M000010000

Illustrated MACHINE-TOOLS of 1885

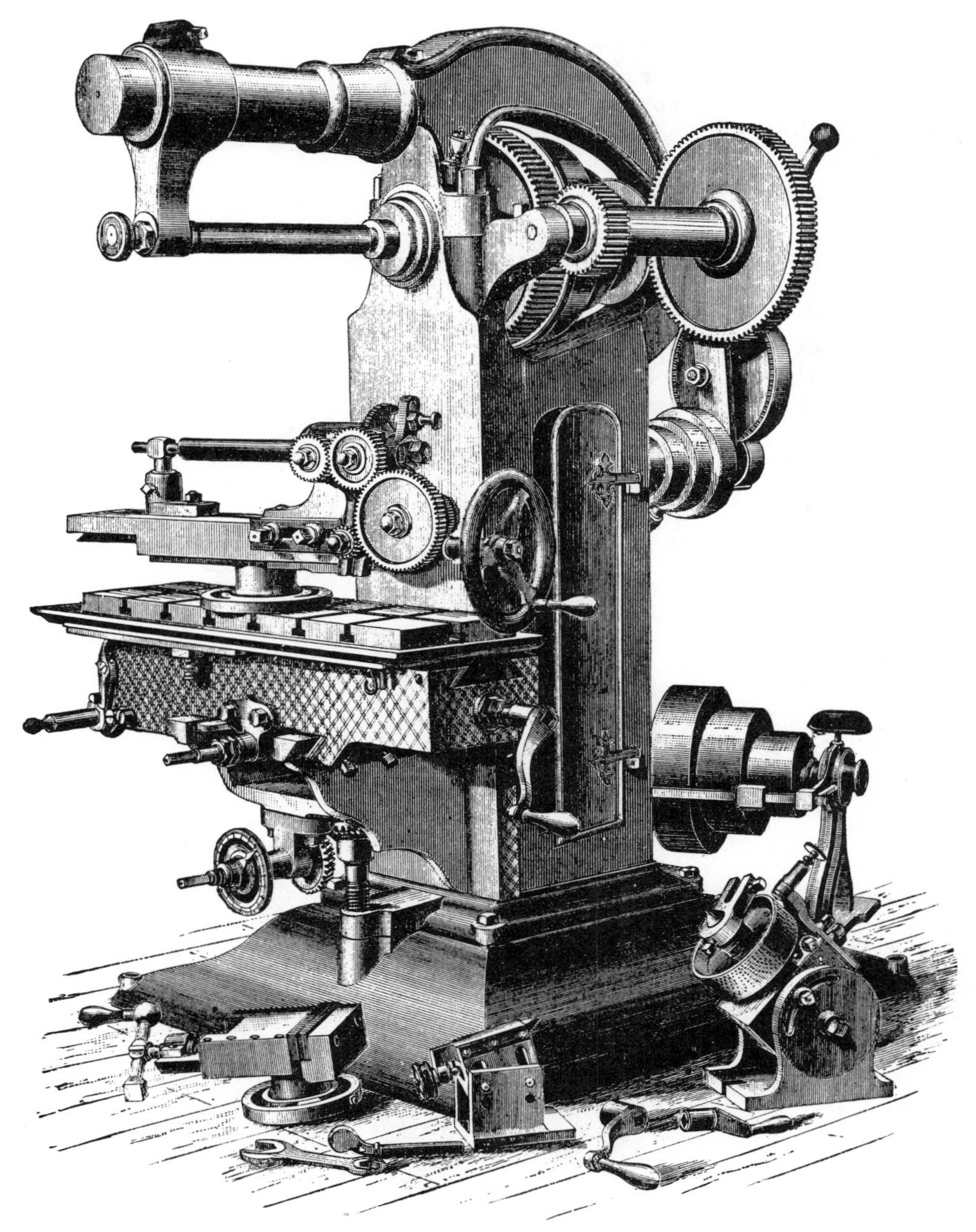

"Lost Technology" Series

Lindsay Publications

Printed in the United States of America

ISBN 0-917914-00-7

This edition was reprinted directly from
a volume released in 1885 by the
Government Printing Office for the
Department of Interior, Census Office.

2 3 4 5 6 7 8 9 10

DEPARTMENT OF THE INTERIOR,

CENSUS OFFICE.

FRANCIS A. WALKER, Superintendent,
Appointed April 1, 1879; resigned November 3, 1881.

CHAS. W. SEATON, Superintendent,
Appointed November 4, 1881. Office of Superintendent abolished March 3, 1885.

STATISTICS OF POWER AND MACHINERY USED IN MANUFACTURES.

REPORT

ON

MACHINE-TOOLS AND WOOD-WORKING MACHINERY,

BY

F. R. HUTTON, M. E.,

ADJUNCT-PROFESSOR OF MECHANICAL ENGINEERING, COLUMBIA COLLEGE, NEW YORK,

AND

SPECIAL AGENT TENTH CENSUS.

WASHINGTON:
GOVERNMENT PRINTING OFFICE.
1885.

Introduction

When the tenth census was taken in 1880, Americans could barely comprehend the whirlwind pace at which new machines were being built and perfected. The United States of America had just celebrated its one-hundredth birthday, and its citizens were watching in amazement as an incredible industrial revolution improved their standard of living and changed almost everything around them. Electricity, telephones, internal combustion engines, phonographs, and a host of other radically new inventions appeared almost overnight. It was an exciting era in which to live.

It may have been because of this technological revolution that the census office was interested in documenting the heavy industrial machine tools that were used to make both other machines and the end products.

F. R. Hutton, a professor of Mechanical Engineering at Columbia College in New York, was hired to compile a pictorial survey of the machine tools in use in 1880. In most cases photographs were taken of the actual machines, but because the process of printing photographs had not been commercially perfected, handmade illustrations had to be engraved by skilled artists. The volume was not completed until 1885.

The result was a book 294 pages in length devoted to machines in nine categories:

PART I — MACHINE-TOOLS

- a) tools acting by compression — hammers, riveters, presses
- b) tools acting by shearing
- c) tools acting by paring — lathes, boring mills, drills, shapers, and planers
- d) milling-machines
- e) tools acting by abrading or grinding

PART II — WOOD-WORKING MACHINERY

- f) saws
- g) tools acting by paring — planers and molders
- h) tools operating by both scission and paring — lathes, boring, mortising and tenoning machines
- i) machines acting by abrasion

Reproduced in this volume are sections c) and d) of part I. Although the lathes and milling machines being used today look much like those of a century ago, many of the specialized varieties of that day are no longer used.

Machinists, experimenters, and historians of technology should find this rare glimpse into 19th century machine shops exciting.

§ 15.

C.—TOOLS ACTING BY PARING.

To this class belongs the majority of the tools of the finishing- or fitting-shop. It includes all those in which the desired figure is produced at the working point by the scraping or cutting action of a wedge-pointed tool. Since they act upon the cold metal and remove relatively small amounts of material in the cut, these tools are much better adapted for working to exact dimensions than those acting by compression or shearing. They can also produce an ornamental finish upon the material which they shape. These features adapt them for the needs of the shop from which the completed work is to be delivered.

Paring-tools belong to two classes. The first includes those in which the relative motion of tool and work is circular or spiral. These can only produce surfaces of revolution, and include lathes, drills, and boring-machines. The second class includes those in which the relative motion of tool and work is rectilinear. These will produce plain surfaces by planers, shapers, and slotters, and also curved surfaces made up of straight line elements by the two latter tools.

The greater part of revolving machinery is made up of surfaces of revolution. The cylinder of these is by far the most important. The lathe will therefore be discussed first.

§ 16.

HORIZONTAL ENGINE LATHES.

The essential parts of a lathe are the bed, the head-stock, the tail-stock, and the arrangements for holding or supporting the tool. This latter device is called the slide-rest or carriage.

It is the primary function of a lathe to produce a truly cylindrical surface, with plain heads perpendicular to the axis, upon the rough material presented to it. The motion of the point of the tool must therefore be truly parallel to the axis of the tool; this latter must be a true straight line, and the secondary motion of the tool must always be at right angles to this line.

The first condition must therefore be stiffness in the bed of the tool. Under the strain of the cut it must not bend downward nor yield laterally. The bed is usually of cast iron, made of two girders of approximate I-section, whose flanges shall give the necessary vertical strength. The newer tools are built with much greater depth of bed than the earlier forms had. To secure lateral stiffness, the two girders front and rear are connected by interior cross-girts about 2 feet apart. These bind the two sides together, and are put near enough to each other to avoid any spring between them. Small lathes are mounted upon legs at sufficient intervals; the lathes of larger swing must be bedded upon a foundation upon which the bed rests directly.

Upon the top of this bed will be the guiding lines for the movable tail-stock and tool-carriage. The finished upper surface of a lathe-bed is called its shears. There are two types of practice with reference to the form of track upon which the sliding parts shall move. In one type the shears are finished off flat, and in the other there are four parallel tracks upon the shear, of inverted V-form, truncated on top.

The advantages of the flat-top shear are its extended bearing surface on the bottom of the carriage and the ease with which the true flat surface may be produced. The large surface reduces the pressure per unit of area, insuring lubrication, and therefore retarding the wear of the sliding surfaces. If hollow places are worn in the shears, the tool-point will fall at those points, producing untruth in the cylinder which is being cut.

The objections to the flat shear are that the tail-stock must move easily in the opening between the shears, that it may be adjusted for work of differing length. For this ease of motion some play must be left between the two sides of the bed and the guiding surfaces of the tail-stock. This play will be enough to vitiate the truth of the cylinders cut by the lathe. Its effect has been avoided by one designer, whose lathes have a V-track upon the under side of one shear. The clamping device fits over this V from below, and when the tail-stock is clamped it is

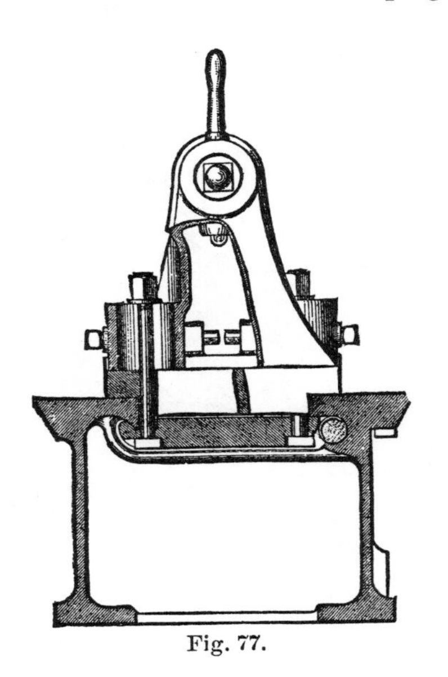

Fig. 77.

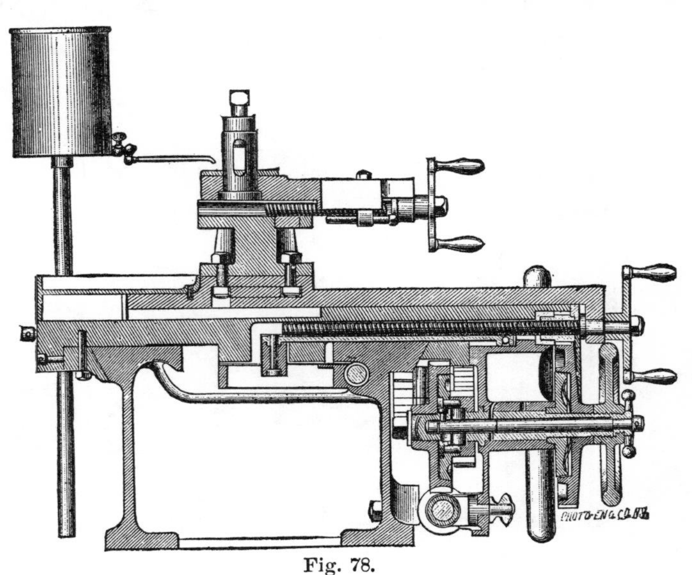

Fig. 78.

certain to be drawn always into the same relation with this V, and the axis of the lathe will be always in one line (Fig. 77). In other designs the stock is kept up to one side by adjustable brass taper gibs, reducing the lost motion to a minimum. The guiding of the tail-stock by the inner edges of the shears is practically universal in the flat shear designs. The carriage or saddle carrying the tool-holder will be guided upon the outer edges (Fig. 78). Otherwise, the wear on the surfaces nearest to the head being the greatest, the untruth of the axis would be increased by the lateral wear due to the carriage-motion.

A second objection to the flat shear is that it opposes its strongest resistance to the vertical components of the strain on the tool-post, while the horizontal components are only taken up by gibs. In turning large work upon a small lathe, where the point of the tool is over the shear, the vertical components will be the greatest. Upon a large lathe also, where the shears will be wide and the carriage and attachments heavy relatively to the strain of the cut, the vertical components will be in excess. But in a lathe cutting work of small diameter, whether facing, boring, or turning, the strain on the tool-post is oblique, passing downward at an angle from the center which varies with the swing of the lathe, and will average perhaps 30°. This strain tends to force the tool downward and outward. The downward strain is resisted by the broad shear; the lateral strain comes upon the gib at the rear only (Fig. 78). This latter strain is not opposed by surfaces at right angles to it nor by surfaces of large area. The freedom for sliding upon the fitted surfaces must also be in this lateral direction, which at the same time is the direction in which untruth will produce the greatest effect to mar the work.

The further objections which have been urged against the flat shear that they make it harder to move the carriage, and that chips from the work get ground into the ways, may be dismissed with a word. The ways will not be clogged when the tool is taken care of as it should be; and a new form of flat shear with a lower step for the tail-stock motion is an effectual preventive of the latter difficulty, even if it were a real one, with shears in one plane only.

The advantages of the V- or track-shears consist, first, in its opposing a resistance normal to the oblique pressure due to a cut on a small cylinder. Upon the top of the bed are four raised rails, of inverted V-form, truncated on top. These V's are of varying angle, around 60° as a mean. The sides of the V's which face the

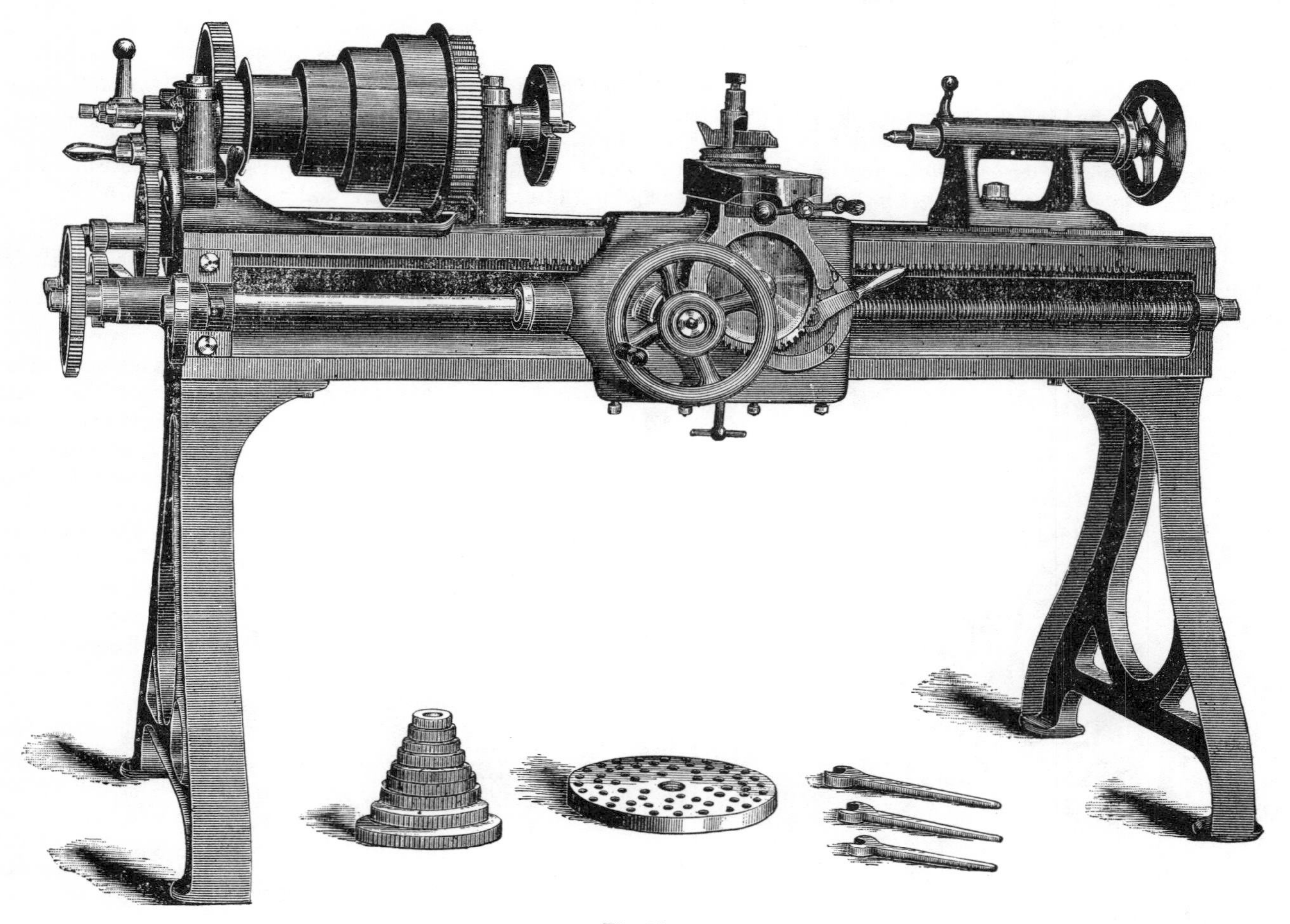

Fig. 79.

back of the tool on each shear are about normal to a strain which presses down obliquely at an angle of about 30°. In some cases of large lathes the angle of the track is about 90°; in others it is 75°. The carriage is carried upon the outer pair of V's, resting upon them in grooves planed in its lower side. It is kept from rising by gibs under the flange of the bed-top, and its own weight secures all the freedom required for ease of motion, without lateral play. The tail-stock travels by similar grooves upon the inner pair of V's, thus securing at all times a perfect alignment with the head-stock. Moreover, the clamping of the tail-stock upon the V's holds the frame from spreading, and acts as a rigid cross-stay where the strain of the dead-center comes. Its freedom of motion is secured by its vertical yielding only. When the tool is at work, therefore, is the time when all its parts come most exactly into line, provided the shear-tracks are perfectly parallel.

Against the V-shears stand the diminished surface for wear by vertical strains, the danger to them from blows, the difficulty of keeping them lubricated, and the expense of accurately fitting them to parallelism and to the grooves in carriage and poppet-heads.

The V-shear is the characteristic American type. It is preferred among all the New England manufacturers, where the tools are built for general work and for jobbing, where small diameters will predominate. Around Philadelphia the flat shear is popular, where the tools are built more for large and heavy work, where the downward pressure will be in excess. For axle or shafting lathes and others, where one diameter is to be prevalent, the shears may be so proportioned as to bring the bulk of the strain vertical, and the flat shear will then be preferable. For large tools in best practice, the moving parts will travel upon three shears instead of upon two only (Fig. 119). This may reduce the swing of the tool slightly, but the gain in stiffness more than compensates for the loss.

One form carries the slide-rest upon the front of the bed only (Fig. 79). This gives large swing over the shears. The carriage does not wear the track of the tail-stock.

Fig. 80 *a*.

Upon the bed of the lathe will be the head-stock and tail-stock, the former carrying the rotating or live center, and the latter the stationary or dead-center. The head-stock will be bolted to the bed securely. The tail-stock must slide along the bed to accommodate work of differing lengths, and should clamp securely fast to the bed with the center in the true axis of the tool. For lathes of small swing Fig. 80 *a* illustrates the general construction of the head-stock in section and in plan. The essential feature of the head-stock is the live-spindle. This is made of steel up to certain sizes, hardened and ground true. Upon the truth of this spindle depends the truth of all work done in the lathes. Any errors in it will repeat themselves, especially in work chucked to the face-plate. In small lathes this spindle turns in hardened steel split boxes. For the larger sizes composition boxes, and cast-iron boxes with babbitted pockets, divide the manufacturers about equally. Many would prefer cast iron alone if they could always insure lubrication. The front journal is always made cylindrical in best practice. Conical journals are apt to "seize" from some variation in temperature and will become cut out of true. Older practice had a collar upon each side of the journal. Newer practice leaves off the outer collar, and the most advanced designers leave off both shoulders and control the end play of the spindle from the outer end. In this system the front or inner journal controls the sidling or lift of the spindle only, and any changes of temperature cannot impair the fit or cause lost motion endwise. To take up the thrust of the tool against the work when facing or when feeding heavily toward the head it is necessary to have some sort of step at the outer end of the spindle. Where the single-shoulder system is in use the rear end turns in a cylindrical box, which is closed at the outer end. Through this closed end passes a hardened steel screw whose axis coincides with that of the spindle. This tail-screw either bears directly against the hardened end of the spindle or else through a washer. The washer is sometimes a disk of hardened ground steel, but in most frequent practice a washer of rawhide is employed. This causes less difficulty from the danger of cutting if it gets dry by accident, and is increasingly popular. The difficulty is the lack of uniformity of the hide. The tail-screw is secured from working loose by a jam-nut against the box, and any degree of closeness of fit longitudinally is obtainable. One designer uses a washer of vulcanized paper fiber, and one uses composition. There are advantages connected with

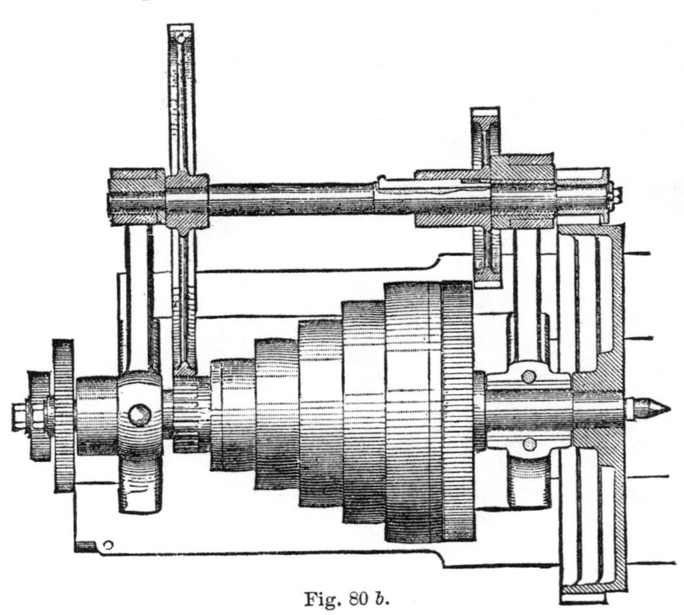

Fig. 80 *b*.

the practice of confining the spindle from end motion in both directions from the tail end. A type of such designs is shown by Fig. 80 *b*. Near the end of the spindle is secured a hardened steel ring or collar, which is ground true and runs between similar washers, from which lost motion can be taken up. When kept well oiled by keeping an oil-cellar full these disks run without liability to stick or jam.

To insure that a lathe-spindle shall always run true, even after wear has begun, beside taking up the end play, is the object of the spindle-journal invented by one of the New England builders. The box is a split cylinder of gun-metal, with conical screw-threads cut on the outside at the ends. Two cheese-nuts fit upon these screws, and by turning them down the box is closed up concentrically upon the journal. A wooden pin prevents the nuts from closing the splits too closely. At the rear box, beside this arrangement, is a bearing-step for motion in one direction, and a pair of jam-nuts bearing against a washer prevent motion in the other direction. The chief point with regard to these thrust bearings is that they have sufficient area. Otherwise they will be apt to wear into rings and cut the surfaces. One designer using steel disks makes them a little smaller than the cell in which they lie. They will turn freely, and yet, being eccentric to the spindle, they must be worn flat uniformly, and will tend to bring up oil from the bottom of the cell upon the step. The advantage of discarding the prevalent step-screw is that the pinion for the feed-gear for the carriage can be put directly upon the end of the spindle. Otherwise this pinion must be inside the head casting, and the latter must be perforated to allow an idle spindle to pass through it, with gears outside and inside. This weakens the head and prolongs the span of the spindle between journals. The alternative way, retaining the step-screw, is to mount the latter upon a separate cross-piece at the tail, supported upon pillar-studs tapped into the end of the head. The Pond box (Fig. 81) permits the spindle to pass through freely, since the thrust is taken up on a steel ring shrunk on the spindle. A hollow steel sleeve flanged at the inner end screws against this ring through the end of the box. The box is hollowed into a chamber around the ring and flange, which is filled with oil up to the horizontal diameter. For the largest sizes of lathes, where the spindle will be massive enough to be made of cast iron, the thrust will be taken up by the collars upon it. The faces of the boxes will often be recessed and babbitted in these designs. One designer of light lathes (Fig. 82) uses a cylindrical box externally, so that the box may be replaced when worn, without replaning the head, to bring the spindle in the center. The boxes are split, and a conical-pointed screw in the crack prevents cramping on the journals.

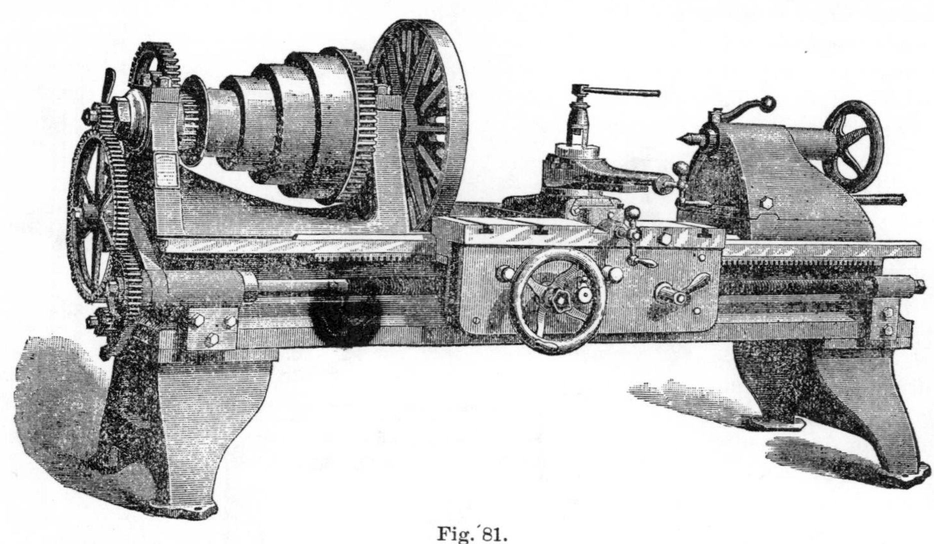

Fig. 81.

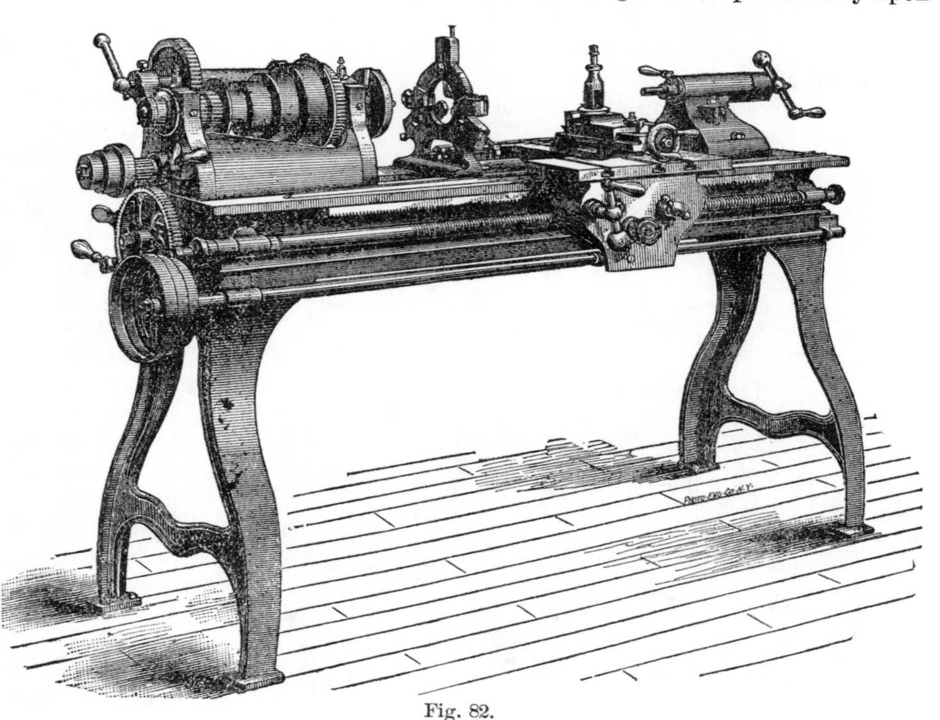

Fig. 82.

The shape of the casting in which the boxes for the spindle are supported will be seen from the various cuts. The top surface curves upward toward the tail, giving effective depth to resist the strains at that part. In one design the hollow underneath the casting is braced by stiffening ribs. The differences required for the lathes of larger swing are solely due to their larger size. The aim of the recent changes of design has been to secure the greatest stiffness and strength against the strains to which the head is exposed.

Upon the live-spindle turns freely the nest of cone-pulleys. This is a series of belt-wheels of different diameters, made necessary by the variety of work to be done upon the tool. The cutting-edge of the tool can act at different speeds upon brass, cast iron, wrought iron, and steel, and a given speed must not be exceeded upon the circumference of cylinders of very different diameters. This variation is most easily accomplished by the use of two nests of cone-pulleys, one on the counter-shaft and the other on the tool. The two nests are complementary, with the sum of the diameters of each pair in the series equal to a constant quantity. The same belt can be used on all, but it

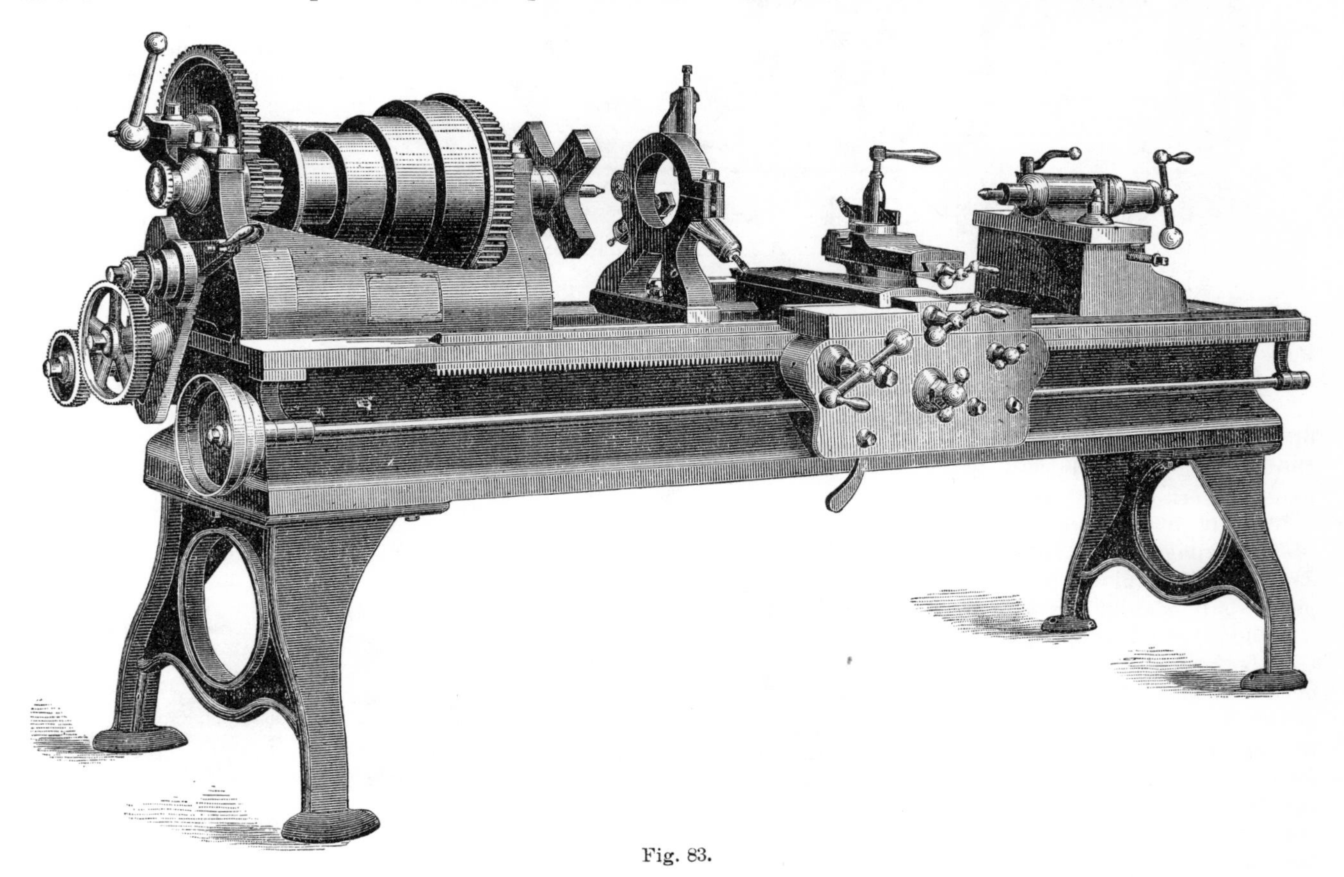

Fig. 83.

will run at different speeds, and therefore produce different speeds of rotation of the work. There are usually four pulleys in the cone. Three only are put on the small sizes, while the very large have five, six, or seven. The faces of the pulleys are most frequently flat; those of a few builders are made crowning. The pulleys are made in one hollow casting, with a long sleeve for the spindle to pass through. The end of the sleeve in larger cones is braced to the large pulley by a spider cast with the cone. For ease of fitting, the sleeve is often cut away in the middle of its length and bears on the spindle at its ends only. The pulleys are sometimes turned on the inside, to insure a perfect balance and smooth running. At the small end of the cone a flange is often put to prevent the belt from running off into the gears. If no flange is used, a guide-pin may be put below, into the casting, to serve the same purpose.

Beyond the flange is a small pinion, either cast as part of the cone or secured to it by screws. This pinion is to drive the "back-gear", or "double-gear", as it is called. This consists of a shaft holding a large and a small gear-wheel, which may carry the motion around the cone-pulleys to a large gear in front of them. This large gear is secured to the live spindle. It will be seen that when the small gear on the cone-pulley drives the large gear on the back-gear shaft, the latter will move at a speed much lower than that due to the cone-pulleys. When again this motion is further reduced, because a small pinion on the back-gear shaft drives the large gear on the spindle, the speed of the work will have been very much lessened. The back-gear usually reduces the speed of the spindle to one-sixth or one-tenth of that due to the cone-pulleys. The back-gear shaft is hollow, and turns upon an interior spindle which passes through it. At each end of this spindle an eccentric-pin is turned, which fits into bearings in the head-casting. It will be seen that if the spindle be turned through 180° it will move the back-gear shaft bodily sidewise through a distance equal to twice the eccentricity. This distance need only be made a little more than the depth of the gear-teeth to furnish a most simple means of engaging and disengaging the shaft with its two gears. Some designers make the eccentricity larger, so as to require less angular motion of the back-gear lever to engage the wheels. The difficulty with this system is that the gear will throw itself out if the bearings are an easy fit. The strain of the gear is a lifting push, and if it takes the eccentrics at a favorable angle it will turn them. Most builders put the eccentric-pins so as to be on the line of centers when in gear. One maker turns the pins a little farther (Fig. 83), so that the strain which tends to separate the gear is opposed by the lower stop. Such an arrangement could not possibly throw out. The engaging-lever on large lathes is often doubled (Fig. 84). Some largest lathes, where the double-gear will be always in use except when polishing, have the composition boxes movable on their seats, so that they can be slipped sidewise, and are then held by a key.

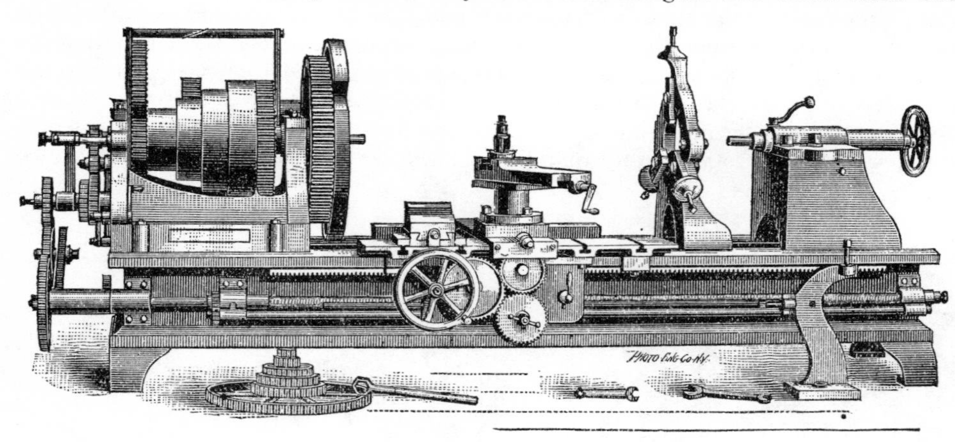

Fig. 84.

Many of the larger lathes are also triple-geared. Beside this back-gear combination, there are often teeth cut upon a circle larger in diameter than the gear which is fast to the spindle. These teeth will be upon the back of the face-plate, and will be driven from a smaller gear on the back-gear shaft prolonged, or else indirectly from it through idle gears (Fig. 85). In these large lathes the face-plate is never removed, since it is inconveniently heavy, and the work can very readily be driven by it. Where the face-plate is driven directly, it is necessary that both pinions on the back-gear shaft should be movable lengthwise on their splines, since they both must not be in gear at once with wheels of different diameters fast to the spindle. Where the power is transmitted through idle wheels, the slip-gear may be the one on the back-gear shaft only. It may slip out of gear with the spindle-wheel and into gear with the face-plate train, with an interval between their planes from which neither will be driven. Sometimes the whole back-gear shaft slides lengthwise and is held in place by a pin, taking into grooves cut in the shaft. The idle-wheel system is specially desirable where the face-plate teeth would come on its periphery. It is much better to make the face-plate teeth internal upon an annular flange in this case (Fig. 85), both for cleanliness, for safety, and to prevent interference with the chucking of large flat work. In many large lathes the cone-pulley spindle drives internal gear on the face-plate through an ordinary back-gear combination. The cone-pulleys are not on the live-spindle in this case (Fig. 86). Where the face-plate is larger than the gear-circle desired the teeth on the latter may be external. Some lathes for special classes of work are driven directly from a pinion on a splined shaft to teeth on the periphery of the face-plate.

Fig. 85.

When the lathe is to be driven at speed for polishing or the like the back-gear shaft will be turned out and the cone-pulley will be clamped to the large gear fast to the spindle. This clamping is effected by a bolt passing through a slot in the plate of the fast gear-wheel. This bolt will cause a short slide to catch between jaws upon the inside of the cone-pulley, so that when the bolt is tightened the cone-pulley and gear become as one; or they may be clamped together by a regular friction device. For some special classes of manufacture, where the work, for example, is to be chucked, faced, polished, and drilled centrally, the back-gears and two speed-changes are all controlled by friction-clutches, so that the speeds may be changed without loss of time to stop the tool and shift belts or loosen nuts. One firm put several lathes upon the market in which the back-gear wheels were made with helical teeth. The object of this was to cause more even working of the spindle and to lessen the vibrations of the work when driven through gears. It was not found to compensate for the trouble in shaping the teeth, and has been abandoned.

Upon the end of the spindle is secured the face-plate. This is simply a disk of cast iron, with radial slots in it, through which bolts and pillars can be passed to secure work to it. The front face of it must be a true plane and perpendicular to the axis of the lathe and of the spindle. It should also be balanced. It is usually screwed upon the end of the spindle, finding a true bearing at the end of the thread. As the lathe always turns in the direction opposite to that of the hands of a watch to one facing the inner end of the spindle, the resistance to the

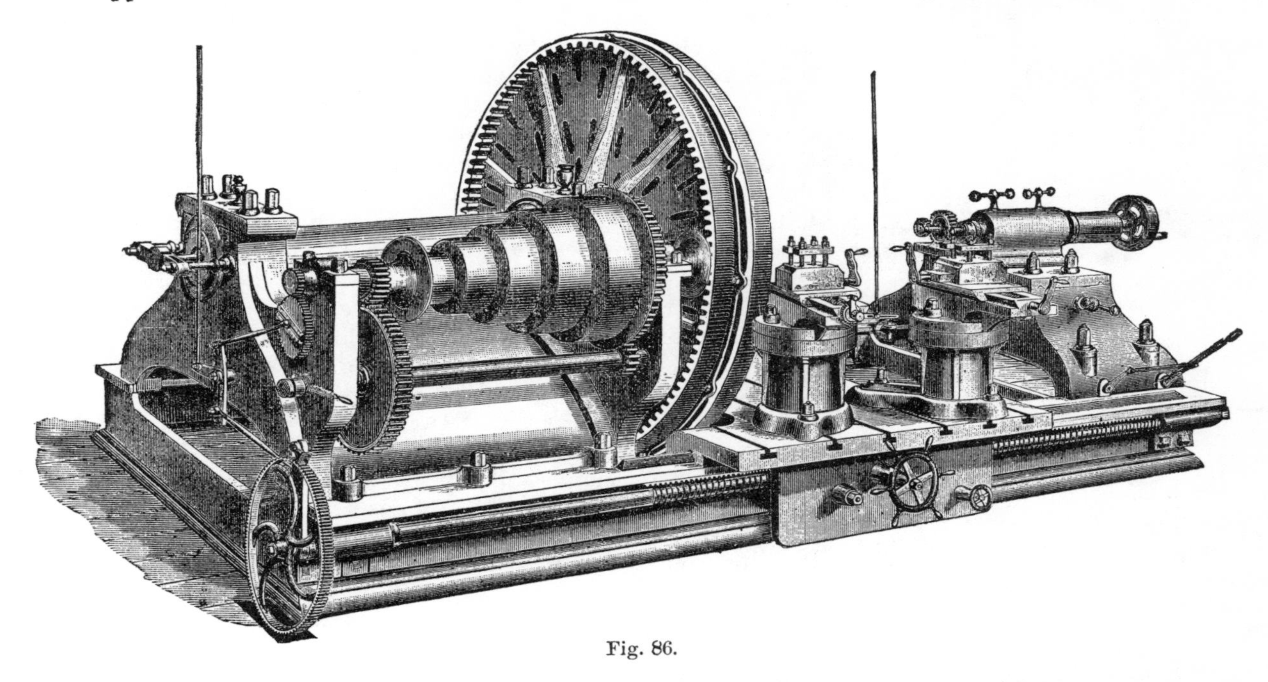

Fig. 86.

cut only screws the plate tighter when threaded on by a right-hand screw. Sometimes, besides the short slots, there are three or four long slots carrying jaws which can be moved upon the plate by screws in the slots. These serve to secure work to the plate, which will then be called a chuck-plate. For rod-work, screw-cutting, and the like, the face-plate is often replaced by a drive-plate, a flat disk with a slot cut on it along a radius to hold the tail of the dogs or drivers (Fig. 82). The four-armed spider is also used for dogged work (Fig. 83). A universal chuck can also be screwed on the end of the spindle when required. Usually the spindle is threaded to its end. In some cases the thread is made much shorter and the end of the spindle made to fit the plate or chucks upon a cylindrical surface left on it beyond the screw. This makes the adjustment of the plate more rapid and lessens the danger of battering the shears in cases where the heavy plate is only released from the screw when it is able to drop.

In the inner end of the spindle is bored the taper hole for the live-center. This, of course, must be truly central, and is made tapering to insure a tight fit at all times and truly in line. The taper is quite long, in order to secure ample bearing for the center when in place. The spindle is often made hollow in small lathes to accommodate lengths of rod, and also to permit the introduction of a rod through the tail-screw by which the center might be driven out when chucks were to be used. Where the centers were made of a long cone fit joined to the short cone center point by a short cylinder this device was very convenient. The newer centers are made with a squared surface outside the fit upon which a wrench can take hold to loosen them. The centers themselves are made of steel hardened at the point and ground truly conical in place. The angle of the cone varies from 60° to about 75°. The former is in many places more general. It is the apex of this cone which determines the axis of the tool, since all surfaces of revolution will turn around the line drawn between the points of the live- and the dead-center as an axis. It is necessary, therefore, not only that both cone centers should themselves be perfectly true, but that both apexes of the cones should remain in the intersection of the same horizontal and vertical planes in whatever part of the bed of the lathe the former may be.

It is the object of the tail-stock to insure the permanence of this axis of the lathe, and to permit considerable variations in its length. There will be a rough adjustment for length of work by hand, and a finer adjustment by a screw, while both must be clamped from moving out of adjustment when in place. The tail-stock is guided from lateral motion by the inner edges of a flat shear, or by the inner tracks of the V-shear.

When at the right position on the bed it is clamped in place by a cross-bearer, which is brought up against the under side of the bed. This clamp may be tightened by one screw from below, by an eccentric-cam, turned by a lever (Fig. 89), or by two or more bolts, one at each side of the casting. On the larger lathes there will be more than one clamp, and therefore more than one pair of clamping-bolts. The eccentric is adapted for medium and small sizes only. The screw arrangement is the most general. Upon the top of the movable stock is the finer screw adjustment for length. This consists of a spindle, cylindrical on small lathes and square upon some large ones, which has a long bearing (Fig. 87). This spindle may be moved in and out from the tail-stock by a screw which is turned by a hand-wheel or ball-handle from the extreme left end. This screw is usually cut with a left thread, so that the spindle may be protruded by an instinctive "screwing-in" motion. When the end of the center enters the drilled hole in the work, the spindle must be clamped to prevent the center from turning out. It is therefore necessary that the spindle shall move in the axis of the lathe independent of the tail-stock, and also the clamp must be such as not to throw the end of the center out of line. There are three types of clamps for the spindle. One form draws up a ring or forces a set-screw or other frictional device upon the center of the spindle from above (Fig. 88). The second clamps the outer end of the spindle by a screw which tightens a collar split upon one side. This collar is often a projecting part of the long bearing (Fig. 89). The third type (Figs. 90 and 87) uses a split sleeve tightened upon the spindle by a conical muff. The muff is drawn upon the sleeve by a screw when a partial turn is given to it. This latter system has the advantage that under abuse it will not be so likely to spring the spindle out of line, either up or down. The casing containing the long bearing for the spindle is cast solid. In the earlier forms, the cap which guides the screw had to be screwed on by a flange. The spindle is kept from turning by a spline.

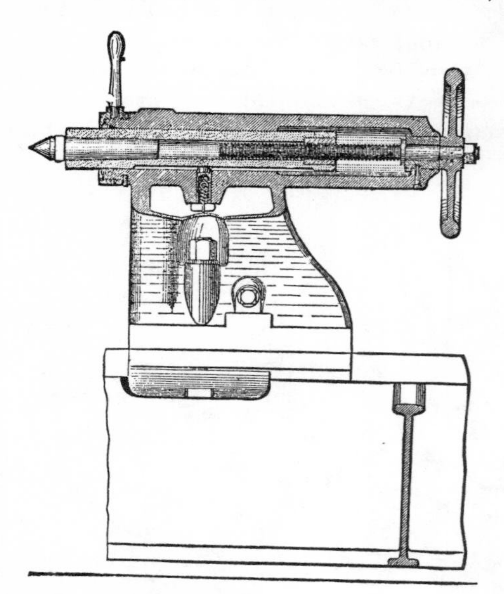

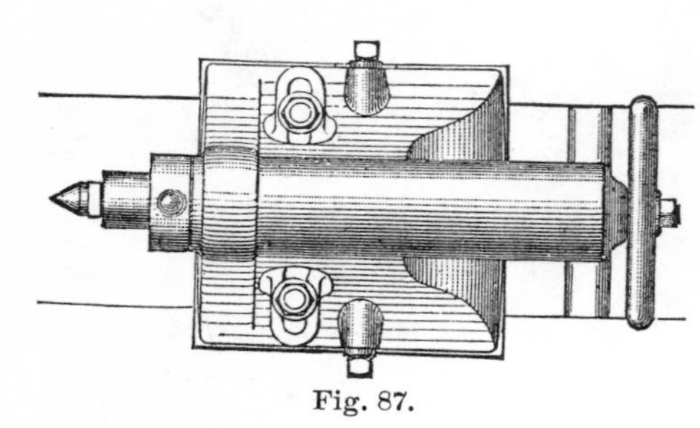

Fig. 87.

The tail-stock in universal practice is made in two parts. These are planed to fit together upon transverse ways, and secured by clamping-bolts or by set-screws.

The object of this arrangement is two-fold. It is desirable to have this lateral adjustment of the dead-center, because in boring the casing for the spindle in the first instance it is hard to get the lateral accuracy of the boring-bar relative to the shear-guides. The vertical adjustment is easy. Since it is desirable to have a little lateral adjustment for the dead-center when in place on the shears, this lateral motion can be easily made larger, and the lathe will then turn conical surfaces as well as cylindrical. Such tail-stocks are called "set-over tail-stocks", and have been hitherto almost universal. Advanced practice of to-day, however, prefers the use of an attachment for turning tapers which controls the motion of the tool. This system not only avoids the difficulty of readjusting the rear spindle after every taper, but also permits the boring of taper holes without a compound rest. When taper attachments are used, the tail-stock has only sufficient motion for adjustment. The older standard form of tail-stock is shown by Fig. 91; the newer shape is that of Fig. 81. Very often a small oil-cup is cast in the spindle-casing, from which the lubricant can very easily be put upon the stationary center. The largest tail-stocks are too heavy to be moved directly by hand, so that a small pinion is made to engage in a rack at the side of the bed, and the squared end of its vertical axis will take the end of a long lever. The rotation of the pinion drags the heavy casting upon the shears. On some of the largest lathes also the tail-spindle has power-feed for boring. This type will be illustrated by Fig. 92 and further in advance.

Fig. 88.

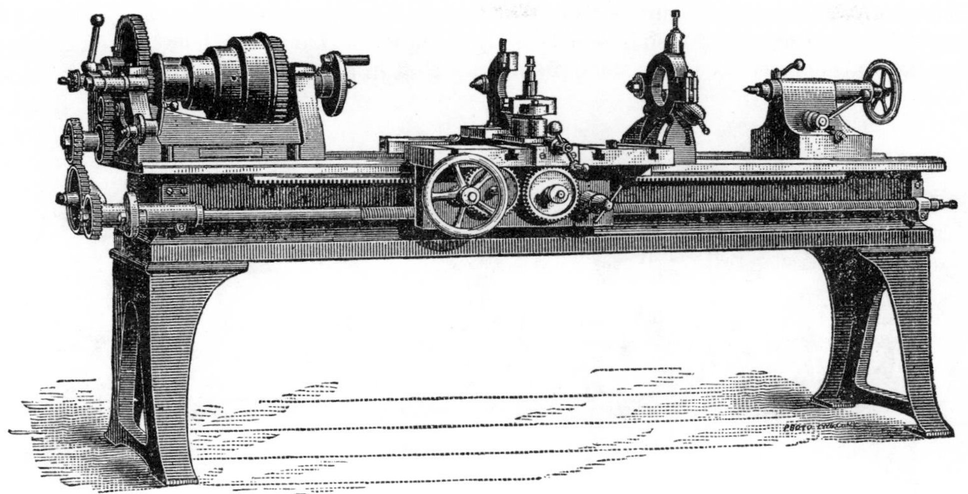

Fig. 89.

Fig. 90.

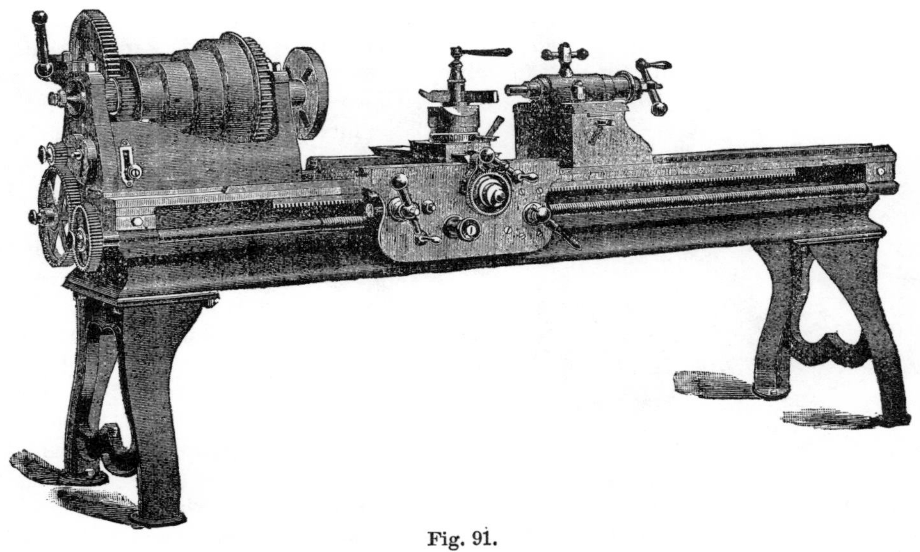

Fig. 91.

The line between the centers being thus made exactly true, it remains to give to the tool-point a motion which shall be truly parallel to that axis, and also one at true right angles to that axis. The motion of the tool parallel to the line of centers must also always be in the same plane with that line. The tool will therefore be rigidly held in a

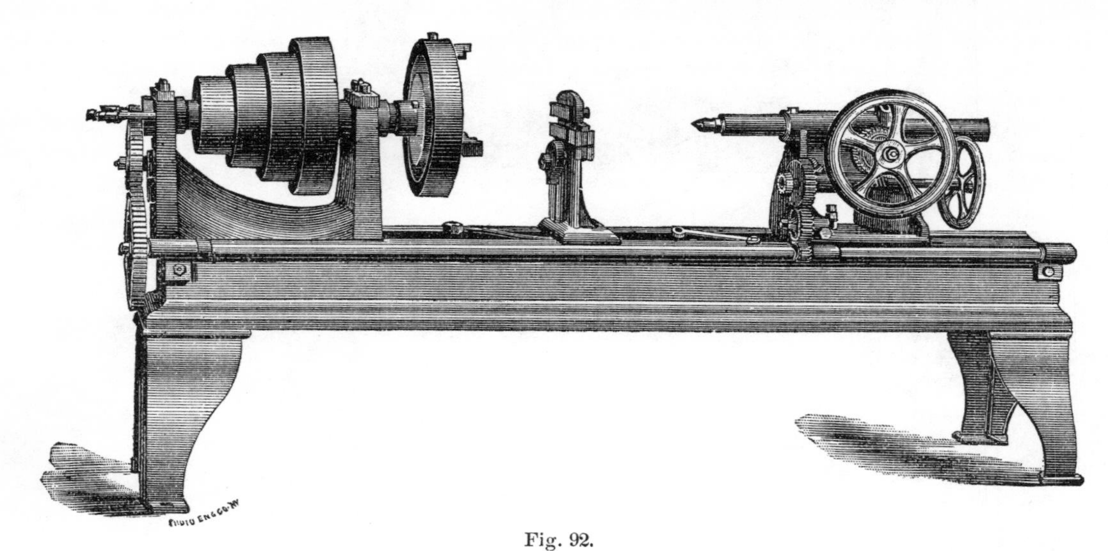

Fig. 92.

tool-post, supported upon a guided carriage. This carriage must receive the two motions at right angles to each other, each motion being independent of the other. The lower part of the carriage will span the opening between the two sides of the bed, so as to be guided by its extreme ends. In the flat shears the tendency to twist the carriage is resisted by the outer surfaces of the shears. These incline inward, and adjustable gibs are fitted against these inclines front and rear, which also keep the rear end of the carriage from lifting under the strain of the cut. In the V shear system the carriage rests upon the outer rail of each shear, and is thus kept from lateral motion. Flat gibs under the square edges of the shears resist what little tendency there may be to cause the saddle to lift. In both cases the bearing surfaces of the carriage are made much longer than is necessary, simply to support the cross-rail or saddle. The plan of the whole would be usually a square, in which the sides were broken away to enable the saddle to come close to the head- and tail-stock. The necessity for these long guiding wings to the carriage results from the method of driving the carriage from the extreme of one side, and also from the leverage exerted upon the tool-point in certain positions. It is an argument urged against the V-shear system that the long span of the saddle to clear the inner rail makes a greater thickness of metal necessary at that part for stiffness, and therefore reduces the swing of the lathe. The shortest radius from the center to the shear limits the face-plate work which the lathe will take in. In long work the limit is fixed by the shortest distance from the axis to the saddle, and the thinner this is the greater the swing of the lathe. This difficulty is met by thickening the metal of the saddle downward between the shears. Nearer the abutments the depth may be reduced. The majority of the carriages are what are called half-gibbed. The gibs take hold below the outer back and the inner front of the shears. Flat-shear and many V-shear carriages are gibbed at the outside, back and front. There are comparatively few which are gibbed on all four surfaces.

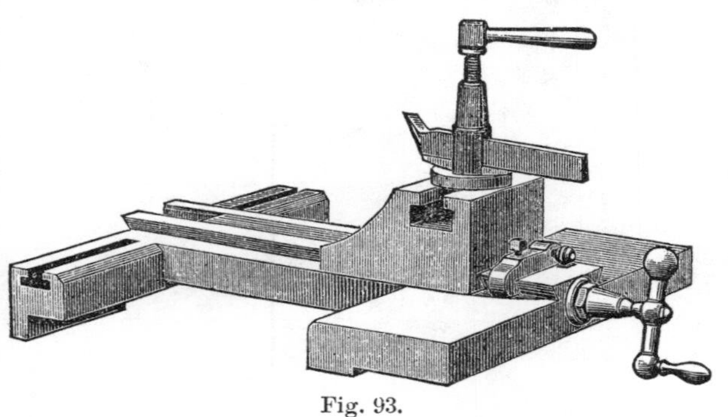

Fig. 93.

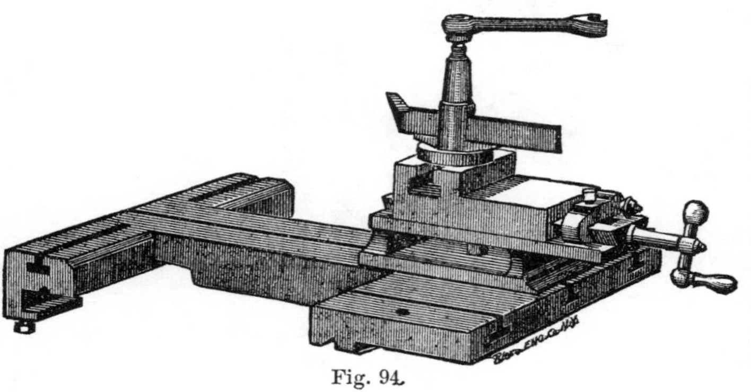

Fig. 94.

Fig. 93 shows the ordinary plain gibbed rest for small and average lathes. The apron which holds the driving gear, to move the rest automatically, is secured to the flat surface at the under side of the front. The cut shows the ordinary tool-post, consisting of a block with a T-socket in its top. The post is slotted out so that the shank of the tool may pass through it, and a set-screw in the axis of the post screws down upon the tool. The abutment is the round head which fits into the T-slot and binds tool and post to the block. For the adjustment of the point of the tool, that it may come opposite the horizontal diameter of the work, is the object of the washer below the tool. This is dished out into a segment of a hollow sphere, and a steel segment of a zone of the same sphere fits into the hollow. The tool rests upon the flat surface of the wedge, whose spherical lower side permits the tool to have a full bearing at any vertical angle within the necessary limits. The same object may be attained by a spiral washer under the tool.

It is the block below the tool-post which receives the cross motion at right angles to the axis of the lathe. Upon the saddle are planed flat, dovetail shears, truly at right angles to those of the carriage below. The post and block can be moved on its shears by the cross-feed screw which holds against the carriage between a shoulder and the ball-handle spacer-washers. The tool-block is made with long bearing surfaces, and any wear in its fit is taken up by screws which bear upon an adjustable gib. The T-slots on the rear wings are planed out to receive a back-rest or any other convenient attachment. On larger lathes, what is known as the "Philadelphia rest" is often used (Fig. 94). An open casting slides in a T-slot across the carriage, to which it can be bolted. The shears for the tool-block are on the top of this adjustable foot. The advantage of this form is that it can be bolted to any part of the rest by the T-slots wherever the exigencies of the work may demand, or the whole tool-holder can be removed, so that the flat carriage only may be left. The cross motion, however, cannot be automatic.

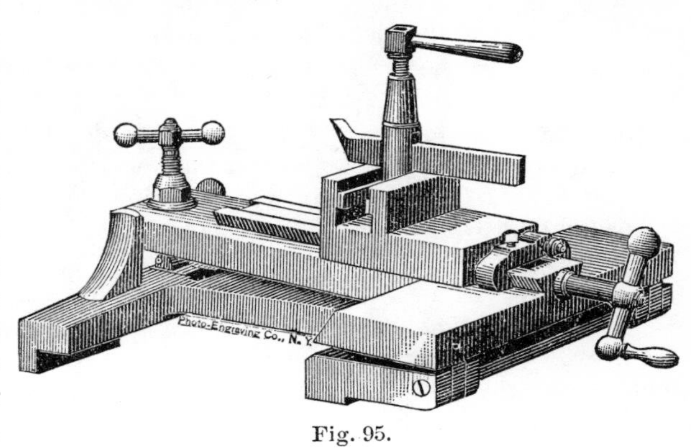

Fig. 95.

For many classes of light job-work the easy, rapid, and secure adjustment of the point of the tool is of considerable moment. To effect this is the object of the gibbed rest shown in Fig. 95. The saddle is made double, the top half revolving around a horizontal hinge at the front. The lifting-saddle is prevented from twisting strain

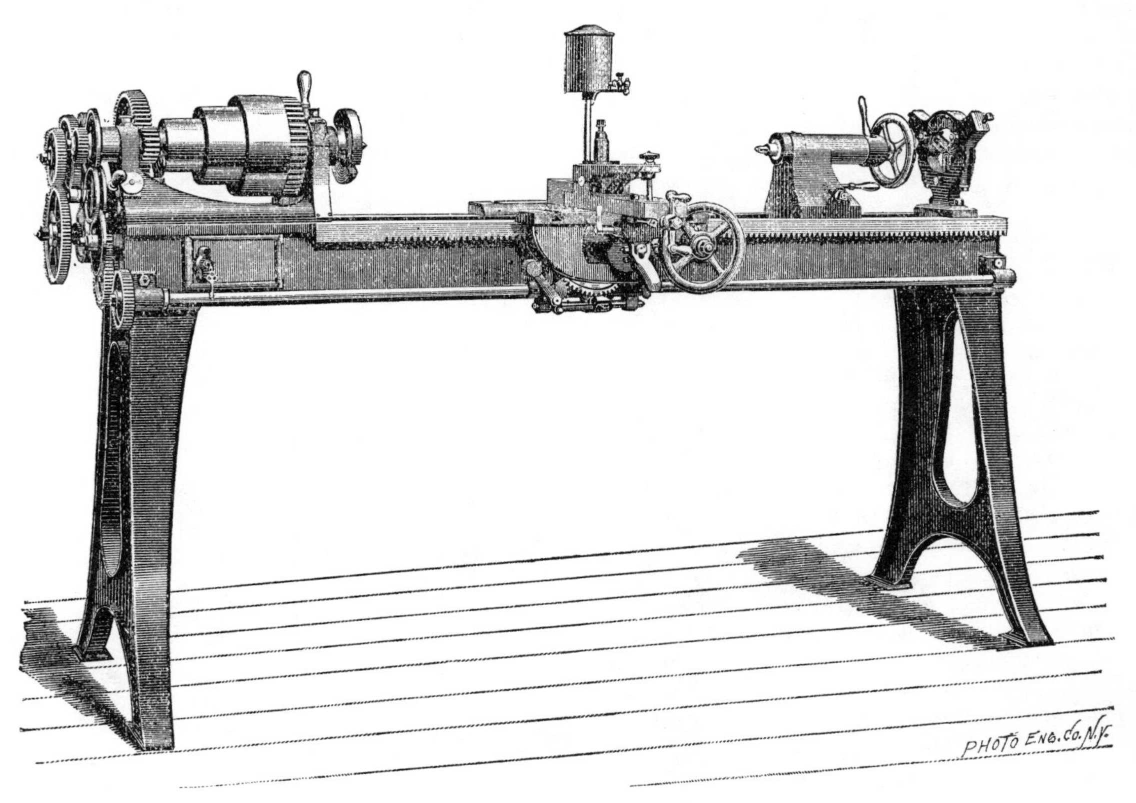

Fig. 96.

by the faced brackets at the back, and the degree of elevation of the rear end is controllable by a screw, which passes down into the lower saddle. The motion of the screw in the upper and lower saddle is circular around horizontal axes (Fig. 96). This is provided for, and lost motion is taken up by several devices. The most usual is to make the lower end of the screw spherical, which fits between brass washers, curved to fit the ball. These washers are confined by a screw-sleeve in the top of the lower saddle, by which any play can be taken up. In the upper saddle the nut for the screw is also made externally spherical and confined by similar sleeves. Others pin the end of the lifting-screw into a slide on the lower saddle, so as to avoid the ball-and-socket fit. Wear is taken up in the nut by splitting it across the axis, and controlling the approach of the two parts either by the sleeve-nuts or by conical-pointed set-screws. In rests of this type the tool-block slot is so made as to give a stiff hold for the tool at a distance from the set-screw. Not infrequently the top of the block is serrated to increase the friction.

Other methods of raising and lowering the tool-point are shown by Figs. 88 and 91. In Fig. 88 the gibbed block slides over a shear on the surface of a horizontal cylinder. A rack on the end of a screw meshes into a sector on this cylinder, and the point of the tool rises in an arc. Another device has the cylindrical surface replaced by a spherical surface, the head of the slotted bolt coinciding with the center of the sphere. This works very well as long as there are no defects in the spherical contact. Still another uses inclined planes on the two halves of the post, controllable by a separate screw. The disadvantage of these methods is that horizontal adjustment of the block must be made after every vertical change. A joint where lost motion may occur is also introduced between the tool and the carriage. Another plan, which has the advantage of stiffness, makes the post with a screw-thread on its lower part. By raising and lowering this large pillar-screw the point rises and falls. One similar design raises the tool by a capstan-nut on the outside of the post, while internal to the post is another which acts to clamp the whole from moving. In still another the pillar of the post is lifted by an elbow-joint, clamped by the screw which controls the joint.

For small lathes an especial practice prevails in New England. The slide-rest carriage, moving on V-shears, is kept to its bearing on the track by a weight, and no gibs are employed. This system gives great steadiness of motion for light cuts, since all lost motion of adjustment and for free travel is absorbed in the weight. The hinged saddle is used, lifted by the end screw by contact joint only, and no "take-up" devices are required (Fig. 97). The cross-feed can be only limited in length on this system. When wide surfaces are to be faced, the post-block must be reset in the slot. No tools of this design are approved at the South or West, but in New England they are preferred by many of the best workmen and builders. As the swing of the lathe increases the height of the tool-post must increase also. To increase the capacity of the tool-holder, the compound rest is approved. The lower block, which may travel across the bed at right angles to the axis of the lathe, carries a horizontal flat disk with a circular T- slot in it. Upon this disk may be bolted at any angle a secondary tool-post, which has a screw cross-feed motion upon its own shears (Fig. 98). So that, beside the two motions at right angles to each other, which are common to the smaller devices and are here retained, the tool may have an angular feed in any direction for turning tapers and conical shapes. On lathes of the largest size, where the pillar on which the tool-holder stands is quite high and the cuts will probably be heavy, the form shown in Figs. 99 or 100 is used. The tool is held by two clampings-crews, and while the large post has the two original motions, the holder on the top has also two motions at right angles for convenient use by hand. In newer practice, even these feeds can be driven by power for smaller work.

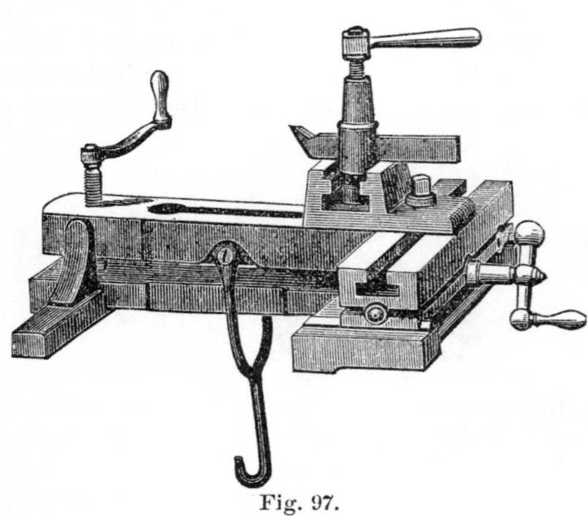

Fig. 97.

To actuate these carriages automatically by the power of the tool itself two general systems are in use. One moves the carriage by a screw, whose nut is held in the apron of the carriage, and the other by a driven pinion in the apron, which meshes into a rack on the under side of the shear. Both systems may be combined in one lathe for different uses. The screw-feed will be used for the reproduction of screws; the feed by the pinion, usually known as the "friction-feed", will be used for the general turning in the lathe. The driving-screw is continuous for the whole length of the bed. It is often called the "lead-screw" or the "feed-screw". In very long lathes it has to be supported to prevent sagging between supports. This is accomplished by flat hooks, which catch hold of the shears and pass under the screw. They are perfectly movable and can be put where most needed. Usually they bear on the tops of the thread of the screw. The thread may be cut away for a length less than that of the nut in the apron if it is desired to give the supporting hooks a complete straight bearing. The lead-screw may be put in front of the bed, at the back of the bed or between the shears.

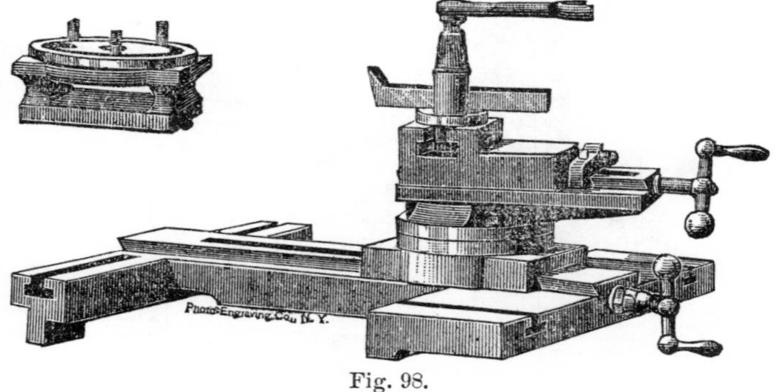

Fig. 98.

There is but one designer using this latter system. In this make, the screw is supported in a trough in the shear casting, and is protected from chips by the projection of the shear. A half-nut or chasing-nut is used on the carriage. The preponderance of practice has the screw in front of the bed. The friction-feed apparatus is always in front.

The screw is driven by a train of gear-wheels from the spindle of the lathe. These wheels come in sets, so

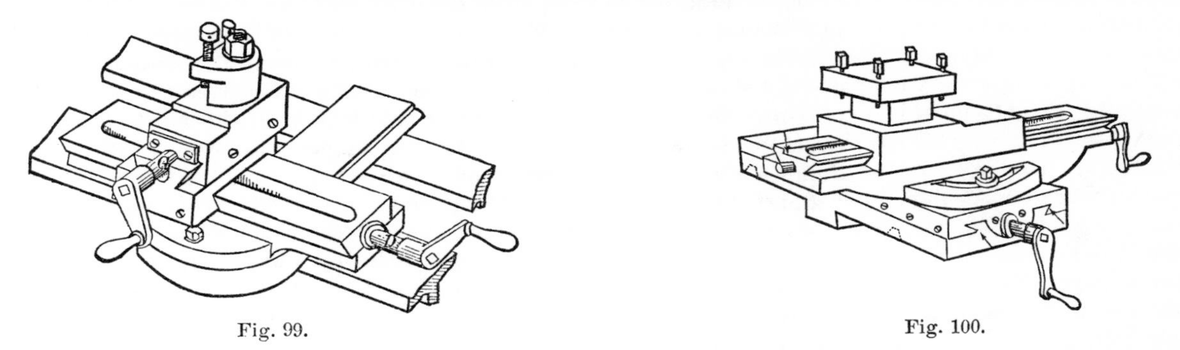

Fig. 99. Fig. 100.

that almost any esired combination may be interposed between the spindle and the screw, to vary their relative velocities. If the spindle and the screw turn at the same rate, the tool-point will cut a duplicate of the lead-screw on the work, since each will have gone round the same number of times while the tool moved over one inch. To cut any other thread the revolutions or the number of teeth on the wheels of the first and last of the train must be as the thread to be cut is to the thread of the feed-screw. It is therefore convenient that the pitch of the feed-screw be a convenient divisor of the usual threads. Very often it has four threads to the inch. One designer uses two threads to the inch, for convenience of calculation and to make it more easy to strike into the thread under the cut. To connect these fixed studs at the two ends of the train the studs upon which the intermediate idle wheels are placed are borne upon a slotted swinging casting, which revolves around the screw or its journal as a center. The studs for the wheels take into these slots, and the casting is clamped by a set-screw to the head of the lathe (Fig. 101).

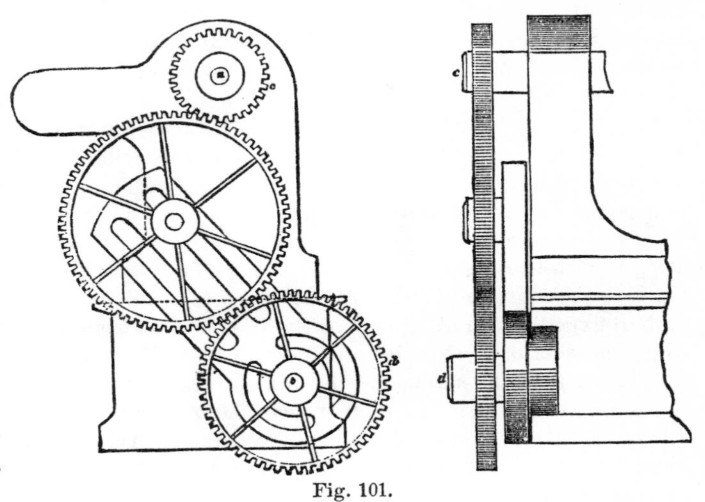

Fig. 101.

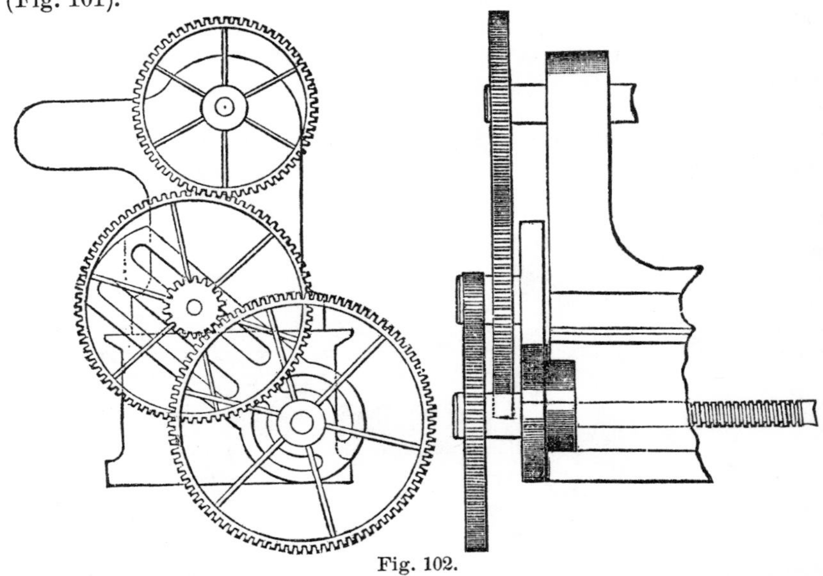

Fig. 102.

Many lathes of large swing having a large feed-screw with small number of threads to the inch will be double-geared or compound-geared. By this is meant that upon one idle shaft are two gears of different diameters turning together. A larger range of speed between the spindle and screw is obtainable with few gears. To avoid confusing the operator with different motions for reversing it is best always to have the same number of spindles in the train. Also, the use of a large gear on the screw may be avoided, necessitating a cut in the floor, and heavy gears are dispensed with. There may be also the gain due to the greater smoothness of working when the driver and follower-gears are more nearly of the same size than would be possible with the single gear. The arrangement is shown by Fig. 102. The tendency is toward smaller diametral pitch in the change-wheels. While it used to be 12 per inch, it is now 6, and some prefer 4 per inch.

For reversing the motion of the screw in general practice one method is preferred. It depends on the principle that in any train of external gears the even numbers in the series will be turning in one direction and the odd numbers turn in the other. By a simple motion of a lever the train of gears driving the screw may be made to contain an odd or an even number of wheels. In Fig. 103 a V-shaped lever turns at its apex on the stud of one wheel as a center. On one arm of the V is one wheel and on the other are two. If the V is rotated so as to bring the driving-pinion D into gear with one arm, the follower at the apex will turn one way; if with the other arm, the follower will turn the other way. There is, of course, a neutral position, in which the driving-pinion will drive neither. The lever which moves the V projects conveniently for the hand of the operator, and is prevented from disengaging itself either by a latch-pin into holes, or by a clamp-screw, or by a little cam. The clamp-screw requires the use of both hands.

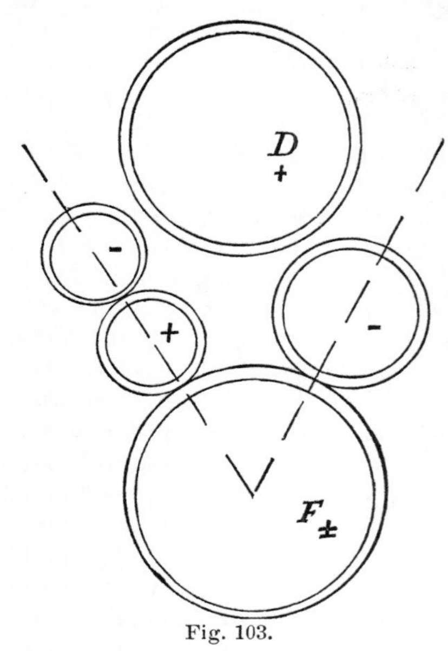

Fig. 103.

Another type of reversing mechanism uses the principle of the two loose bevel-gears driven by the third between them. The combination is put under the cone-pulleys, and a clutch is engaged by a rod from the apron with one or the other of the loose gears. The advantage of engaging and reversing at the head also rather than at the carriage only is that, when speeding the lathe for polishing, the gears need not be clattering and wearing each other out. For engaging and disengaging at the carriage, the universal device is a split nut. This is divided along a plane through the axis into two parts, which approach to clasp the screw or recede to release it at the will of the operator. This clasp-nut has the halves moving in guides so as truly to come together and make a nut, the motion to open and close being given to both parts. Usually this motion is given by a disk in which are two spiral slots. In these slots fit two pins, of which one belongs to each half of the nut. The slots are so laid out that when a partial rotation is given to the disk the pins come equally toward its center or recede from it, carrying the sliding halves of the nut. Another device draws the halves together by fitting them to a bolt with a right thread on one half and a left thread on the other.

This clasp-nut device is practically universal in lathes driven from the screw in the apron. A New England design, with the screw at the back, uses a solid nut, which bolts through a bracket to the saddle by easy working tap-screws, when required. This system of solid nut renders obligatory the use of reversing counter-shafts—a system expedient in all cases for the economy of time and exactness of screw profile. Left threads are cut in this single-connection system by putting an extra idle-wheel in the gear-train.

The use of the screw and nut for ordinary turning-feeds has two objections. The principal one is the wear of the screw, which will be greatest near the head-stock where the greatest amount of work will be done. Therefore a long screw cut on such a lathe will not be uniform or regular. The nut will also wear and permit lost motion. A second minor objection is that the ordinary feeds are so much slower than a screw-cutting feed that considerable rearrangement of the train is necessary to get the proper speeds when the work varies. To avoid these difficulties, nearly all the smaller and medium lathes of to-day are provided with a second feed system, known usually as the "friction-feed". Motion is imparted to a train of gears in the apron of the rest, by which a small pinion is made to turn in gear with a stationary rack upon the shear. This train of gears is engaged and disengaged by a friction-clutch in the apron.

Figs. 104 and 105 show a plan and elevation of a very usual form of the gears in the apron. The rod *f* is driven by a narrow belt from a cone-pulley on the first spindle of the change-wheel train. There are usually three changes

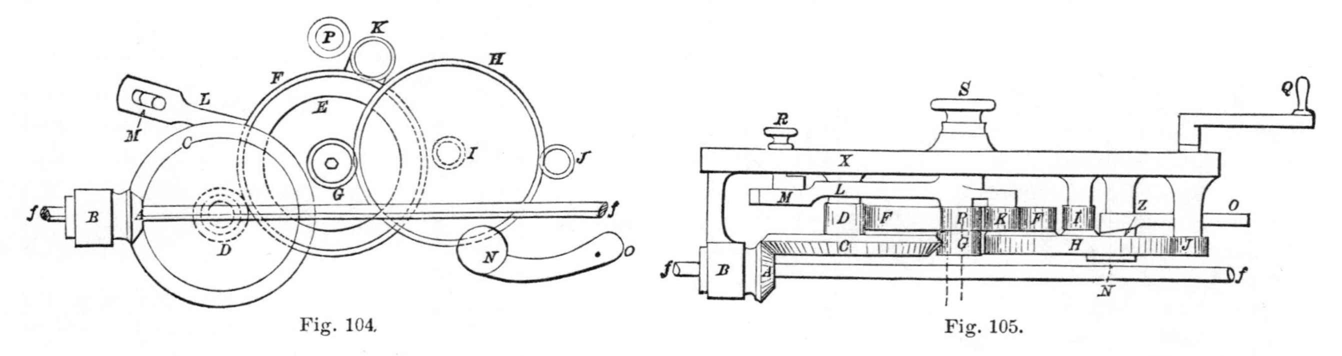

Fig. 104.

Fig. 105.

on the cone, and the reversing is done either by the lever with the one and two gears, or by crossing the little belt, or it may be done in the apron. This rod is splined, and carries a bevel-wheel, A, mounted on a bracket, B, from the apron. The rotation of *f* will therefore turn A wherever the latter may be upon the rod. When A revolves, it turns the wheel F, which is the female part of a friction-cone. The rest of the train, up to the rack, is connected with the male part of the cone (Fig. 105) through the pinion G. The cone is engaged by the screw Y, controlled from outside by the hand-nut S. The wheel H catches in the rack under the shear, and on the axis of the pinion J is put the ball-crank or hand-wheel for traversing the carriage by hand. It will be seen that if a second bevel-pinion be put opposite to A, so that either may be at will engaged with C, a very simple reversing and disengaging gear is designed, which is worked from the carriage entirely, without stepping to the head. In many designs the bevel-gear A is replaced by a worm. This permits the reduction of speed to be made with few wheels in the train. For reversing in the apron, one designer has one right and one left worm on the rod, either of which can be brought under the worm-wheel by a lever in front.

The worm-system is objected to by many builders on account of the danger to it if allowed to get dry by neglect. The wear of the surfaces becomes very rapid. The wheel is made of cast iron, the worm of wrought iron, steel, or cast iron. In some cases it turns in an oil-pan to keep it lubricated. Very often, instead of driving the wheels in the apron from a separate splined rod, the feed-screw is splined to carry the worm on the bevel-gear. This is objected to by some on the ground of the wear on the top of the thread and at the points of the threads where they are cut by the spline. One designer gears the rod to the screw and drives both at once (Fig. 89). The end play of the screw is prevented by a steel step-screw or by a washer of some material like rawhide. When a lathe has both feeds in the apron there have been devices to prevent the operator from throwing in both at once. For reasons of simplicity of mechanism this attachment is not often applied. The gears are usually carried on studs bolted into the apron. To avoid the strains on the overhanging bearings one designer makes the apron with two walls (Fig. 81). Another plan has all the gearing on the outside in front (Fig. 89); this is a gain in cleanliness, but there is more danger of accident to a careless operator. The rod-feed of the lathe shown in Fig. 80 is driven by a friction device by means of which the speed of feed may be varied. A smooth disk of cast iron is the driver, which is clasped by two disks of brass upon its sides. These disks of brass are kept against the iron by a stiff steel spiral spring. A second disk of cast iron upon the splined rod is driven by the contact of the brass plates on the side of their axis opposite to that of the driver. The axis of the connecting plates is movable along the line of centers of the driver and follower disks, so that any ratio of radii within the limits of the design can be secured. In this lathe also the screw is not clamped between the two halves of a nut, but a half-nut presses against the screw laterally, and flexure is prevented by the shape of the shear casting. In the Sellers small lathe the rod-feed is often driven by their frequent device of a concealed worm or spiral pinion. In the Miles lathe the feed is driven by an original device to avoid the loss of time in changing the gear-train (Fig. 106). The live-spindle is

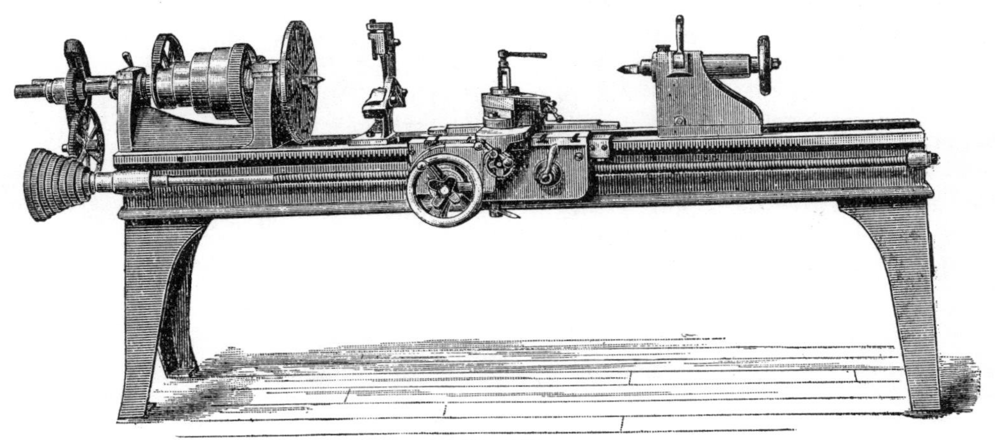

Fig. 106.

prolonged for some distance at the head of the lathe, and is splined to carry a spur-wheel and pinion. At the rear of this spindle is a round horizontal pillar, upon which slides an arm, carrying an idle wheel on a horizontal stud which can connect either spur-wheel or pinion to a nest of gear-wheels of different diameters fast on the screw. The pillar is graduated so that the edge of the arm may be rightly clamped to cause the proper thread to be cut. Changes of feed speed by this arrangement are very simple and rapid and the gear is durable. The racks under the shears are usually in segments, screwed in place. They are of wrought iron, steel, or cast iron. Steel is preferred by some because of the weakness of the teeth of fine racks under strain of the feed.

The screw for the cross-feed of the tool-post is most frequently engaged by a second friction-clutch operated like the other by a screw (Fig. 78). This takes hold of the gear before the other, so that both may be used at once or only the one which is required.

The arrangement shown in Fig. 104 is a type of another system where the connection is made by moving an idle pinion into the train. The pinion K is on a stud upon an arm which turns around the axis of the driving cone-wheel F. A slight motion of the arm around its center will put the idle pinion into gear with the pinion on the cross-screw P. This can only be reversed by reversing the motion of the rod. For large wheel-turning lathes and the like, the cross-feed has often been driven by a click and ratchet motion by a weighted lever (Fig. 107). A

Fig. 107.

rope passes from an adjustable crank at the head-stock to a pivoted lever overhead, and from thence a second rope comes down to the ratchet lever on the screw. The intermittence of the motion is compensated for in the spring of the tool. A longitudinal ratchet-feed is not now used to any extent (Fig. 86). The saddle may be clamped against longitudinal motion when cross-feeding by a movable gib, or by any convenient device.

To avoid the inconvenience that the friction-cones in the apron will sometimes set themselves, a designer in Philadelphia makes the clutch cylindrical, of a split steel ring, kept open by a little cam. When the cam is turned the ring closes and engages the gear. There are several devices in use to prevent the unintentional seizure of the conical forms.

Every lathe has certain accessory appliances as part of its furniture. One of these is called the "steady-rest". It is intended to support long cylindrical work which might sag by its own weight between centers. It consists of a frame to support three radial sliding jaws which can be moved toward the axis of the tool by screws. The rest

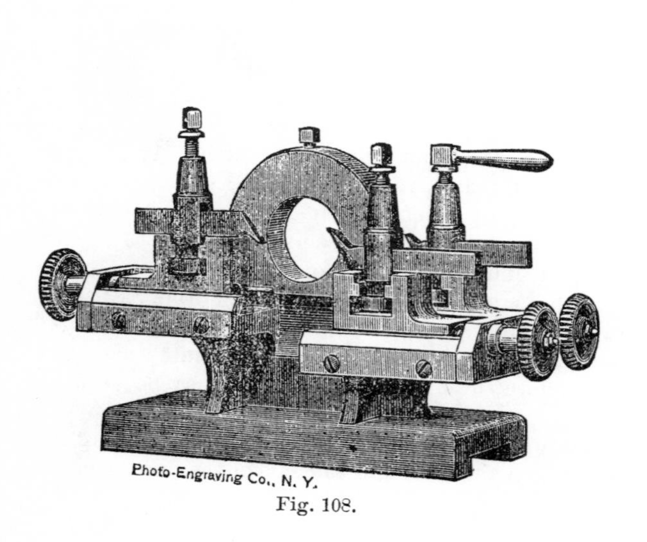

Fig. 108.

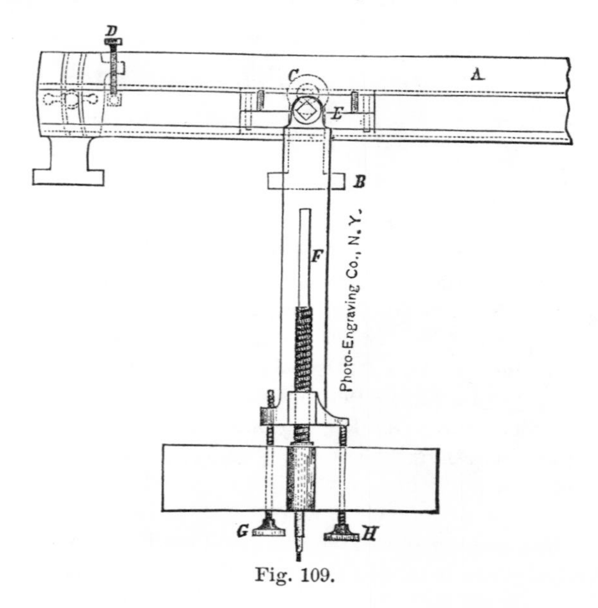

Fig. 109.

stands on the shears and is clamped by a cross-piece below. The cylindrical frame which holds the jaws is split at the horizontal diameter for convenience of inserting and removing work, two of the jaws lying at angles of 30° below the horizontal line. When the work is not cylindrical, a shell "doctor" with radial set-screws in pairs can be secured to the work so as to turn centrally upon the jaws of the rest. To resist the horizontal spring of light work away from the tool-point, a "back-rest" is used. A curved upright bolts in T-slots in the carriage, and adjustable jaws oppose the pressure of the tool. These difficulties are overcome in lathes for turning shafting by making the rest on the duplex system (Fig. 108). There are two tools opposite each other, one turned up and one turned down. A third tool may produce the finishing cut, and the shaft may be sized perfectly by a hollow reamer.

A type of the attachments for turning tapers on a lathe is shown in plan in Fig. 109, and in place on the lathe in Fig. 110. At the back of the bed are three brackets which carry a grooved bar. This bar can be adjusted

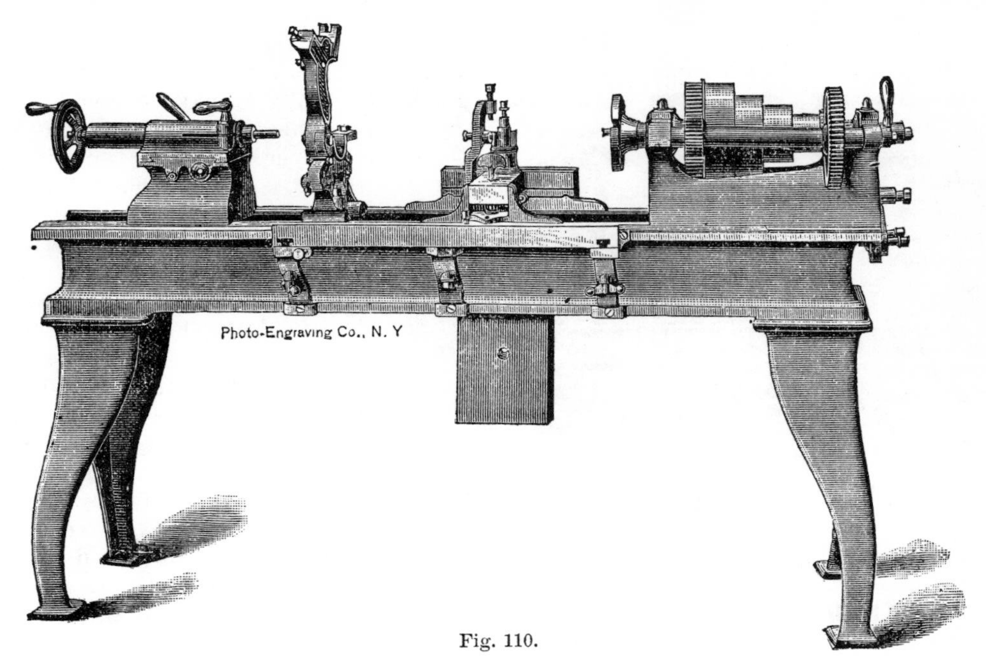

Fig. 110.

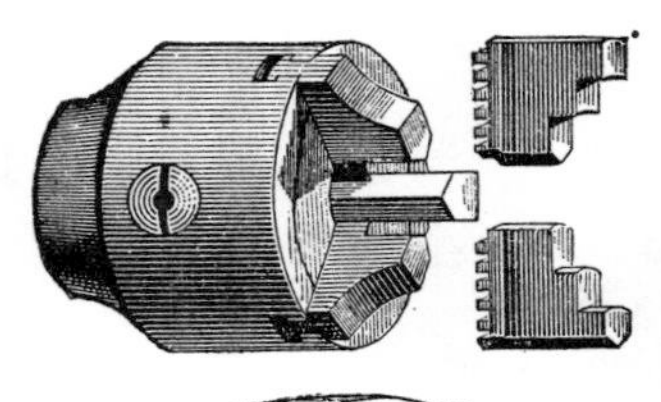

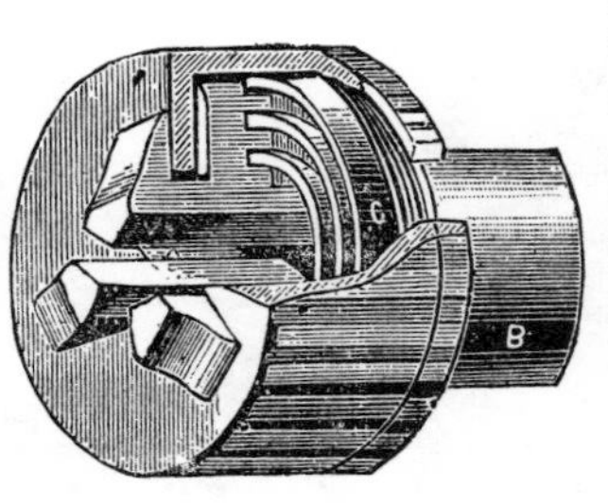

Fig. 111 *b*.

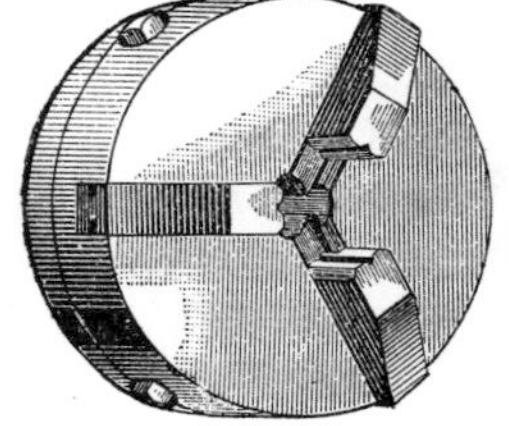

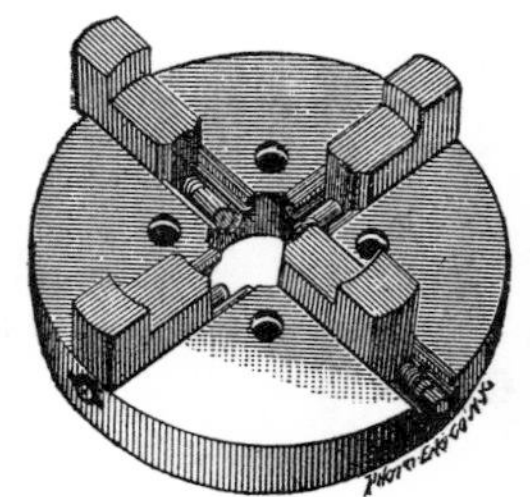

Fig. 111 *a*.

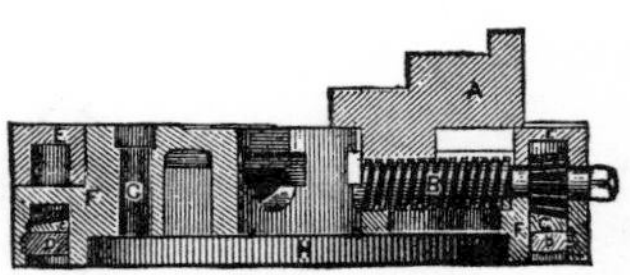

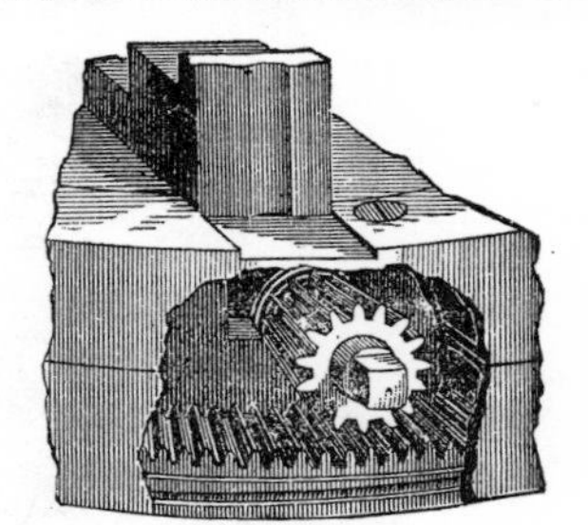

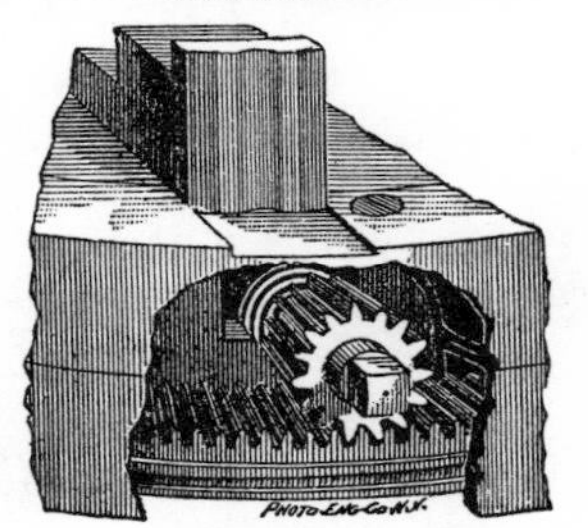

Fig. 112.

parallel to the axis of the tool or at any angle with its horizontal projection. In this groove slides a block, E, which is pinned to the nut-bar F, which slides in a groove in the lower part of the tool-carriage. G and H are stop-screws to be used in outside and inside work respectively. When the bar A is swung around its center pin, C, and clamped into the required position as determined by the tangent-screw D, a gradual transverse motion is imparted to the upper part of the tool-carriage in and out from the centers. This type of attachment is unaffected by the length of the piece, requires no preliminary cuts for trial of the taper, works as well for inside work as for outside, and avoids setting the centers out of line. A similar type which avoids any lost motion of the slide in the groove holds the guiding surfaces in contact by a weight over a pulley.

A universal or self-centering chuck is a usual accessory. These are made for small and medium lathes upon two principles. The jaws are usually three or four in number, sliding in radial grooves. The scroll-chucks have a plate with a continuous flat spiral groove cut in it. The jaws have projecting lips, which enter the groove, and when the scroll-plate is turned the jaws all move equally toward the center (Fig. 111 *b*).

The second type has the jaws mounted and moved inward by screws. These screws have each a small pinion near the outer end meshing into a large gear concentric with the chuck. When one of the screws is turned the others must all turn equally and the jaws will move to the center. Fig. 111 *b* shows a type of scroll-chuck. Fig. 112 is a screw-chuck of the second type. The screw type enables the lost motion due to wear to be taken up. Each screw can be separately tightened by the wrench in this form, since the two gears may be disengaged. The special chucks, the drill-chucks, and the eccentric-chuck, the mandrels, and the dogs and drivers, are articles of especial purchase or manufacture.

§ 17.

SPECIAL FORMS OF LATHE.

Special constructions of lathes are adapted for special uses. Where a large chucking capacity may be called for, but only average swing over the rest of the bed, a gap-lathe (Fig. 113) may be used. This gap may be permanent, or the shears may be in two tiers, the upper or working bed sliding over the gap when it is not needed. Where work is always to be of large diameter and flat, of such a shape as to be worked best on the face-plate, the bed may be made short and the tail-stock may be omitted. This form of lathe will be called a chucking-lathe (Fig. 114). For very large fly-wheels and work of that class a chucking-lathe only is required, and very often the face-plate and tool-carriage rest upon separate foundations, and are really separate machines.

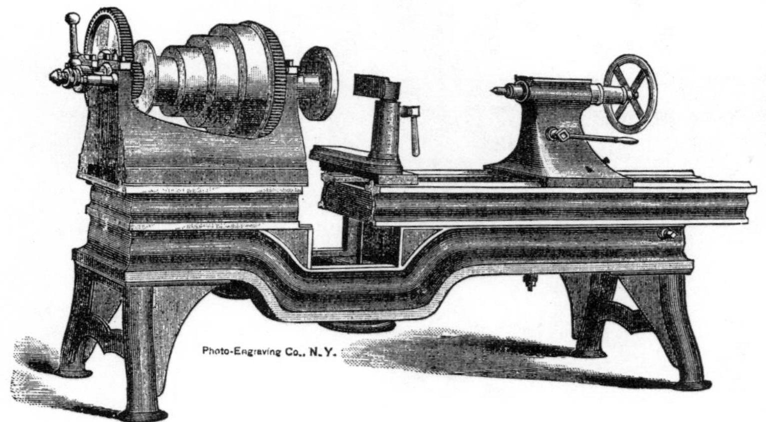

Fig. 113.

A lathe especially adapted for locomotive driving-wheels is shown by Fig. 115. There are two large face-plates driven from pinions on splined shafts. This avoids the twisting strain on the axle when the resistance comes at the end of a long lever. The frames of the heads are of the box pattern, giving great stiffness. There are two tool-

Fig. 114.

posts, and a facing-rest may be secured to the face-plates. Upon the tool-posts may be secured a quartering device for boring the holes for crank-pins at exactly 90° with each other. In other forms of this same tool the quartering attachments are secured to the frames, so that the spindle passes through the face-plates. The tool-posts clamp in place and are fed from overhead.

Fig. 115.

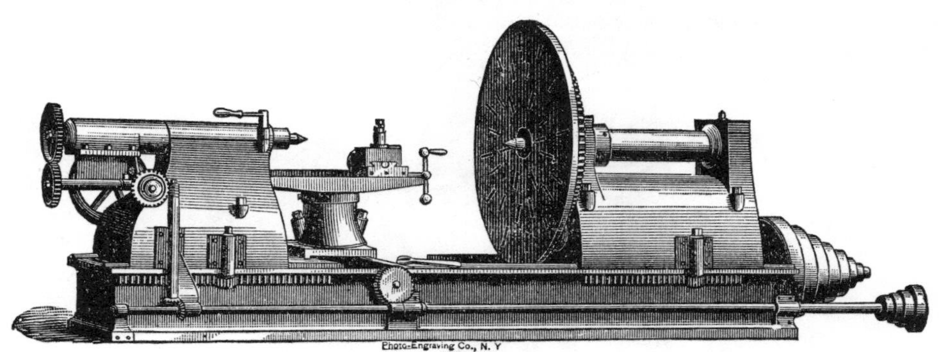

Fig. 116.

Fig. 117.

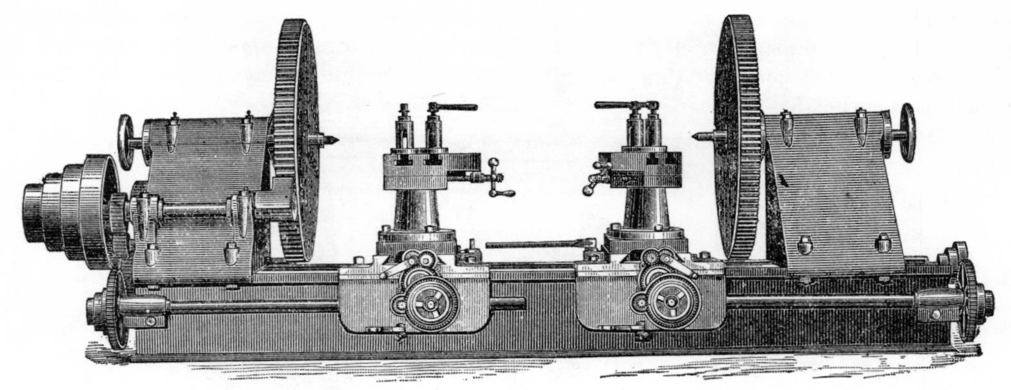

Fig. 118.

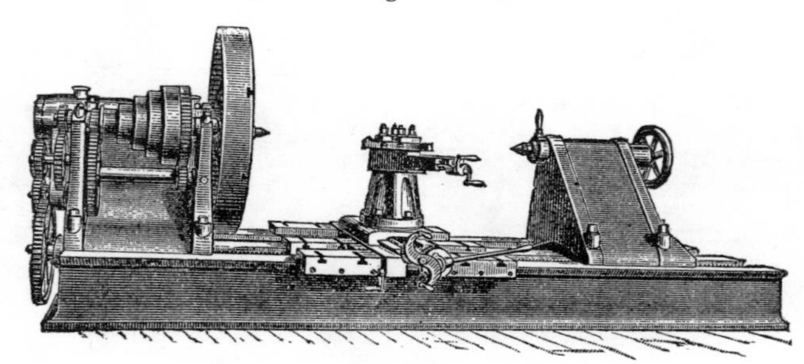

Fig. 119.

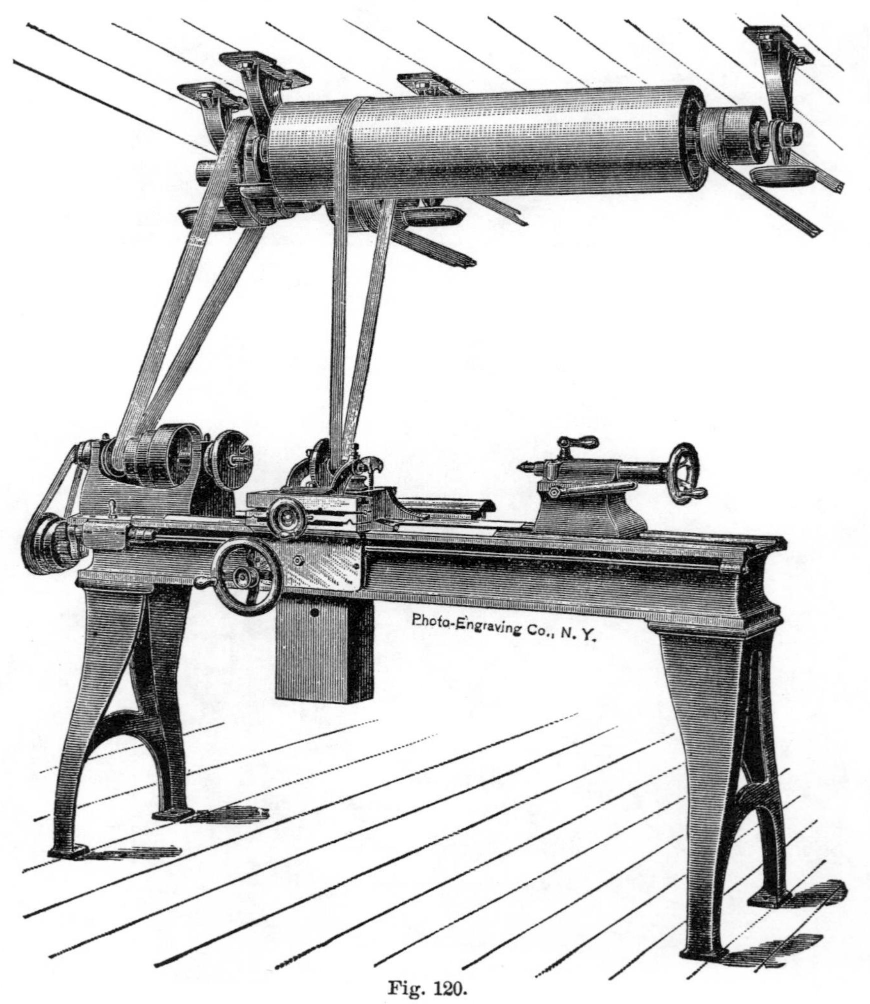

Fig. 120.

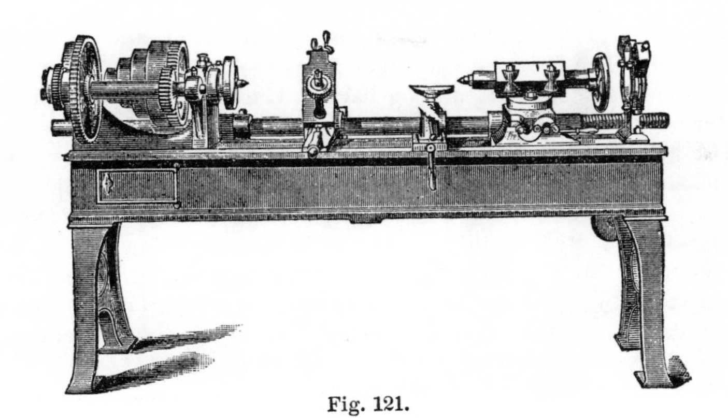

Fig. 121.

Fig. 122.

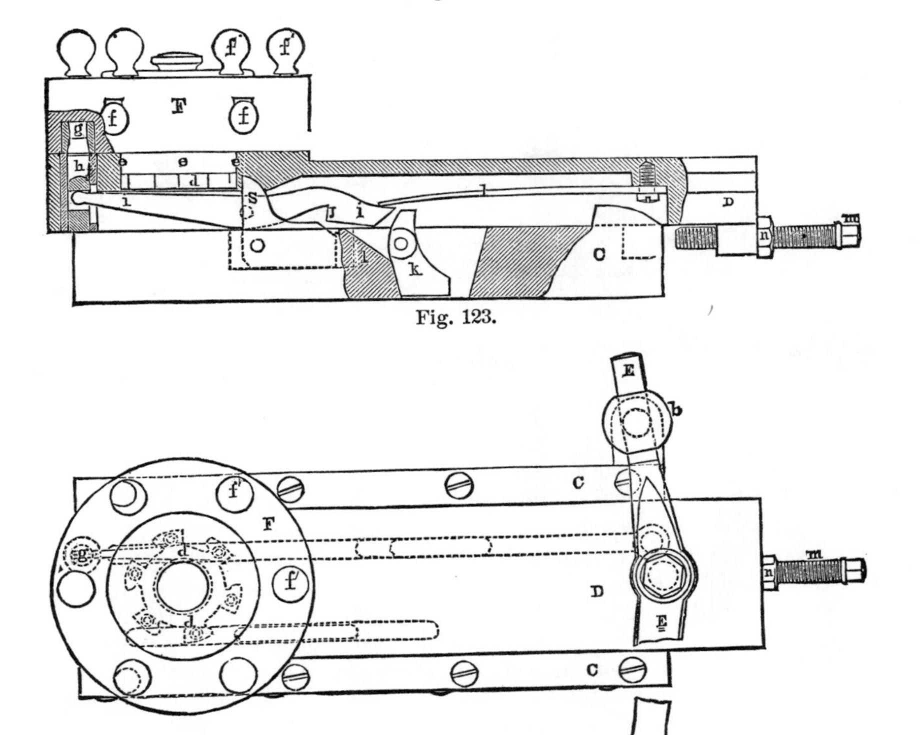

Fig. 123.

Fig. 124.

The lathe of Fig. 116 has one or two stationary tool-posts. The head- and tail-stock are both made movable by rack and pinion along the bed. The face-plate is driven from a splined shaft below the shears. The tail-spindle has power-feed for boring from the feed-shaft at the back. The feed for the tool is carried up vertically by bevel-gear through the center of the post, and at the top is carried to the feed-screws by double bevel-gear, giving motion forward or backward at will. The driving-axis, being central to the post, permits feed at any angle. The movable heads with stationary post gives great steadiness and stiffness. A slightly different tool with similar facilities is shown by Fig. 117. Figs. 118 and 119 show types of lathes of very large swing.

For the exact sizing of hardened steel spindles and the like the cutting has to be done by an emery-wheel. Fig. 120 shows the arrangement for such lathes, the grinding-spindle being driven by a separate counter-shaft, with a long drum. The shear-tracks are protected from the emery-dust by guards. The slide-rest has an automatic longitudinal traverse in both directions, the reversing being done by double bevel-gears and a clutch connected with the feed-rod. It can grind tapers as well as cylindrical surfaces.

For reduplicating small chucked work in the soft metals what is called a chasing-lathe (Fig. 121) is in very general use. It is not intended for turning work between centers, but it can be so used if desired. The head-stock receives motion in the usual way by cone-pulleys and back-gear. The tail-stock has also two motions, so that a tool can be inserted in the squared spindle, and by working the cross-feed to a stop any standard diameter can be reproduced without the loss of time for calibrating. It can also be set to cut tapers. The slide-rest is clamped upon a guided bar at the back, and is brought to its work by a handle, which is pressed down upon the front shear. The tool-post is fed upon an inclined shear by a screw. An arm on the guided bar carries a half-nut, which is brought into gear with a chasing-hob, driven from the live-spindle by the movement of the handle which brings the tool to its cut. The spindle carrying the hobs can carry two of different pitches, and a single-pointed tool can cut single, double, or quadruple threads. The slide-rest is counter-weighted so as to be brought up against a collar on either side at will when released from the chasing-hob. This collar can also serve as stop to prevent any given operation from being carried further than a certain length on the work. A hand-rest enables small finishing and chamfering cuts to be made by hand. A tool of this kind is adapted for miscellaneous work in brass, such as globe-valve and lubricator work, which it does very rapidly, exactly, and at one chucking.

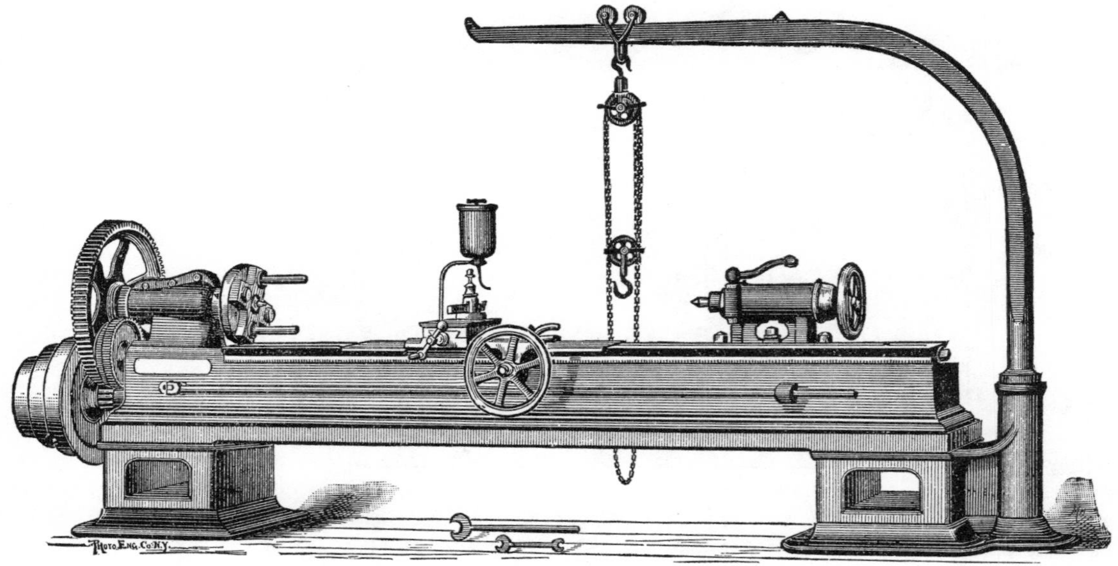

Fig. 125.

A similar tool, differing only in the construction of the tail-stock, is shown by Fig. 122. This tool is fitted with what is called a turret-head. A vertical cylinder, like a monitor turret, has six radial openings in the vertical surface, each of which carries a tool adapted for a different operation on the work. After the lower block has been clamped, the turret may receive its various motions by levers or by screws acting against adjustable stops. The interior construction of the turret-head and slide of one of the best forms is shown by Figs. 123 and 124. The lever E moves the slide D to the right and to the left. As the slide D carries the turret F to the right, the lug S strikes projections d on the bottom of the turret and gives it a partial rotation around its axis. That the proper amount of rotation may be given and the turret locked in the right place is the object of the pin h. This pin is thrown up into spaced holes in the bottom of the turret by the lever i, when it is released from the catch k. When D is moved to the right the pin is withdrawn from the hole g, and the end of i passes over the catch k. The movement of D in the other direction causes i to be released from k, and when the hole comes opposite the pin the spring *r* forces the former upward and locks the turret. The pin and the bushing *s* of the holes are made conical, so as to come to an exact fit, and are hardened to prevent wear. In the lathe illustrated the disagreement of the centers, which is such an annoyance in turret-lathe work, is avoided by an especial device. The head-stock swivels, and at its juncture with the bed is a tongue which permits the head to be raised by the elevating-screw under the head while preventing lateral displacement. If the centers do not agree, standard tools in the turret will turn work out of size.

For turning locomotive- and car-axles an especial design of lathe is preferred. These are of two kinds, the single head and the double head. The single-head machine acts on one end at a time only. Such an one would

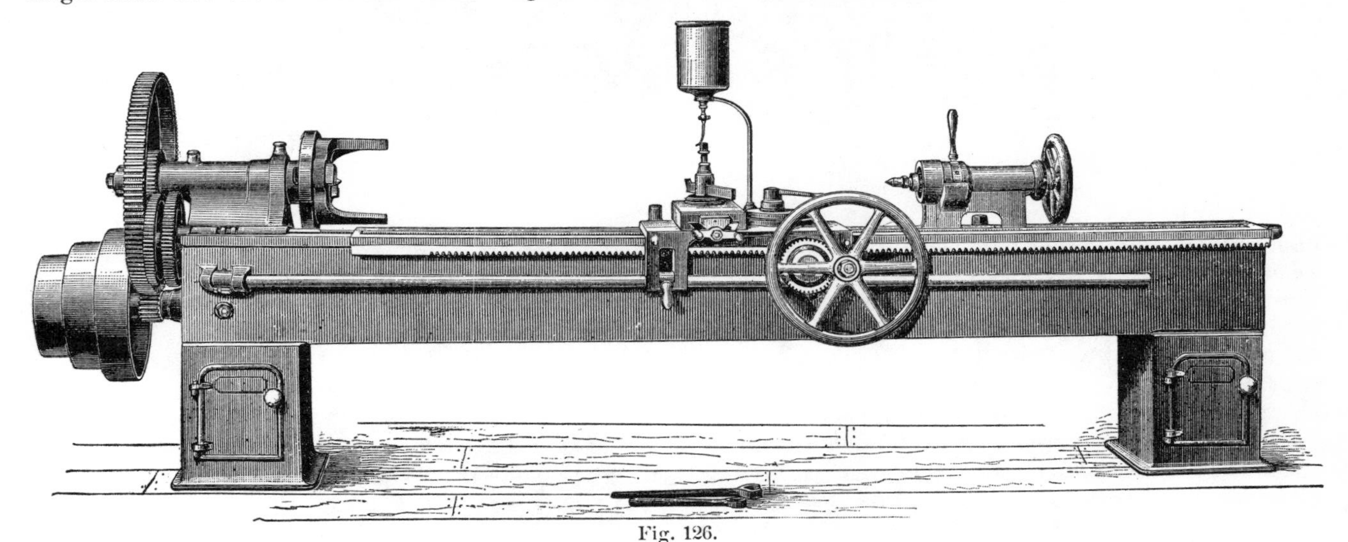

Fig. 126.

be illustrated by Fig. 125. The shears are flat, since the strain can come inside of them, the tail-head moving on a lower plane than the carriage. The head-stock is made adjustable for wear by the split in the casing, which is

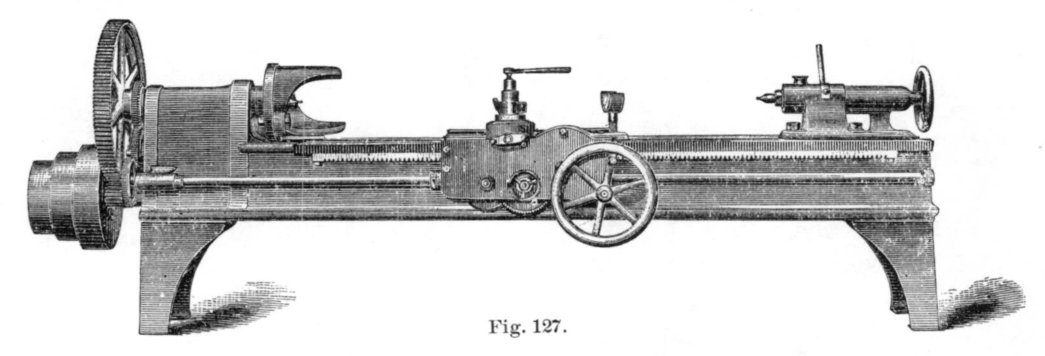

Fig. 127.

kept together by bolts. To equalize the turning strain on the axle when under the cut it is driven by two pins on the face-plate. There are two speeds of the tool for roughing and finishing which are caused by the two sets of pulleys on the counter-shaft. The two sets of feeds are produced at the head by the rod in front of the bed. The crane with differential pulley-gear enables the work to be handled easily.

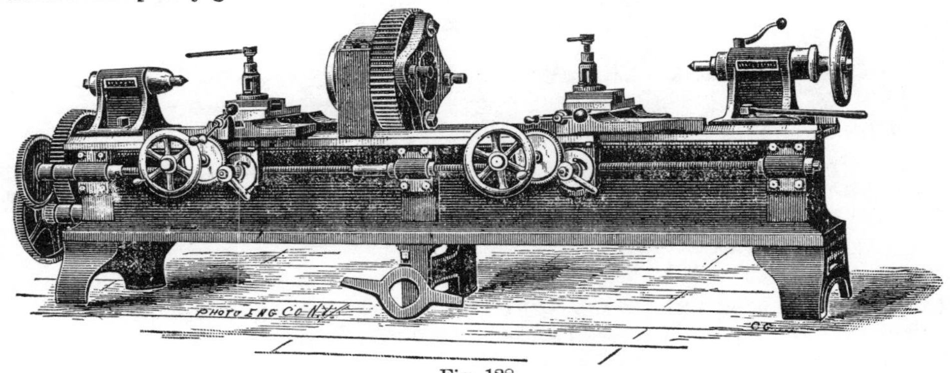

Fig. 128.

Differing only in some of the details are the car-axle lathes shown in Figs. 126 and 127. The lathe of Fig. 128 is one of the double-headed type. The axle is driven by a driver from the middle, and there is a tool-post for each

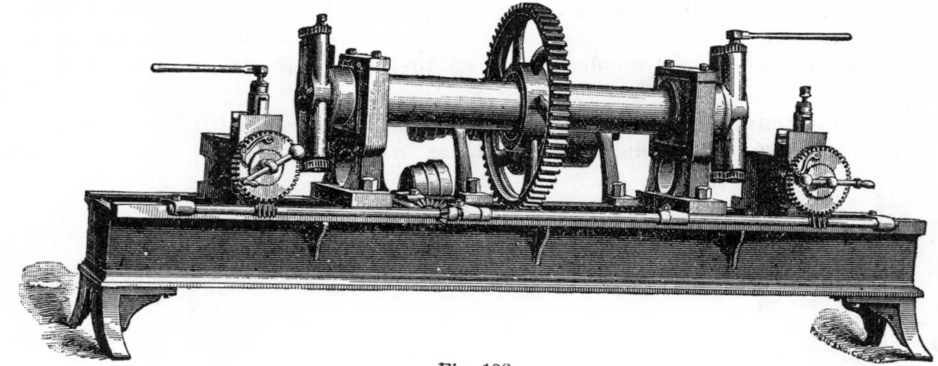

Fig. 129.

end, so that the two ends may be worked at once. The driving-pin plate is not rigidly bolted to the gear-wheel head, but has a certain diametral adjustment in slots. This enables the driver to be acted on equally by both pins,

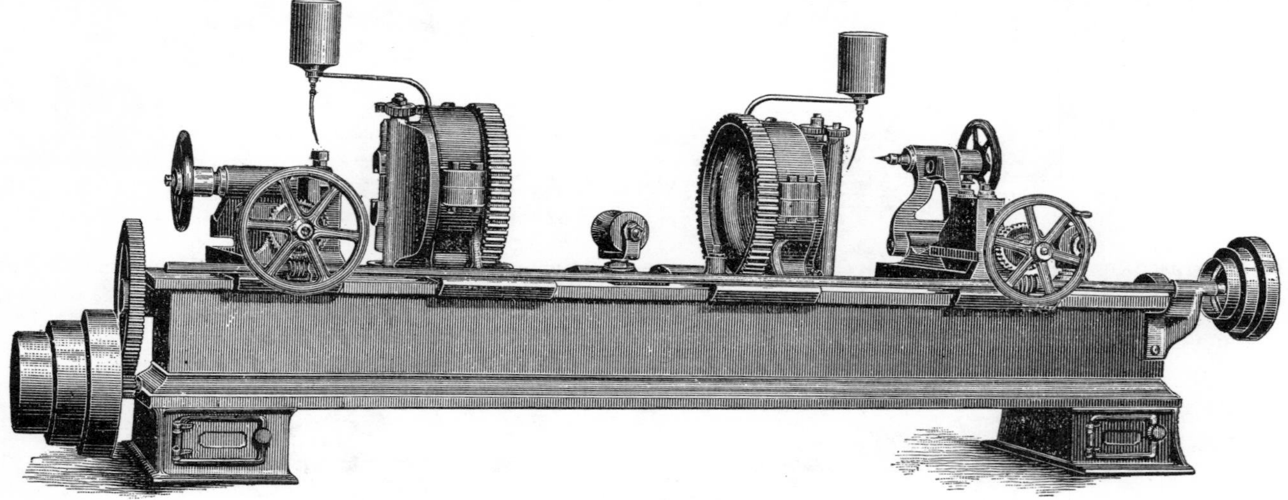

Fig. 130.

and avoids the tendency to spring sidewise which is not infrequently manifested when the axle is driven from a jaw-chuck. When this happens the work is out of round when released.

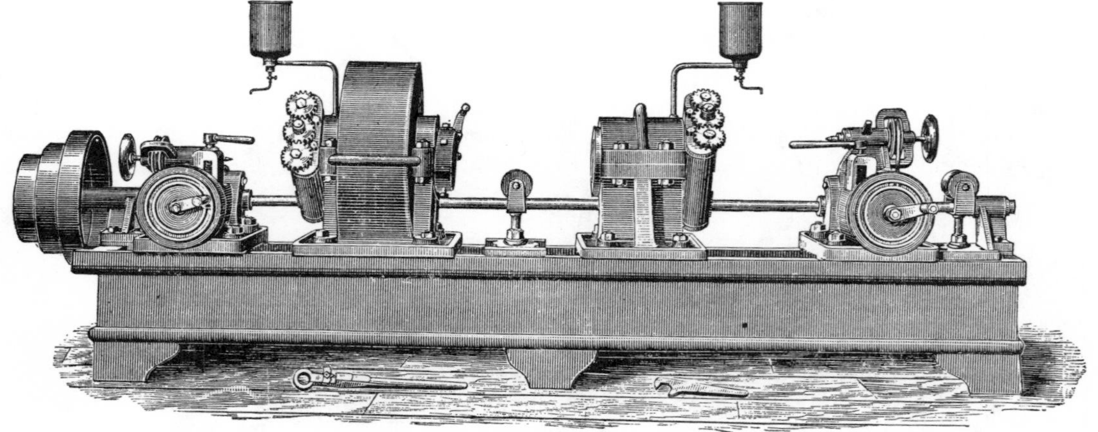

Fig. 131.

Another type of double-headed lathe is shown by Fig. 129. The axle is driven by jaws close to the cut, and the slide-rests have lateral and longitudinal power feed. By this system it is unnecessary to center the axles after being cut.

For cutting off and centering axles as they come from the hammer the tool shown by Fig. 130 is in use. The axle is driven at each end from the splined shaft within the bed, and cutting-off tools are fed against them at the proper length. When the crop-ends are removed the centering-heads may be fed into the end to drill and countersink for the center of the lathe which is to follow. The centering-heads can be swung out of the way when not in use. Fig. 131 illustrates another form of the same tool. A machine for centering only, after the crop ends have been removed, is shown by Fig. 132. The jaws are moved by right-and-left screw, and the center drill is fed rapidly by a rack and hand-wheel. An axle can be centered in three minutes by this machine.

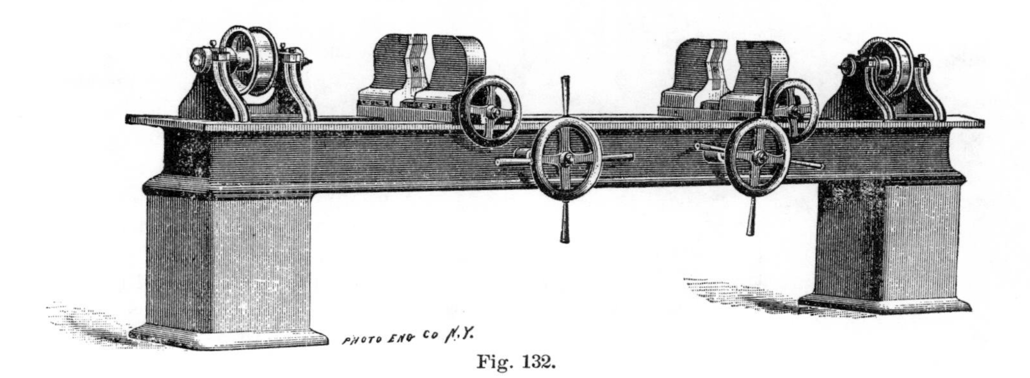

Fig. 132.

The lathe shown in Fig. 133 differs from the preceding in using a bed of a cylindrical section, with flats raised for the poppet-head and slide-rest. The feed is by a worm of four threads meshing into a rack on the front of the bed. The axle is driven by what is known as Clements' driver on the face-plate. The gearing is strong enough to rough out the journal in one cut of a depth of $\frac{3}{4}$ or $\frac{7}{8}$ of an inch. For centering the rough axle and sizing the wheel-fit the machine shown in Fig. 134 is used. The axle is driven from a powerful chuck lined with brass. This

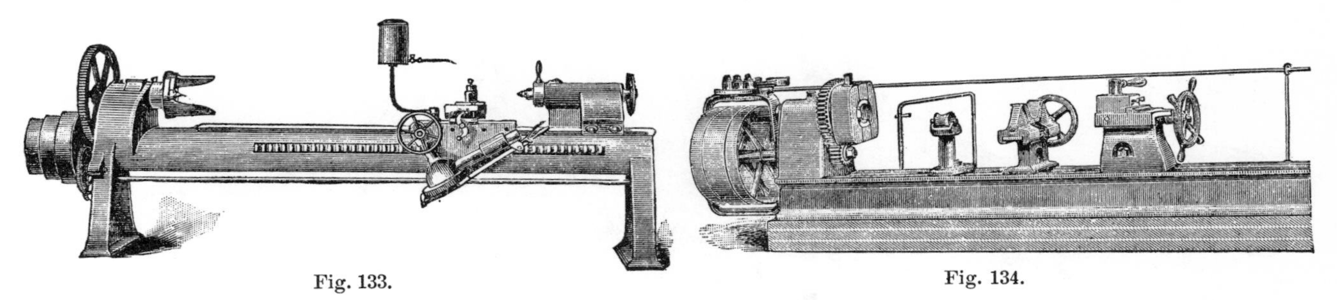
Fig. 133. Fig. 134.

may clasp the axle by its collar when it is finished. The free end is held in an adjustable V-guide, and the end of the axle is squared and centered by a tool fed to it. The wheel-fit is sized exactly by a hollow reamer with adjustable blades. With these conveniences it is claimed that this tool and the lathe make it possible to produce from eighteen to twenty axles per man per ten hours.

With the lathes for axles should be discussed those lathes designed specially for finishing pulleys. Fig. 135

Fig. 135.

shows an ordinary lathe design of large swing, specially altered for pulley-work. The chief differences are in the use of two tool-rests of variable ratchet-feed, and in the arrangements to permit the face to be turned crowning.

Fig. 136 shows a special pulley-machine for taking bored pulleys on a mandrel. This system has the advantage over the chucking system of turning the pulley more under the same conditions in which it is afterward to be run on a shaft. The pulley is secured on the mandrel by its own set-screws or keys, although it is driven by driver-pins on the gear-wheel, resting against its arms. A former attachment will turn the face crowning. For filing or polishing the mandrel may be driven directly by the belt-wheel on the spindle.

Fig. 136.

A similar tool is shown by Fig. 137, except that worm-gear is used to drive the mandrel, and the driver-pins are adjustable upon the face-plate to equalize the strain on the pulley-arms. The crowning is effected by setting over one end of the tool-post rail, according to the graduations. The worm-wheel on the feed-screw is relieved to permit this adjustment. The turned pulley is polished by securing it to the end of the worm-shaft, and the two operations of turning and polishing may go on at once.

Fig. 138 shows a double pulley-lathe on the mandrel system. The mandrel may be supported on a head with adjustable center, and the faces may be turned flat or crowning. Each slide has an independent self-acting feed, with automatic disengaging gear.

Fig. 137.

An objection to the mandrel system in these forms is that the pulley must first be chucked and the hole in the hub must be bored before the wheel can be put on the special lathe. This requires two tools, and some of the forms of boring-machine must precede the pulley-lathe.

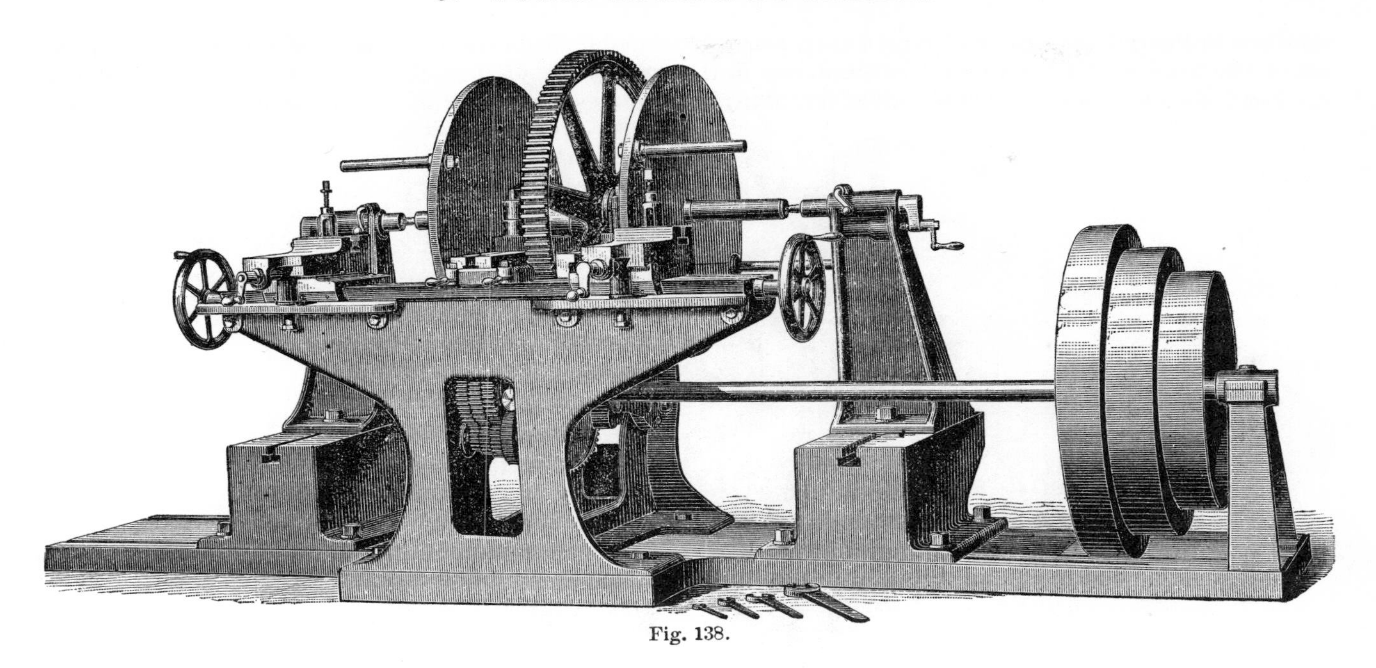

Fig. 138.

§ 18.

VERTICAL LATHES AND BORING-MACHINES.

The distinction between a lathe and a boring-machine is somewhat one of convention. Any lathe can be used as a boring-machine, either by securing the work to the chuck or by securing the work to the carriage and supporting a boring-bar between the centers. Especially is the distinction elusive when applied to the vertical machines. To carry out a possible analogy from the horizontal machines, a lathe would be a tool where the work revolved while the tool has only linear motions, while a boring-machine would be one in which the work was stationary and a cutting-tool described the surface of revolution. Many vertical lathes, however, on this classification are currently known as boring-machines, because they are designed for one class of work only, such as pulley or car-wheel boring-machines. There are certain of them which come unmistakably under the class of lathes, since they can turn as well as bore.

Fig. 139 shows one form of turning- and boring-mill. The work is secured to the horizontal face-plate and the tool is carried by the holder upon the cross-head. The feed of the tool is self-acting in all directions by the twisted belt at the right. The idle shaft, connected to the driving-shaft by a link, keeps the belt tight by its weight and permits the cross-head to rise and fall. The cross-head is only finished to guide the tool-post for a little over one-half the swing of the tool, since the cut is intended to be resisted by the compression against the cross-head. The slide on the cross-head is fed horizontally by the screw and vertically or at any angle from the splined shaft above the latter. The shaft carries a bevel-gear, which turns the rod parallel to the axis of the holder through an idle pair of bevel-wheels. As these mills have large capacity, swinging from 84 to 120 inches in the different sizes, the large face-plate must be steadied. This is accomplished by making a V-ring on the lower side of the plate which projects into and fits a corresponding V-groove in the bed. This makes the motion as steady as that of a planer bed. An adjustable step at the center can be made to take up any desired amount of vertical strain in the preliminary work of chucking and centering.

Fig. 139.

Fig. 140 shows a similar design, with two tool-holders. The holders are each counter-weighted by a weight on a wire-rope over pulleys. ' The rope winds on a pulley with a spiral groove at the back of the holder, the circumference of the pulley being in the axis of the holder. This prevents the action of the weight from departing very much from the line of the action of gravity. The axis of the grooved pulley turns a pinion meshing into a rack on the side of the holder. The feeds for the tools are automatic in every direction and independent. The facing traverse is by screws which can feed in either direction. Their motion is received from the vertical shaft at the right, which

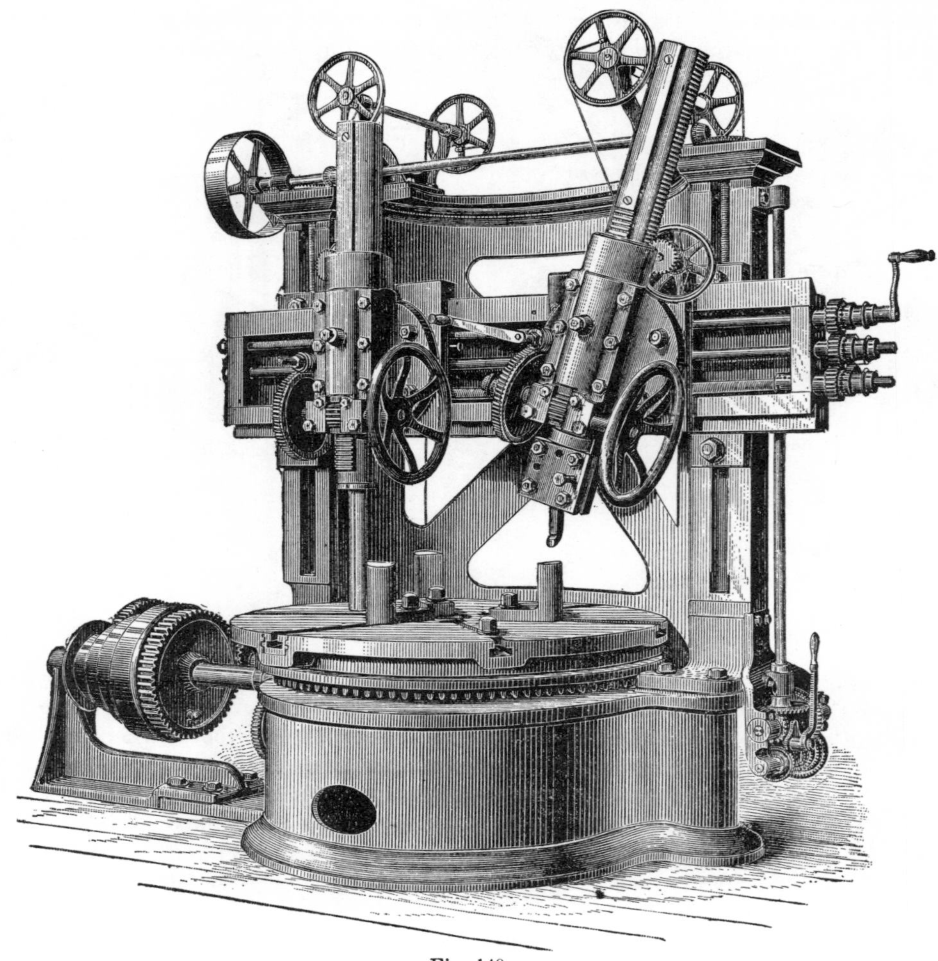

Fig. 140.

can be driven in either direction by the combination of three bevel-gears and a clutch from the cone-pulley shaft. Either cross-feed may be disengaged by a slip-jaw clutch on the end of the screw. For the downward and angular feeds the central splined shaft is used. A pair of bevel-gears, with clutch, is carried on the cross-slide. Between them is a third wheel, on whose shaft is a worm which turns a pinion-shaft and lifts and lowers the holder by a rack. The clutch to the worm-shaft is worked from behind the cross-head for change of direction, and the pinion-shaft is disengaged for convenient hand-feed and quick return by a slip-jaw clutch. The face-plate on the large sizes is driven by internal spur-gearing (Fig. 141) to avoid the lifting or bending action produced by bevel-gearing. The entire revolving weight is borne upon a central step. This consists of a loose steel disk, hardened and ground, which is placed between two others of a hard alloy of copper and tin. One is fast to the foot-step, and the other is on the revolving spindle. These disks are grooved for the distribution of oil, delivered through a tube under the center. Chips are kept from the lower bearing by guards.

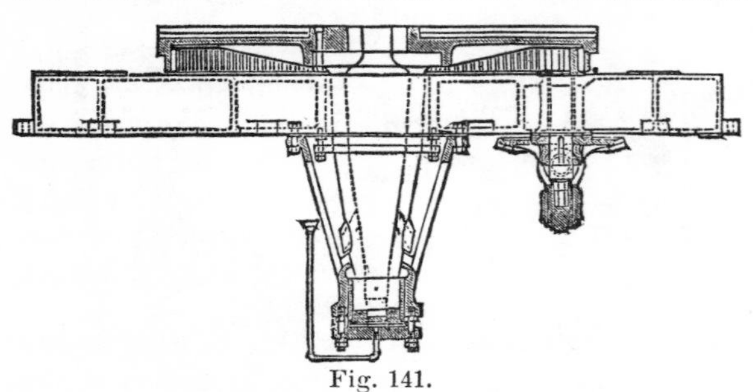

Fig. 141.

By the use of two holders a piece of work may be exposed to two operations at once. A pulley may be faced and bored at the same time, or a ring may be turned and faced at one operation. In another design the down-feed is given by a worm and wheel in front of the holder. The worm is driven by extensible shaft and universal joints for turning tapers. These tools are also made up to 12 feet swing. Some of the smaller sizes have the face-plate carried on a Schiele anti-friction curve, and a slotting attachment may be added for pulley-work.

A similar tool to the latter is shown by Fig. 142. It has the adjustable step for the spindle, controllable by the screw in front of the bed. The feeds are made variable in speed and direction by the brush-wheel combination at the right of the bed. The movable wheel is faced with leather, and adjusted by the hand-wheel. The tool-bars are counter-weighted, so as to have the pull of the weight always in the line of the axis without oblique stress on the guides. For pulley-work the adjustable driver-plate and carrier-pins are employed, and an adjustable dead-center is made use of. By setting the bars slightly oblique and feeding in opposite directions the pulleys will be

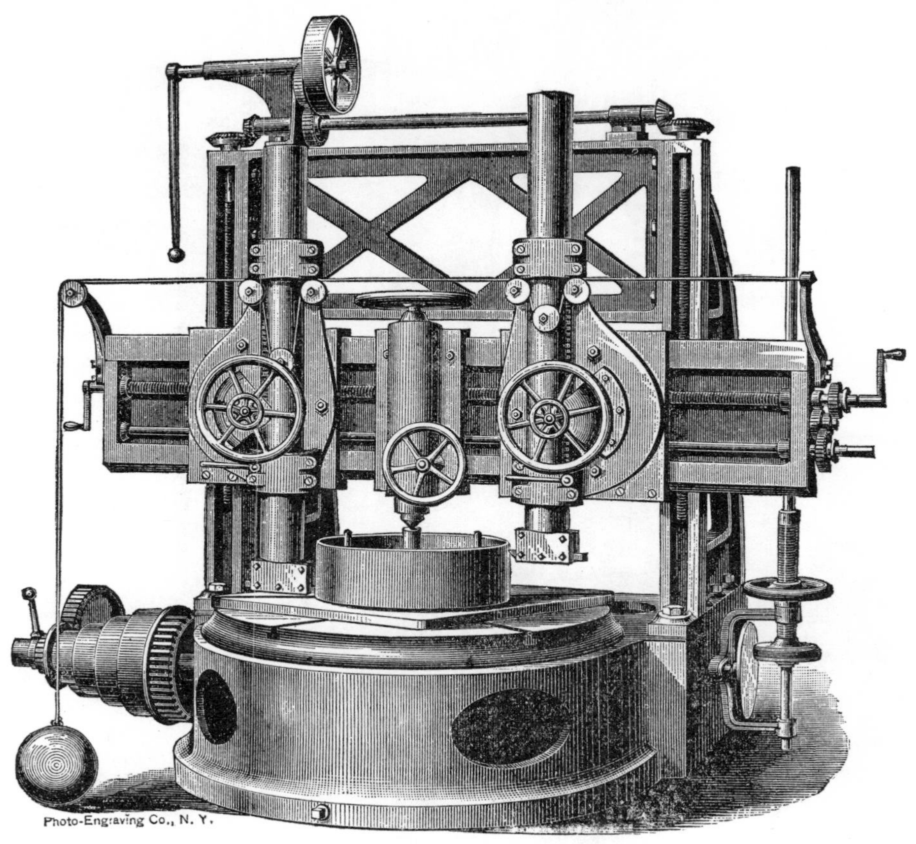

Fig. 142.

faced off with a crown. These tools are built of sizes to swing from 5 feet to 16 feet in diameter. In common with the other vertical lathes these tools have the advantage of simplifying the labor of chucking large and heavy work. All the time required to secure the work for the tests of its position on the face-plate is saved. The work will lie by its weight on the horizontal bed until located, while, when gravity has to be overcome on a vertical plate, the piece must be bolted fast. This property, with the conveniences of the double tool-bar, makes these tools of very wide and general usefulness. By removing the uprights of a very large mill of this class it may be used as a fly-wheel lathe for the largest diameters. The tool is held on a special upright on a floor-plate, and is fed by hand. Many drawbacks of the old chucking-lathe are thus avoided.

A very large number of vertical lathes of small swing are made for boring only and for special work. A type of these is shown by Fig. 143, adapted for boring-pulleys and car-wheels. The stiff boring-bar, counterpoised overhead, is held in the long adjustable bearing. It is fed downward by rack and pinion, driven by worm and wheel. The hand-feed quick-return is released by a friction-clutch. Specially for car-wheels the same builders have the tool shown by Fig. 144. The crane attachment is very convenient for chucking rapidly. Such tools are made with chucks of the self-centering and independent-jaw variety. They have capacity for wheels of 42 inches diameter.

Another form of car-wheel boring-machine is illustrated by Fig. 145. The adjustment for the bearing of the bar is effected by tightening the bolts upon the split casting. The counterpoising of the bar is by means of the weighted lever, which has a floating fulcrum to avoid side strain. The face-plate is adaptable for boring tapers, for the few conical fits which are used by some. It is made of two disks, the faces of both being beveled as they lie together. By changing the relation to each other of these two disks the horizontal adjustment is destroyed and a conical hole is bored. There is also a hub-facing attachment. The boring-mill of Fig. 146 feeds the tool down by a different mechanism. The hub-facing attachment has a slide independent of the boring-machinery, so that a

Fig. 143.

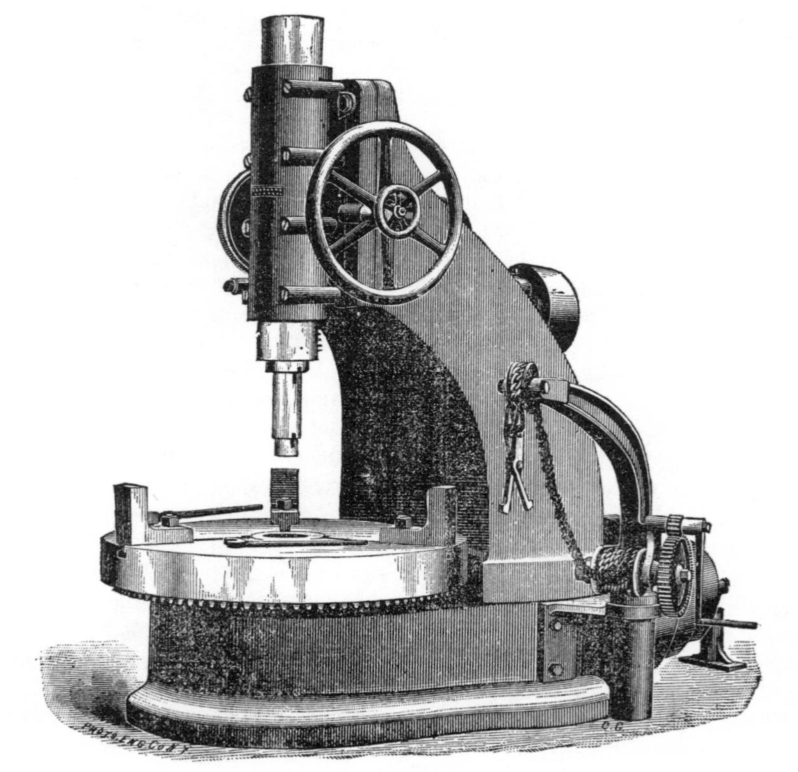

Fig. 144.

hub may be bored and faced at the same time. The crane attachment for lifting the wheels is hung from a davit overhead. It is a geared hoist. This machine has a claimed capacity for fifty wheels per ten hours.

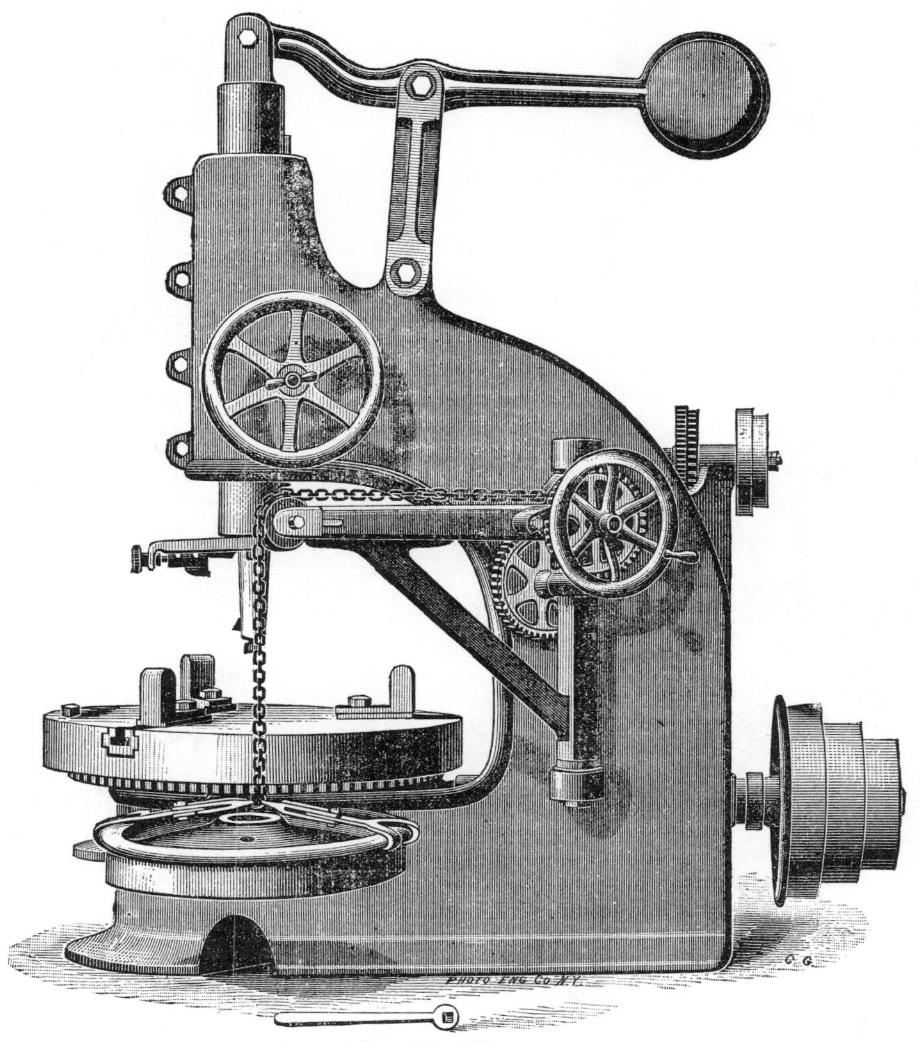

Fig. 145.

The borer of Fig. 147 takes up any lost motion around the bar by the glands at the top and bottom of the long bearing. These compress centrally a conical split sleeve when tightened down. The face-plate is carried upon a Schiele curve bearing, with a shoulder and ring at the top to prevent lateral jarring. The feed is by rack and pinion through worm-gear, engaged by friction. The gears are all external but boxed from dirt and accident. The roughing cut which should size to within $\frac{1}{32}$ of an inch is made with a feed of $\frac{1}{4}$ of an inch. The finishing cut is made with a feed of $\frac{3}{8}$ of an inch. By this machine a wheel can be chucked and bored in four minutes, as against seven minutes in the previous forms. The lifting-crane is also driven by power at the back.

For smaller work than this the table-borer (Fig. 148) is in use. The boring-bar is steadied and held by a counterpoised cross-head below the table. The feed is varied in either direction by the friction-disks between the desired limits, exactly as in the lathes of the same builders. The objection to these disks is their tendency to wear into rings, because of the sliding action where they overlap. All the borers of this type use the double cutters wedged into a slot in the bar (Fig. 149 *a* and *b*). The roughing-cutters wear more rapidly of course than those used for finishing. The first will probably lose its edge after boring four or five wheels; the other will last for more than ten times that number.

In all these forms of tool the horizontal chuck-plate permits very rapid adjustment of the wheels in place. Light hydraulic cranes are sometimes arranged to accommodate a number of tools, without requiring a special one for each.

For the boring of large vertical cylinders large shops usually have an especial apparatus, put up most frequently in a corner. A heavy boring-bar carries a spider or tool-carrier, which is moved up and down by a screw in the deep spline which compels the rotation of the carrier (Fig. 150). A large gear drives the bar and the carrier-head, and reducing gearing feeds down the screw. Sometimes the feed-gear is driven by an epicyclic

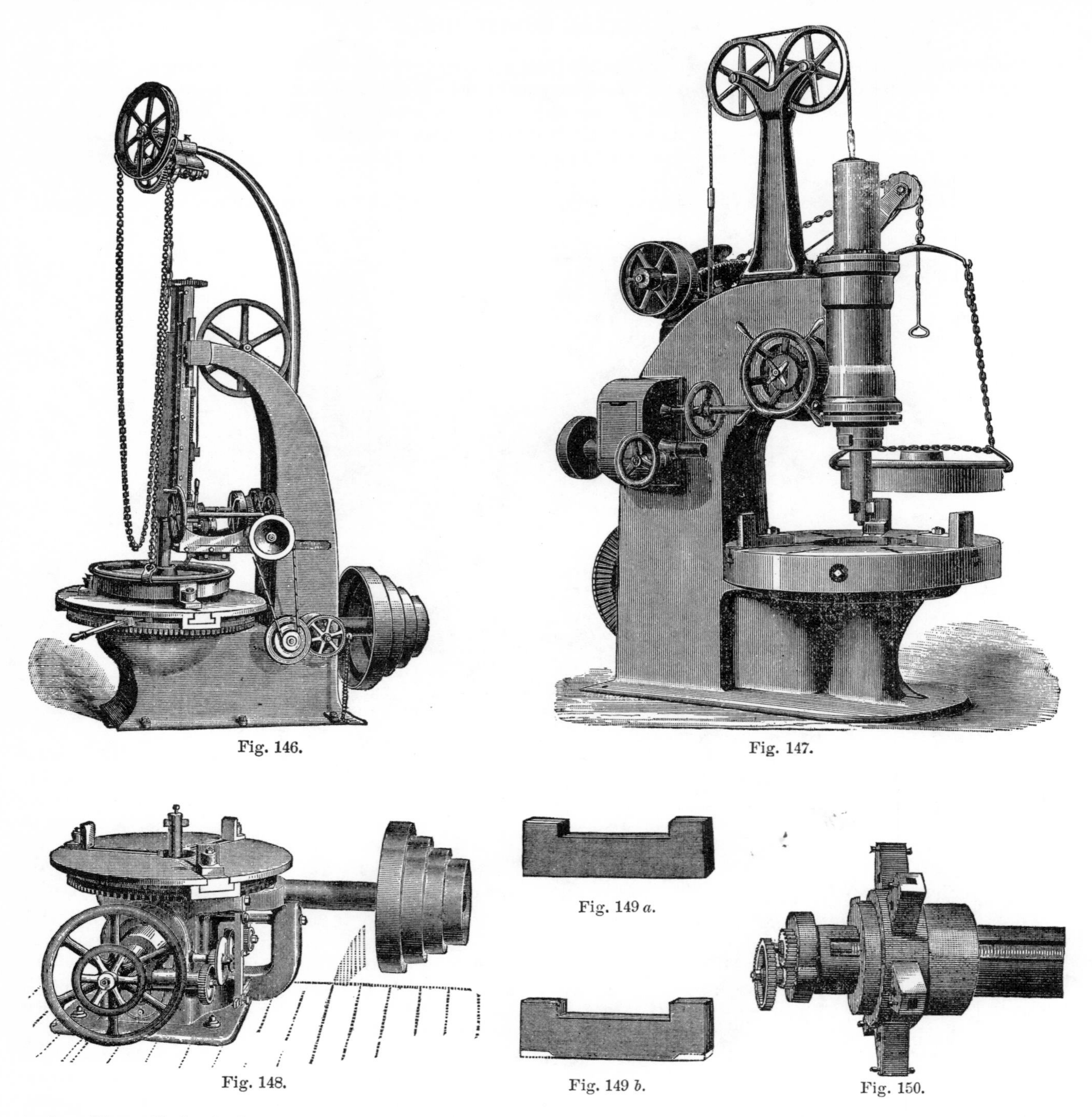

Fig. 146.

Fig. 147.

Fig. 148.

Fig. 149 *a*.

Fig. 149 *b*.

Fig. 150.

train. The cylinder is dogged and braced to a floor-plate at truly right angles to the bar. These machines have capacity for the largest cylinders.

§19.

HORIZONTAL BORING-MILLS.

The horizontal mills are especially adapted for bar-boring, either between centers or in bearings. The work is dogged to a table or carriage, which may be automatically fed or not, the feed in most cases being on the cutter-bar only. This type of tool is especially adapted for work in which the axis of the hole to be bored is parallel or not perpendicular to the chucking surface. It therefore lends itself easily to the boring of journal-boxes and hangers, of horizontal cylinders for engines and pumps, of elastic cylinders, and of cylinders without flanges, and work of that class.

For bar-boring between centers the machine of Fig. 151 is a type. The live-spindle is strongly back-geared,

Fig. 151.

turning in long bearings at each end. The bearings of both head- and tail-stock are lifted by screws geared together by bevel-gears to a longitudinal shaft under the shears.

This arrangement insures that the two centers shall always remain in line. The hand-wheel at the dead-center permits accurate adjustment. The carriage is compound, having a longitudinal motion in either direction by power, and a cross-feed by hand. The power feed is reversed by a clutch between two bevel-gears. In some forms of this tool, when using a compound boring-bar, the carriage and work are stationary and the feed of the carrier is moved by a star-wheel on an arm from the head of the bar. Like any boring-mill with centers, this tool can be used as a lathe by simply bolting a tool-post to the slotted carriage; and conversely, of course, any lathe can be used as a similar bar-boring mill. This tool has the advantage over the lathe, in that the work does not have to be blocked up into the axis of the centers. The work can be bolted to the carriage, and then the centers can be rapidly adjusted into place.

For bar-boring in journals, and for horizontal drilling, the type of machine shown in Fig. 152 is used. A column supports a head like a lathe poppet-head. The spindle is long and has a longitudinal traverse. It is heavily back-geared, and is fed forward by a screw driven by friction-disks. This permits wide variation of feed for holes of different diameters. There is also a hand-feed over the spindle. The front end of the spindle is bored tapering, and can receive either a drill or the end of a boring-bar. The table in front is carried upon screws which are moved together by a hand-wheel convenient to the operator. The carriage has a longitudinal traverse, by a screw moved by the second hand-wheel, and also an adjusting cross-traverse. For the use of a boring-bar, an adjustable bearing to steady its outer end may be clamped on the carriage. More frequently, however, when bar-boring is to be done, the yoke-system is preferred (Fig. 153). The hole in the top is in the center line of the spindle, and can be bushed for different diameters of bar. It can be bolted to any part of the bed-plate for different lengths of bar, and also serves to steady the free end of the table. The front of the column carries the long gibbed knee of the table, giving great stiffness when at work. The thrust of the spindle is taken up at the collars which embrace the bracket at the back. This bracket is guided at its foot, below V-guides, and is fed forward by a rack. This rack is driven by a worm and wheel, which is engaged with the hand-feed and quick-return by a friction-clutch. There are six changes of feed, three of which are for drilling and three for boring. The slowest feed will permit small holes to be drilled in steel; the fastest gives $\frac{1}{4}$ of an inch feed for finishing cuts in boring. The cut shows the raising and lowering gear driven by power. The tool may be run forward and backward at the same speed, so as to cut in either direction with the same cutters. The back-gear is compressed for ease of handling and compactness.

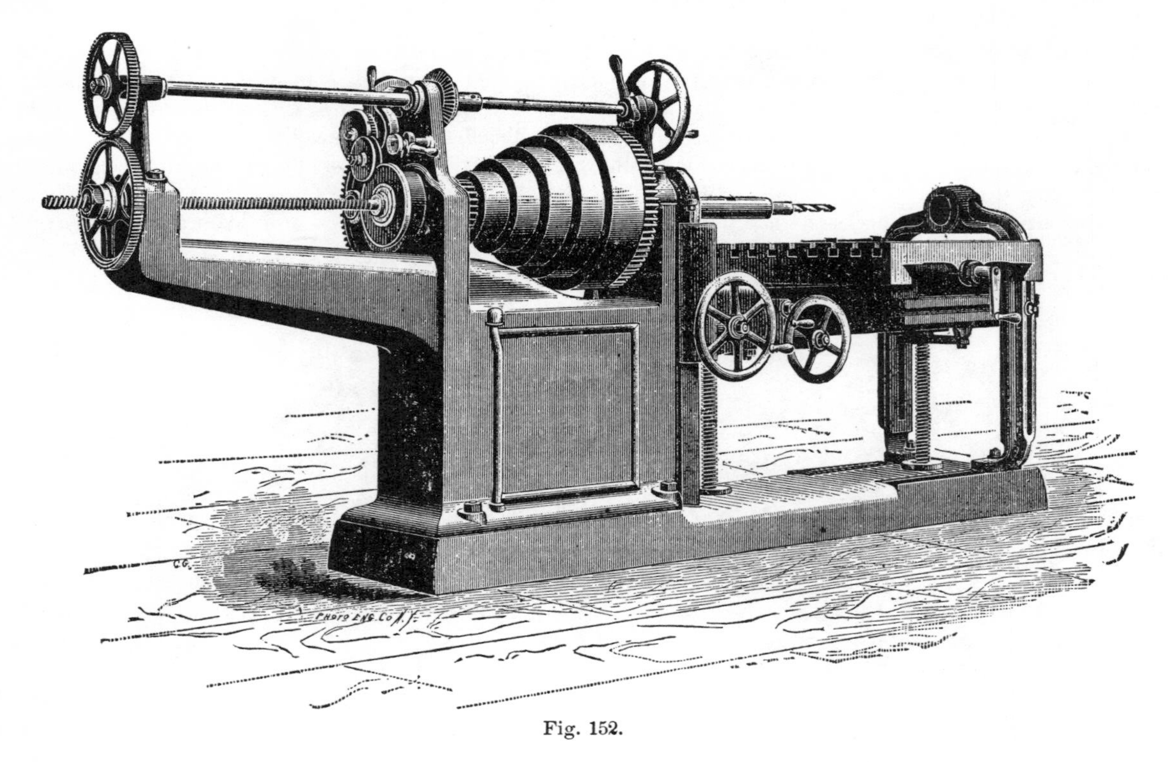

Fig. 152.

Fig. 154 differs only in the arrangement of the feed-gear. On one of the shafts are three loose gears. Each has a keyway cut in it. On the shaft is cut a spline till it meets a hole in the axis, in which slides a rod from the end. A key, fixed to the end of this rod, may be moved along the cut spline so as to come opposite the key-way in any of the gears, when it will slide into it, and make that gear fast to the shaft for the time. There is also a

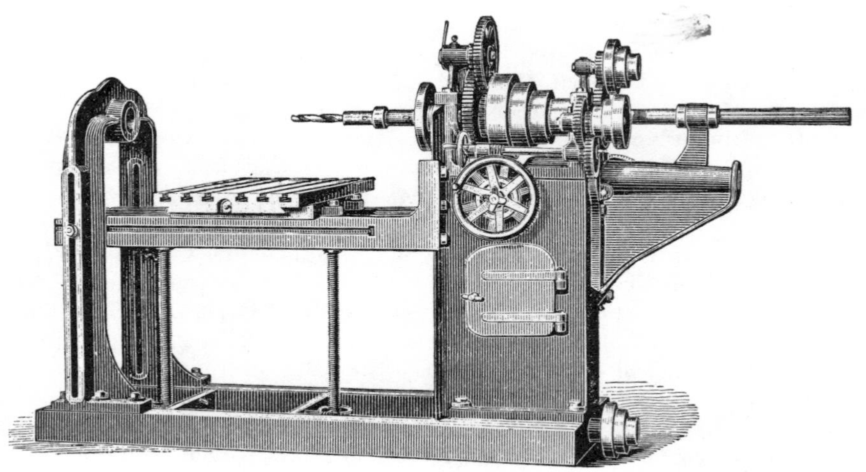

Fig. 153.

slow hand-feed and quick return. A facing-rest may be bolted to the face-plate, and will be fed by the star-wheel. The driving-pins are lightly bolted to the top of the head-casting. The thrust is taken up as before by collars against an arm from the guided slide, but in this design the arm is quite short. Sometimes a tail-screw is arranged on the slide to take up lost motion and to receive the thrust.

Where the work to be bored or drilled is very large or heavy, it is convenient to bolt it to the floor and to move the live-spindle into the proper position. Such a design is illustrated by Fig. 155. A large floor area is covered by a sole-plate with intersecting T-slots planed in it. In any position on this plate may bolt the lower block of the spindle upright. The upright has an adjustment laterally on guides upon this block for distances less than the intervals between the slots. The spindle may be clamped at any elevation above the plate within

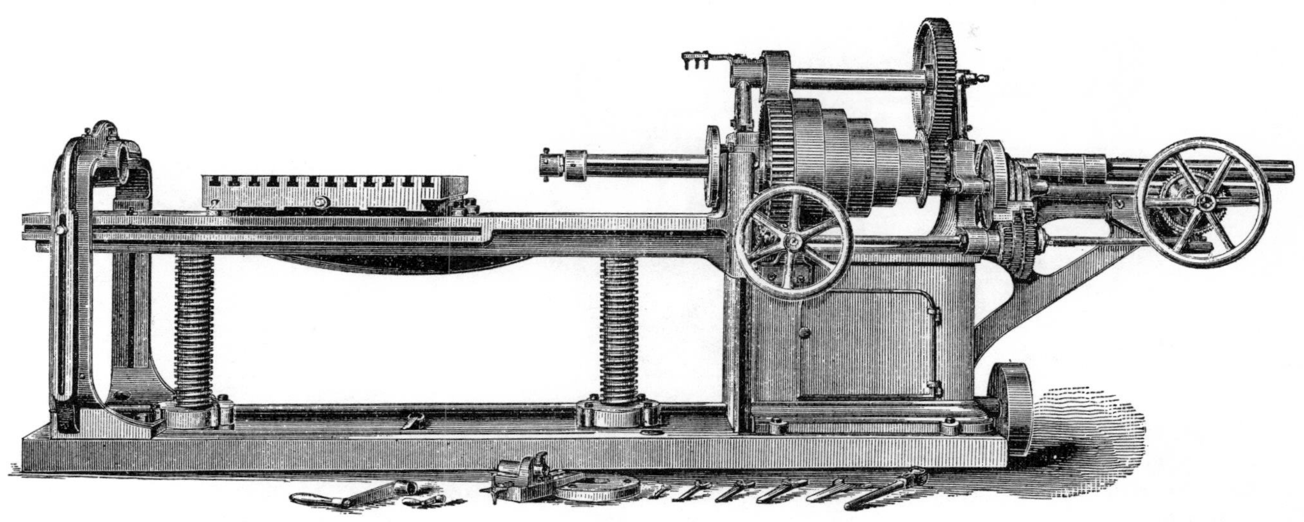

Fig. 154.

the limits of 6 feet 4 inches, and 14 inches. The casting is raised and lowered by screws driven by power. The power is transmitted to the tool by belts from swinging frames to take up the slack of adjustment. The bar is fed by a screw driven by friction-disks. To support the outer end of the bar a similar. but smaller, upright may be used, bolted to the slotted table where needed.

Another tool, with greater vertical capacity but less convenient horizontal adjustment, is made at Providence, Rhode Island. A tall upright, 15 feet high and braced from the roof, carries the gibbed slide with the horizontal

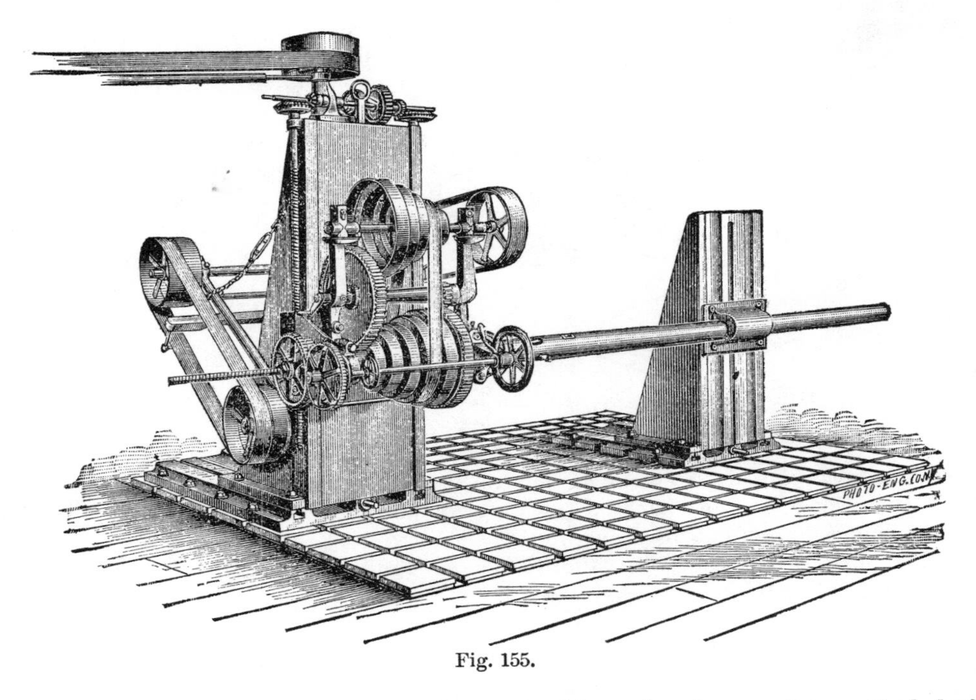

Fig. 155.

driving-spindle. Motion is imparted to the spindle by a pair of brass bevel-gears, the vertical shaft being splined and moving upward with the slide. The spindle is made long, and the thrust and feed are provided for by an arm from a guided slide. The feed is by hand and power, the adjustment of the slide being only by hand. Its weight is counterpoised. To secure the work a heavy table moves transversely on rails, the adjustment being effected by a pinion in the table taking into a fixed rack on the floor. There is no outer support for a long bar at high levels. The machine is more used for drilling, or for boring with short tools held in the end of the spindle.

A special tool for boring and facing flanged cylinders for locomotives and other engines is shown in **Fig. 156.** **A 6-inch steel boring-bar is driven at both ends by the face-plates from a splined shaft in the bed. The bar can**

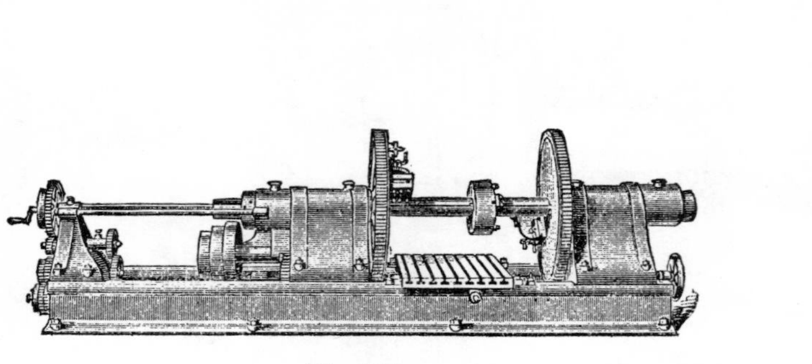

Fig. 156.

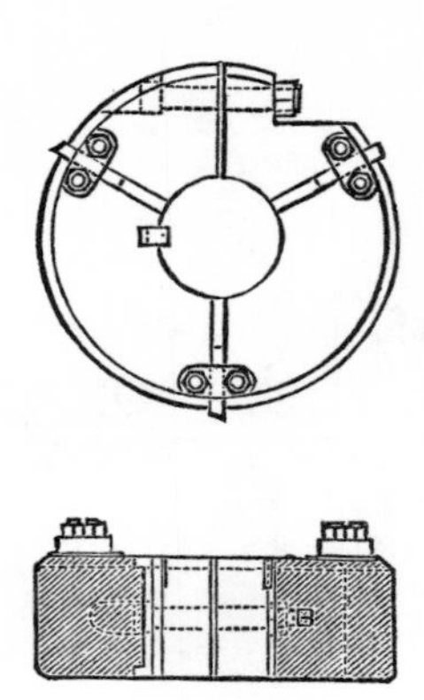

Fig. 157.

be withdrawn from the work by hand or power, and the cutter-head may be similarly fed in at the proper speeds for the heavy rough cut and the finer finishing cut. Facing-rests bolt to the two face-plates so that the sinking head may be cut off and the flanges faced up while the roughing cut is in progress. This arrangement gives truer

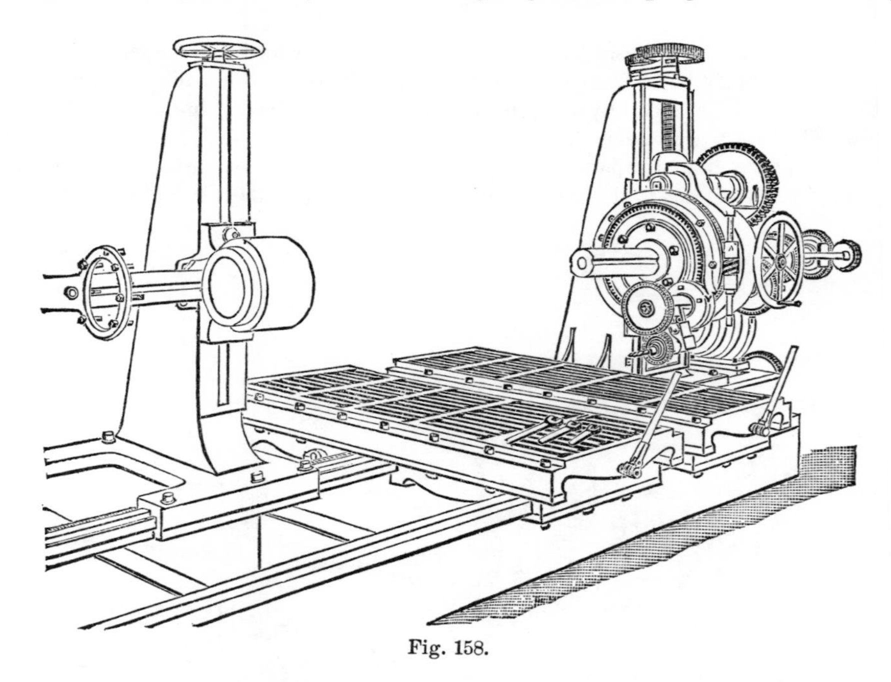

Fig. 158.

work than when the facing-tool is driven from the bar, since the variation in resistance will cause a springing of the joints in the latter case. By this machine the time for boring and facing a locomotive cylinder of usual dimensions has been reduced to a little over one-third of that required with less perfect machines. The boring-head for these bars is made to clip the latter (Fig. 157). The head is cut at one element, and is held by a bolt, which clamps firmly and yet can be instantly released.

A similar tool, designed for large horizontal work, is shown by Fig. 158. Beside boring and facing cylinders of large size, by this machine the holes in the flanges for the cover-studs can be drilled. The whole live-spindle head can be raised and lowered by power, and the post is arranged with a bracket bearing which will support the outer end of bars of different diameters by means of inserted bushings. Its longitudinal and vertical adjustment are effected by screws. The flange-drill E is revolved around the center of the spindle by the worm A′ and held in place by it. By this system the holes can be adjusted to be on the circumference of any circle around the axis of the cylinder and can all be spaced equally.

Fig. 159 shows a third upright with a longitudinal and transverse motion beside the vertical adjustment. This head is used for surfacing work. The tables have compound motion. The bed of this machine is 39 feet long.

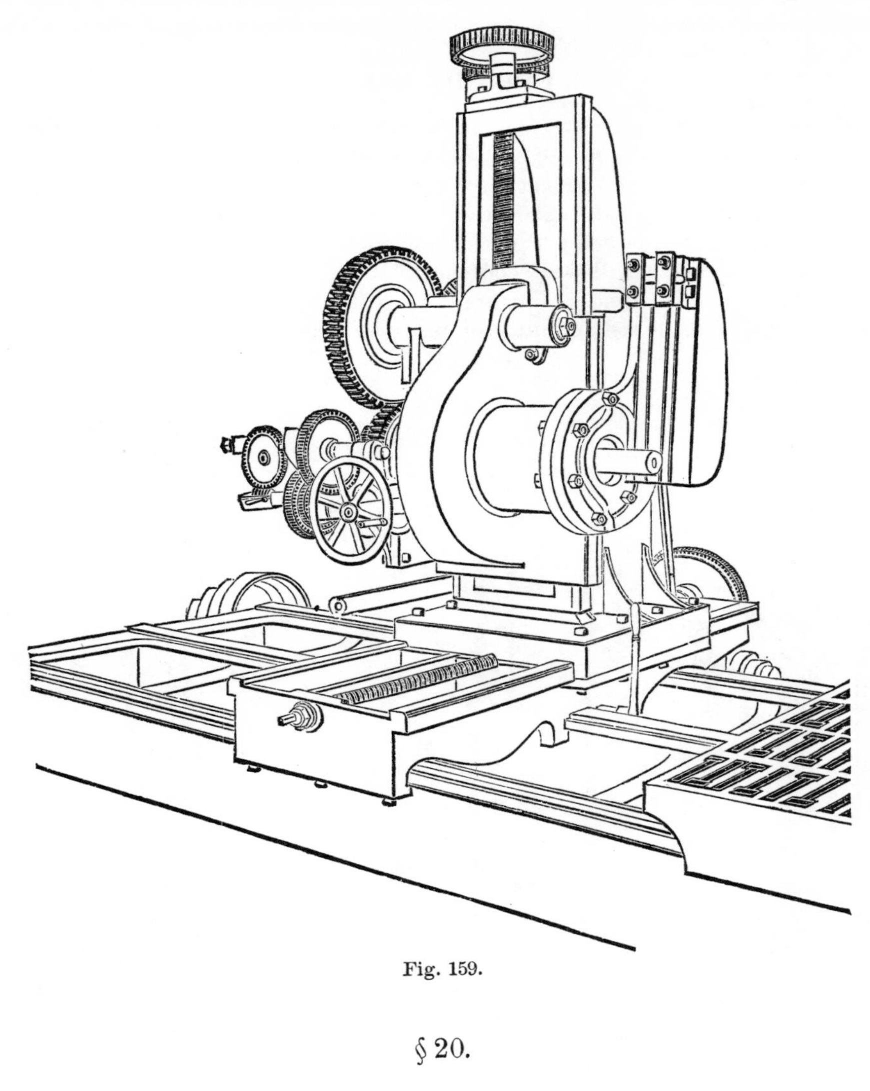

Fig. 159.

§ 20.

DRILLS.

The distinction between drilling-machines and boring machines is not very marked with respect to their function. Usually, however, the drill cuts only at the bottom of a hole in the solid metal, while the boring-tool cuts at the side or bottom of a hole already made. It is possible in the case of most large holes to have them either punched or cored, whence their enlargement to exact size will be effected by boring. Drilling will be usually resorted to for small holes. A drill will, therefore, turn more rapidly than a boring-machine, and will usually be a much lighter and smaller machine.

The question of feeding the drill-point forward against the work was for a long time debated. Some held that it was unwise to have power-feeds; others approved them. Practice of to-day favors a disengageable feed from the spindle, permitting a quick-return by hand, or a hand-feed if desired.

The prevailing drill properly so-called has its spindle vertical. The motion from the horizontal shafting of the shop must, therefore, be transmitted to the spindle through a pair of bevel-gears or else by belt over guide-pulleys. The bevel-gear combination is in the majority. The work will be secured to a T-slotted floor-plate under the spindle, or to a table, according to its size, and according to the type of machine.

The drill-presses may be variously divided, according to their form. For convenience they will be discussed under the heads of upright drills, radial or column drills, and other forms. The latter will include such types as the suspended and multiple drills and special designs.

§ 21.

UPRIGHT DRILLS.

The upright drills (so-called) are usually made to be self-contained. The counter-shaft, with fast-and-loose pulleys and the nest of cone-pulleys, is put at the back of the machine and conveniently near the base. This position of the cone-pulleys makes the shifting of the belt quite easy. The horizontal driving-spindle will be at the top of the machine, both being carried in journals which are on brackets from the main upright of the tool. There are two types of practice with respect to the manner of securing these brackets. Some designers cast the upright and brackets all in one piece. This type is called a "gooseneck" drill, and is illustrated by Figs. 162, 167, and 168. It has the advantage of stiffness and cheapness of fitting. The other type has the brackets bolted to flat seats made for them. By this means is avoided the risk of failure of an entire large casting because of defects of small parts of it.

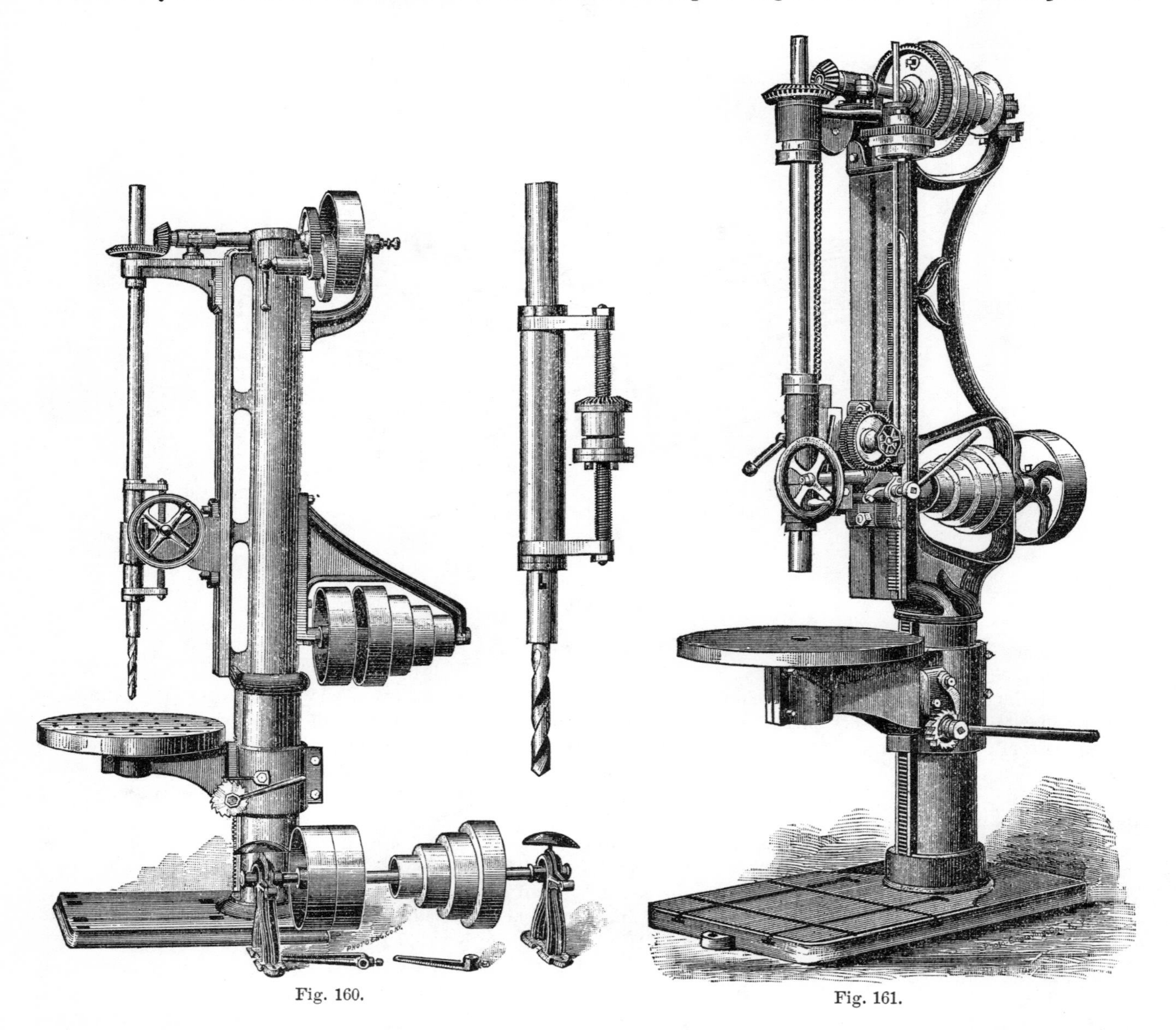

Fig. 160. Fig. 161.

A type of this design is shown by Figs. 165 and 170. Upon the lower part of the principal upright a cylindrical surface is turned. Upon this fits a bracket, very usually split so as to clamp in place, which carries the table. This table is made with slots and T-holes in it for securing work, and its top surface must be truly horizontal when the tool is in place. This table is made to raise and lower by a pinion meshing into a rack. This pinion will be turned directly in lighter tools by a crank or ratchet-lever, or indirectly by a worm and wheel. One form uses a worm (Fig. 167) meshing directly into the rack whose teeth are inclined to conform to the obliquity of the screw. This rack is not cast on the cylinder but fits between collars at top and bottom of the turned surface, and is kept in its vertical position by its fit through the knee. By this expedient, not only is the fitting of the table made more easy, but the table can be made to swing around the upright out of the way of the spindle, if desired.

The foot of the upright rests in a foot-plate in a long, deep socket. In newer practice this foot-plate is planed and slotted to secure deep work to, that it may serve also as a table. The table is usually held in the bracket by

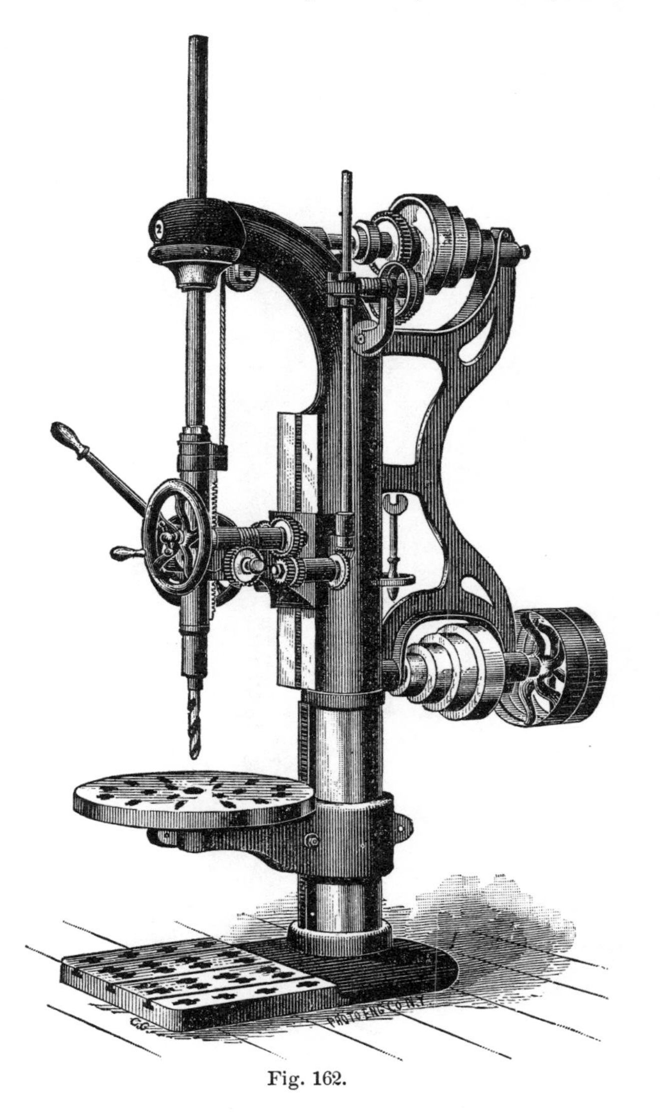

Fig. 162.

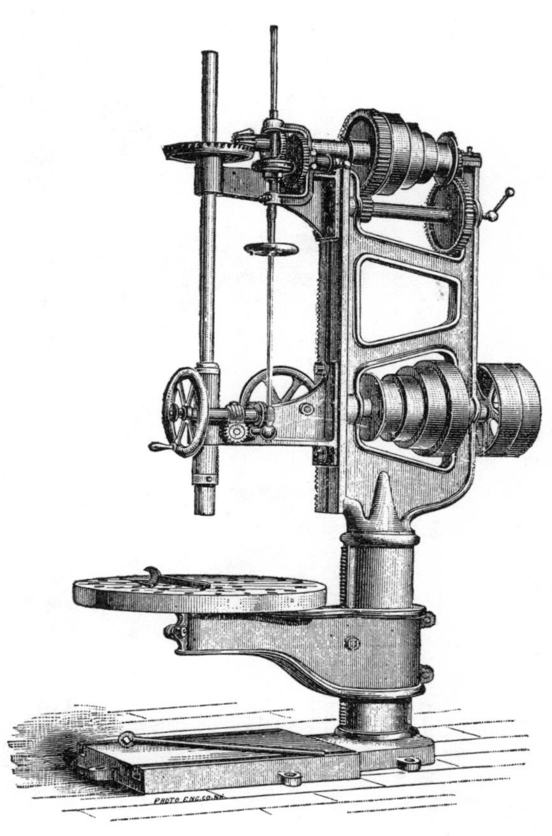

Fig. 163.

a clamp, taking hold upon a cylindrical post, on the lower side central and perpendicular to the finished face. Sometimes this post is screwed into the clamp-nut of the bracket, for finer vertical adjustment. Perpendicular to this table and to the planed foot-plate must turn the spindle of the tool. This is driven from bevel-gear on the upper spindle, the horizontal gear being usually the larger, that the belt-pulleys may turn at high speeds. The horizontal gear usually turns in the bearing in the upper bracket, being provided with a very long hub. This avoids the cutting and wearing of the bearing by the sharp edge of the spline. The vertical spindle must be splined to permit the motion for feed and for adjustment, while the driving bevel-gear remains stationary. The lower bracket, which guides the lower end of the drilling-spindle, is made adjustable vertically for work of differing depths. It is provided with a long knee, which clamps to a planed slide in the front of the tool. Where the bracket is not counter-weighted, the bracket is lifted by a pinion turning in a rack cast in the slide (Fig. 161). The newer types are arranged to move by the unaided hand.

Fig. 160 illustrates one of the older types with separate counter-shaft and hand-feed only. The feed was by a screw bracketed out from a sleeve through which the spindle passed. The sleeve only is fitted to the bearing in the bracket. At the bottom of the sleeve is the point at which the thrust of the cut is borne. Present practice puts a brass washer, or a hardened steel washer, or a washer of rawhide at this point, and any lost motion or wear is taken up by different devices above the sleeve. In place of the screw, the practice of to-day favors a rack, usually cast as part of the sleeve and fed downward by a pinion, driven through worms.

Fig. 161 shows the rack and ratchet device for lifting the feed-bracket. This is made necessary by the fact that the spindle only is counter-weighted. It is of course more important to counter-weight the spindle in order that its weight may not be released suddenly if the drill-point enters a blow-hole. The edges would be likely to catch,

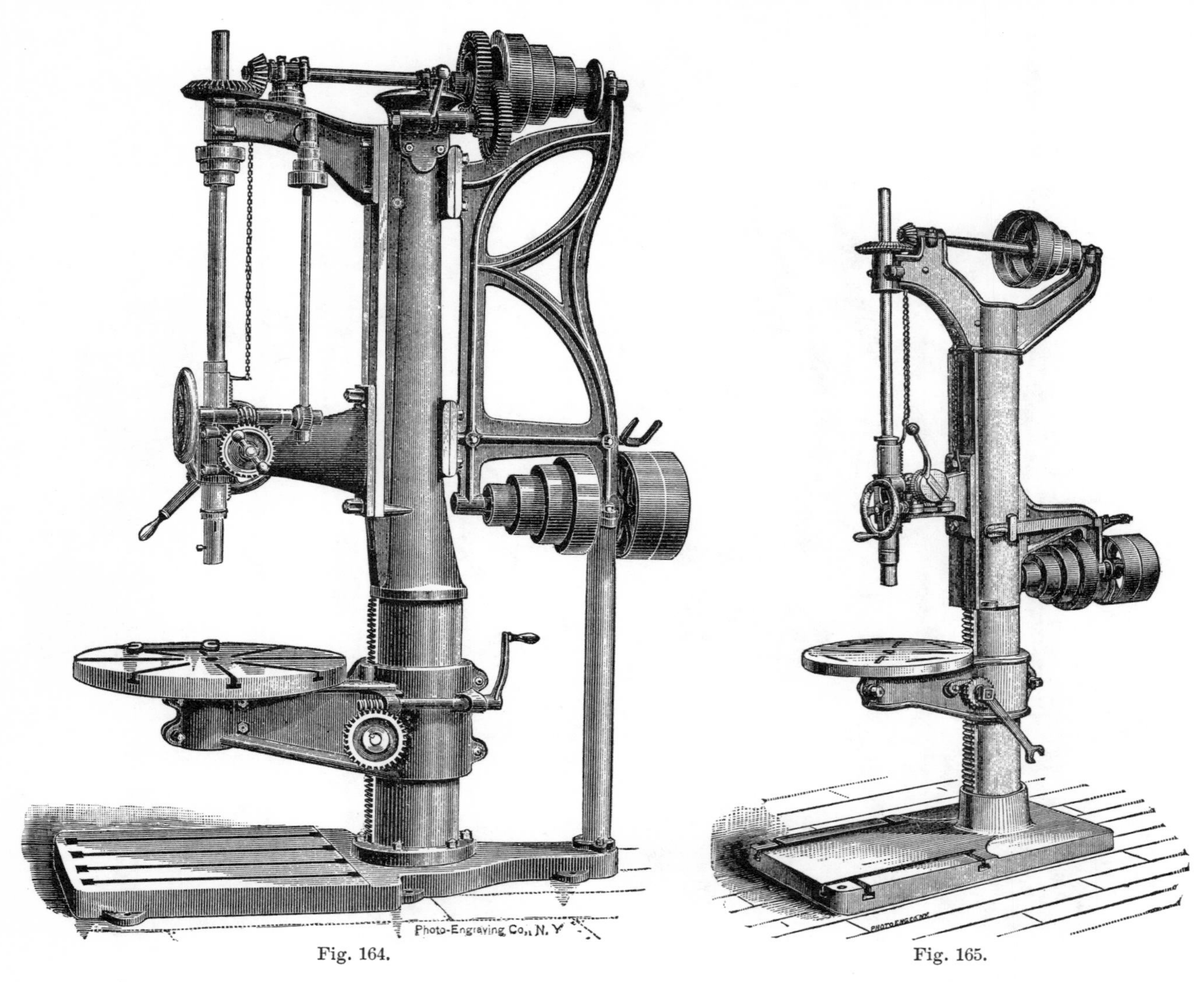

Fig. 164. Fig. 165.

and the drill would break. The power-feed is from cone-pulleys on the hub of the horizontal driven bevel-wheel, which drive a splined worm-shaft by reducing gear. Hand-feed through a second worm is disengaged by friction, and a quick-return lever, for use when both are thrown out, is on the farther side.

Fig. 162 shows the typical gooseneck drill. The counter-shaft is on the back of the tool, and the bevel-gears are incased from dust. The feed changes are made without shifting the feed-belts by shifting-splines on the movable bracket spindles. The hand-feed and quick return are engaged by friction. The counter-weight hangs in the column.

Fig. 163 shows a drill of 48 inches swing, fitted with a variable power-feed by a brush-wheel combination. The power is gained by two worms. The hand-feed is disengaged by friction.

Fig. 164 shows a counterpoised spindle design. The rear post is introduced to stiffen the frame against the thrust of the cut. This flexure of the upright is one of the great defects in the single upright system. The same drill illustrates the lifting of the table by worm-gear.

Figs. 165 and 166 show a counterpoised drill in which the quick return and hand-feed are original. The bent lever swings on a pivot in the diameter of the disk, and a tooth on the end of the rectangular part may catch in notches in the face of the worm-wheel. The power-feed may be disengaged by a friction-clutch.

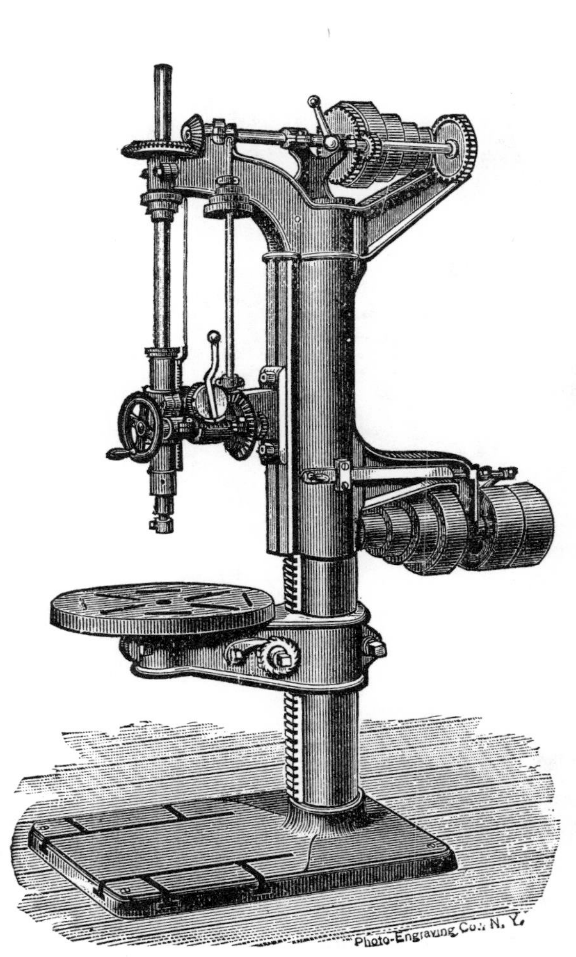

Fig. 166.

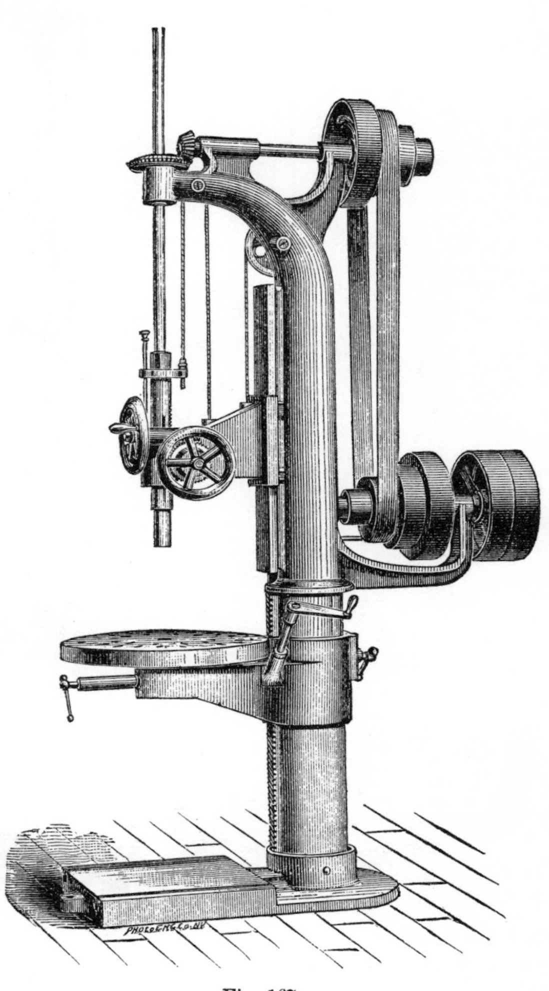

Fig. 167.

Fig. 167 uses but one weight to counterpoise both spindle and bracket. The wire rope is continuous, and passes under a sheave in the bracket from over pulleys in the upright. There is also an adjustable depth-gauge attached to the lower stock. This is an accurately graduated scale, which enables the operator to determine the penetration of the drill by an index on the feeding-sleeve.

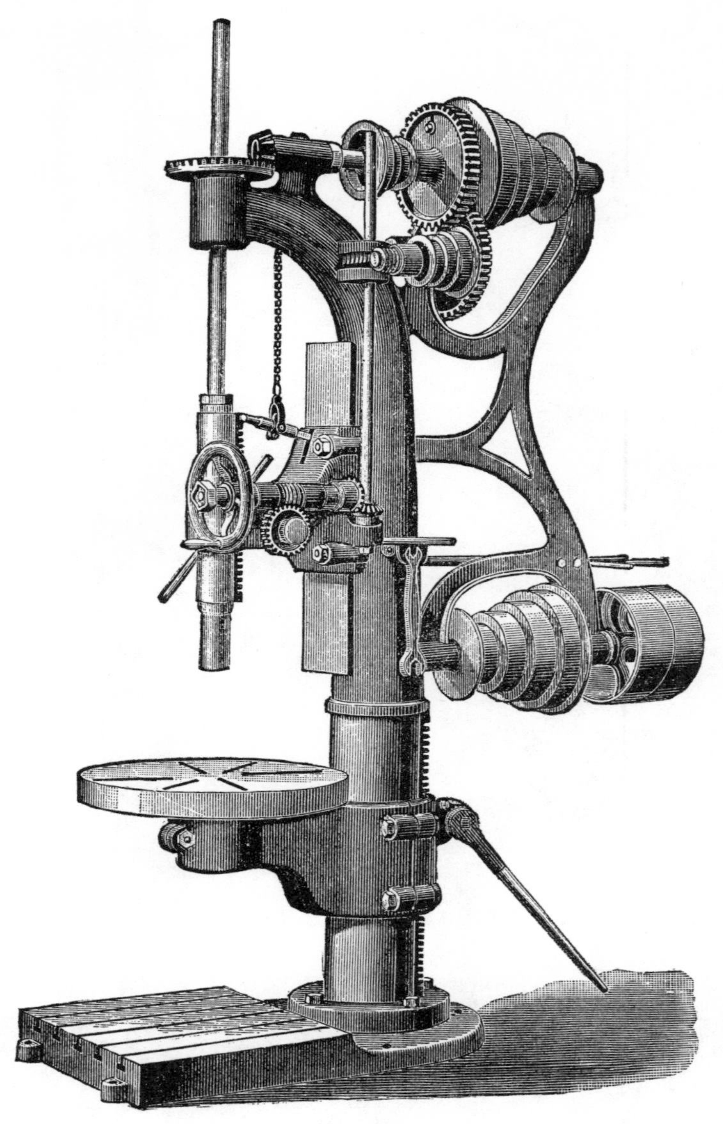

Fig. 168.

Fig. 168 shows a New England design where one weight counterpoises both spindle and bracket. The chain lifts both by a hinged lever, attached to the bracket near its center of gravity by a link. This link compensates for the motion of the spindle, and the adjustable clamp of the clevis D permits any proportion of the counter-weight to be distributed upon the spindle joint as the weight may vary in the socket. The power-feed and quick-return are controlled by friction-clutches. This tool also illustrates the compacting of the back-gear mechanism upon a short axis. This is very general in the newer tools.

Fig. 169 illustrates the same arrangement of back-gear, but the spindle has but one long bearing instead of two. The table has a very long vertical adjustment by a screw let into a slot in the column. The brass nut of the screw can be disengaged by the pin below the table in front, so that the table may swing aside. The changes of feed are accomplished by the three bevel-gears on the worm-shaft. The vertical gears are engaged with the geared spindle by a movable spline operated by the rod and milled head at the rear end. The counterpoise is annular over the top of the spindle-cap.

Fig. 170, by the same builder, illustrates the bolted system for the upper brackets.

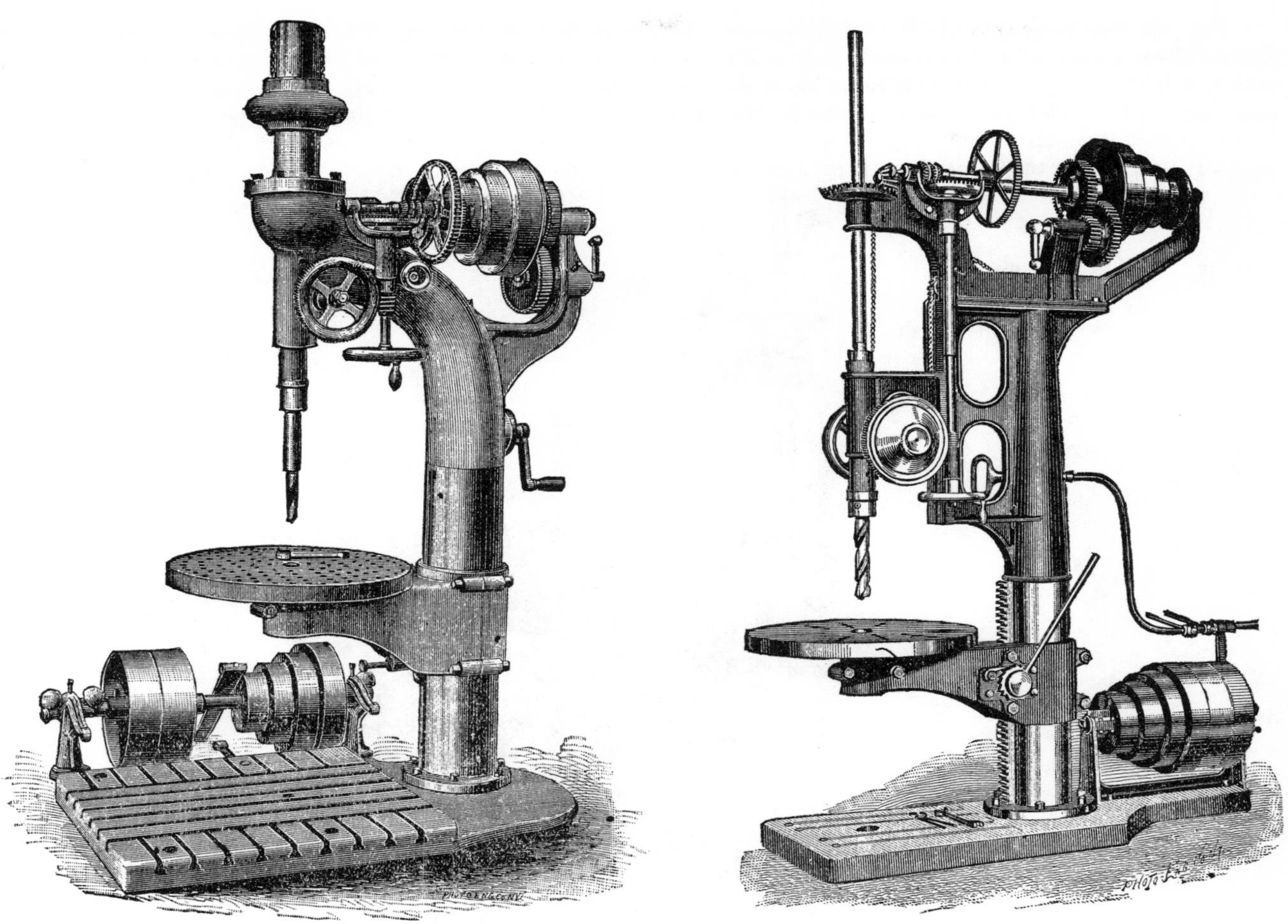

Fig. 169.

Fig. 170.

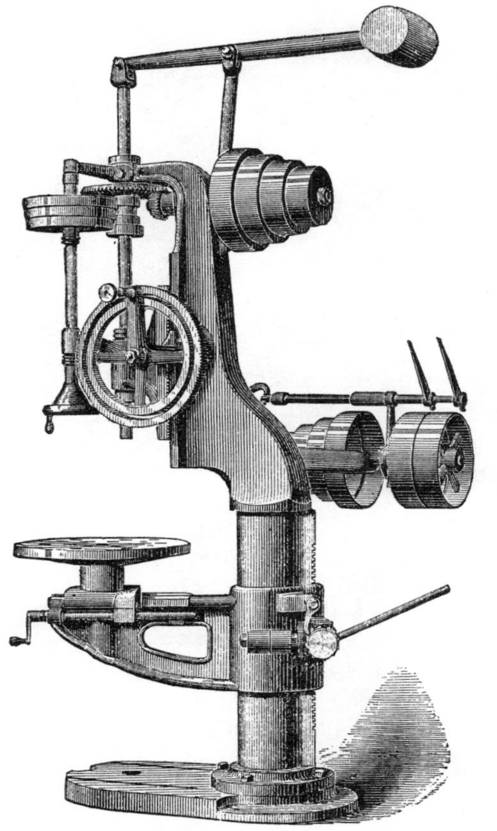

Fig. 171.

Fig. 171 shows a lever counter-weight drill, with the feed driven by a cone of belt-wheels. The hand-feed and quick-return device is by a frictional clip in the sunk ring of the worm-wheel. The handle of the crank forms a screw-clutch. The table has a horizontal traverse by screw.

Fig. 172 shows a lever counterpoise drill, the links being curved so that the short lever may not cause binding upon the spindle. The quick-return is by a lever on the left-hand side, the worm of the feed-motion being moved laterally away from the pinion wheel by an eccentric on the vertical rod at the right. The power-feed has three

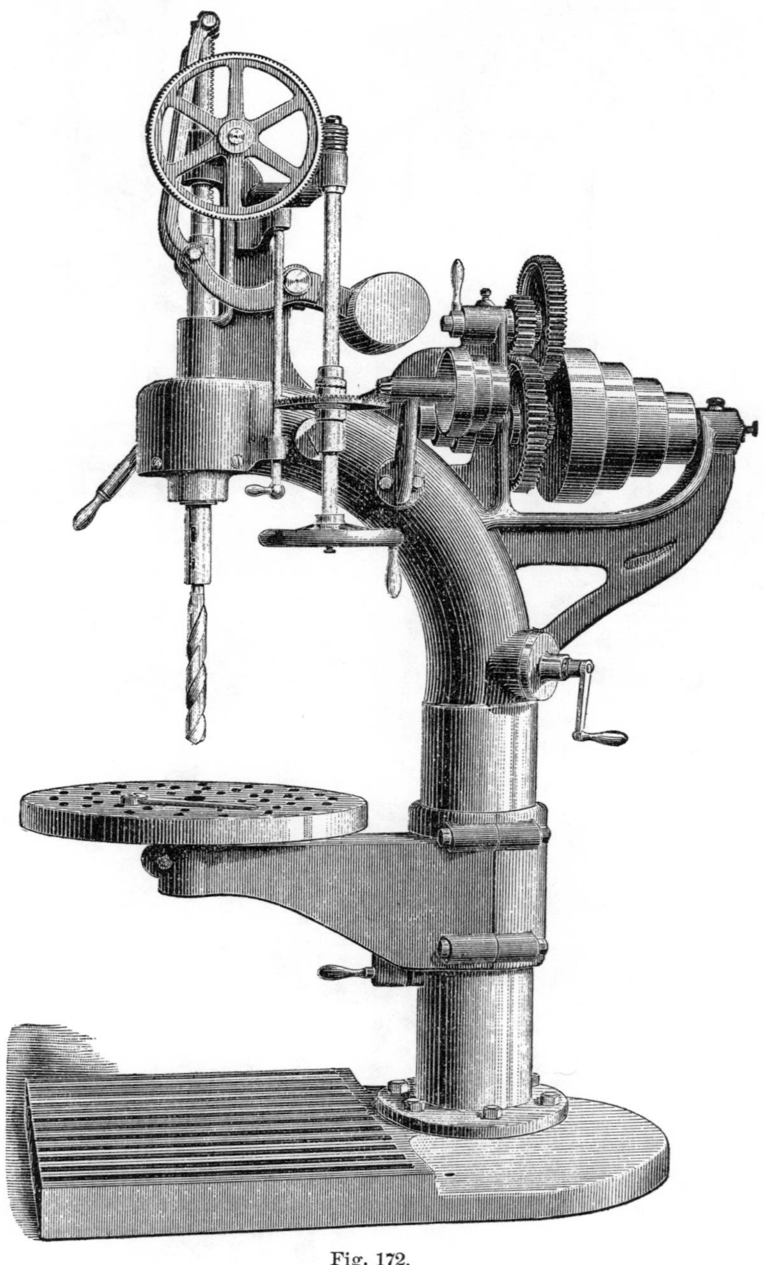

Fig. 172.

changes by a belt cone, the horizontal gear being disengaged for hand-feed by a jaw-clutch. This is lifted by the rod, in the axis of the worm-shaft, by the milled button below.

Fig. 173 illustrates a type of drill in which the spindle may be driven by belt only, when the back-gearing is not required. The belt passes over guide-pulleys, on the back of the square upright. The direct use of a belt gives a smoother running for very small drills. The feed is by a screw of steep pitch engaged by a clutch worked by the latch-lever. The thrust is borne on the very long nut of the feed-screw. The table is gibbed to a flat slide in front of the upright, but by loosening two bolts the table is released and swings to one side. The axis of the swinging of the table is the lifting-screw, which is at the left side, and is turned by power. The power for this motion of the table is obtained by clutching a horizontal internal shaft with bevel-gears. The clutch is worked by the lever near the base of the upright, and access to the gears is had through the small door. The table has screw traverse in both directions, which is often found a great convenience in miscellaneous or spaced work.

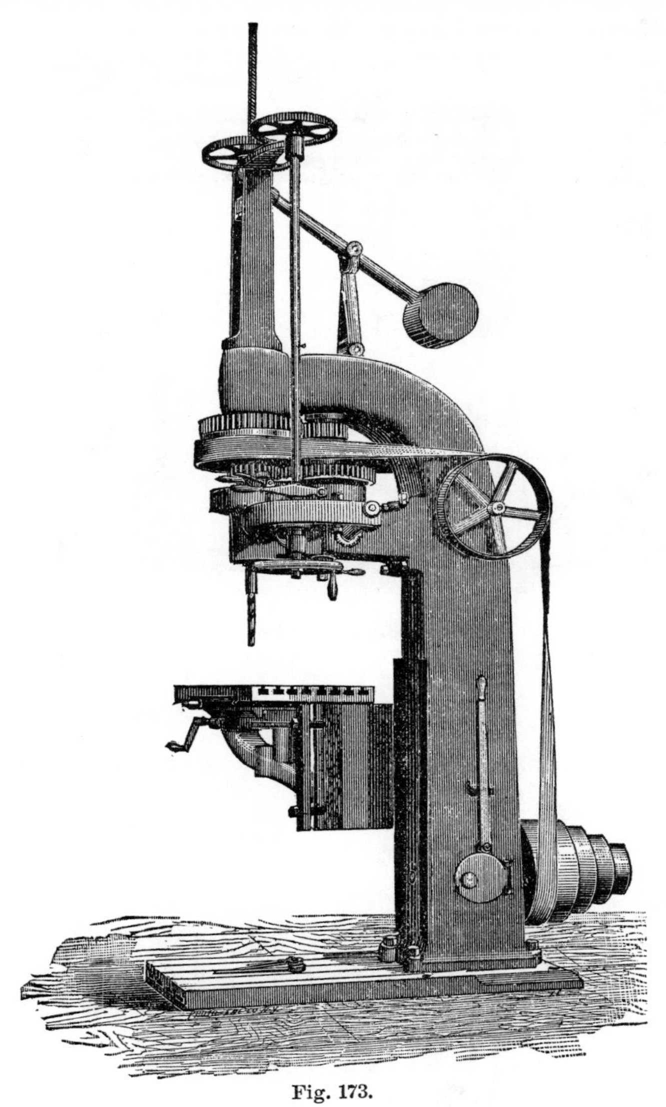

Fig. 173.

§ 22.

RADIAL OR COLUMN DRILLS.

This class includes those in which the carriage bearing the drilling-spindle is adjustable upon a horizontal arm, which swings cranewise around a vertical column. The drill-point can therefore command any point in an annular area, determined by the outer and inner swing of the radial arm around the center of the column. A tool of this sort is especially adapted for heavy work, inasmuch as the drill can be moved to any point of the work more easily than the work can be adjusted under the point of the drill. Moreover, the swinging of the radius permits the drill to command a variety of tables of different levels.

Such a tool is illustrated by Fig. 174. The radius arm is double, to give firm bearing on both sides of it for the spindle-carriage, and has a long internal bearing from the collars upward. The radius is clamped in place by the split in the sleeve at the collars. There is a slotted floor-plate, a tilting-table, adjustable by a screw and clamp, and on a third side may be a pit, if desired, to work on the ends of very long pieces. The tilting-table permits the drilling of angular holes, and is preferred by the builders to the use of an inclined spindle. The tool is driven by a central vertical shaft from a cone-pulley shaft below. A splined shaft takes off the power in any direction from the bevel-gear on the top. The carriage travels over the radius by a rack and pinion from the hand-wheels, and the

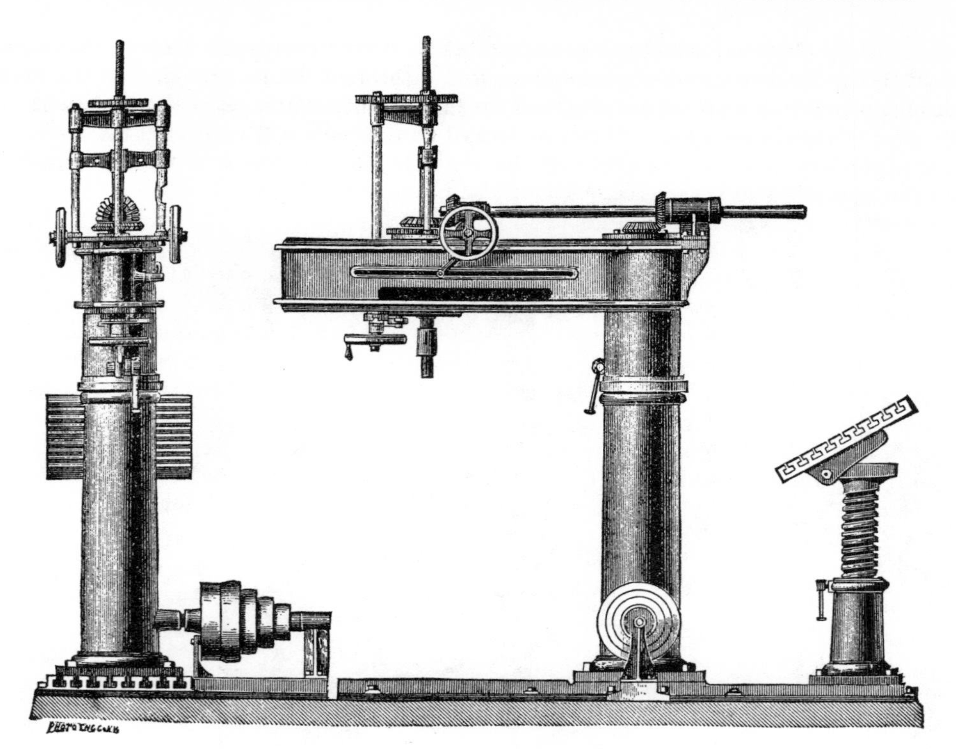

Fig. 174.

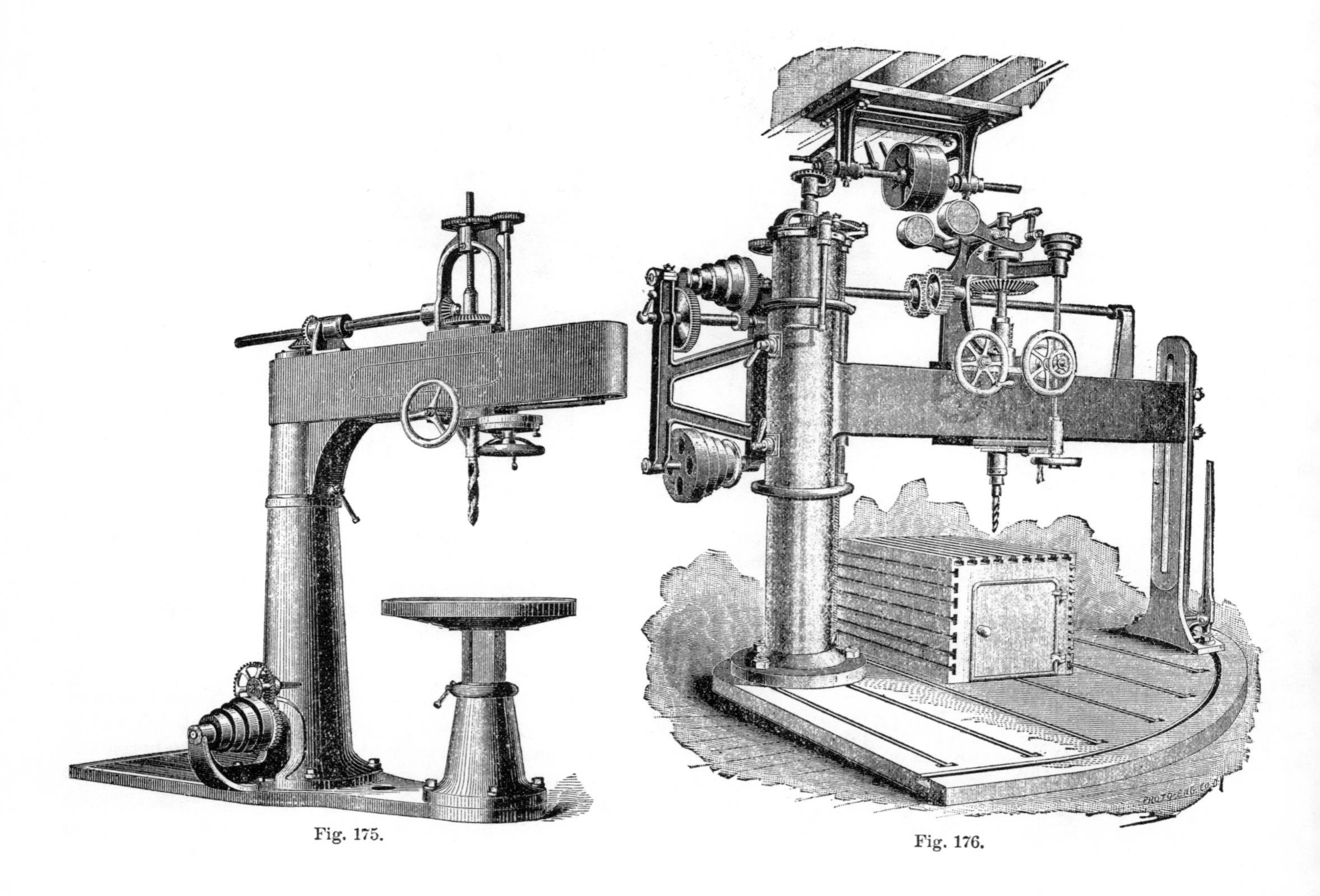

Fig. 175.

Fig. 176.

tool is fed downward by a screw. The back-gear connection is very compact. Fast to the large pulley of the cone is a small gear. This meshes into a second whose stud is carried by an arm fast to the spindle. This arm is counterpoised on the other side of the spindle, and by this sector the arm can be locked to an internal wheel with which the idle gear is always engaged. When so locked the spindle will turn with the cone. When the internal wheel is locked to the base-plate of the drill and the sector is released, the arm will be carried around as the idle-wheel rolls on the internal wheel, and the speed will be much reduced.

Fig. 175 illustrates a very similar design.

Fig. 176 shows a design intended to increase the vertical capacity of the tool, by making the whole radius move vertically upon the column. This enables the tool to act easily upon very flat, heavy work. The lifting-screw is driven by power from the central shaft, engaged by the lever motion from the handled rod. This tool also avoids a difficulty which results from the overhang of the radius when heavy cuts are made. A slotted post, moving on the arc of the end of the radius, may bolt the latter to the bed, when the tool becomes as rigid as could be desired. The spindle is driven by a pair of gears from the splined shaft, which may be driven directly or double geared. The feed is from cone-pulleys to a worm and wheel, disengaged by friction for hand-feed.

Fig. 177 shows a similar design, where the drilling-spindle is universal, and holes may be drilled at any angle. The spindle is driven from the splined shaft, below the radius, by two pairs of bevel-gears, the axis of the idle pair being in the center of the swivel clamp-plate. The tool is driven directly from a horizontal belt, and the arm is

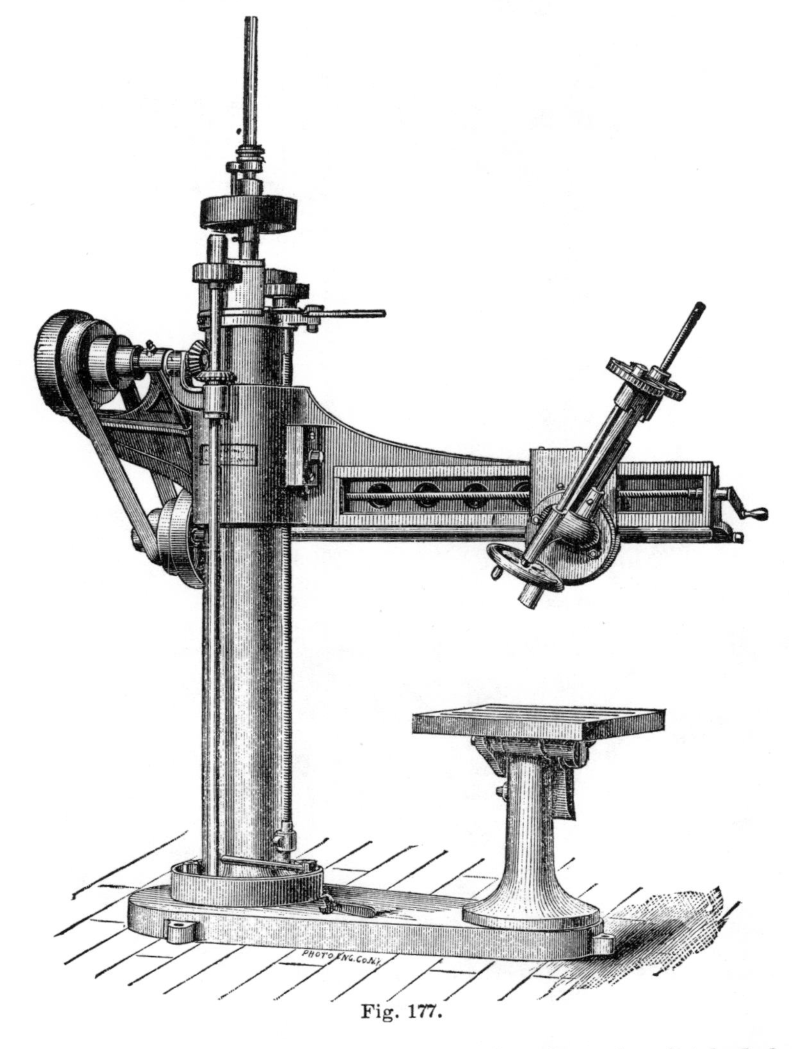

Fig. 177.

raised and lowered by power. In all the tools with this feature the column is a finished shell which turns upon an internal post with a long bearing. The shell is clamped in place by the bolts in the flange at its foot. It will be seen that by the two motions of this tool, a hole may be drilled in any direction and at any angle with the horizontal plane. The radius can bring the spindle into any vertical plane, and the swivel-plate permits the drill to be presented at any angle in that plane. Horizontal holes can be drilled in work of any length, the work lying on the floor or on trestles. Holes may be bored in erected locomotive-frames by using a long false socket.

Fig. 178 shows the spindle mechanism of Fig. 172 applied to a radial drill, and Fig. 179 shows a universal drill by the same builders. The radius slides on a faced slide, and the shell of the upright need not be finished all over. The raising and lowering is by power, the gears being engaged by the handled lever on the upright. The feed is by a screw, and may be made automatic with three changes, also as well as by hand.

Fig. 180 illustrates a belt-driven radial drill. The arm swings cranewise around a splined shaft through a little more than 180°. The guiding-slide is made very long for stiffness, so long as to need no clamping in place

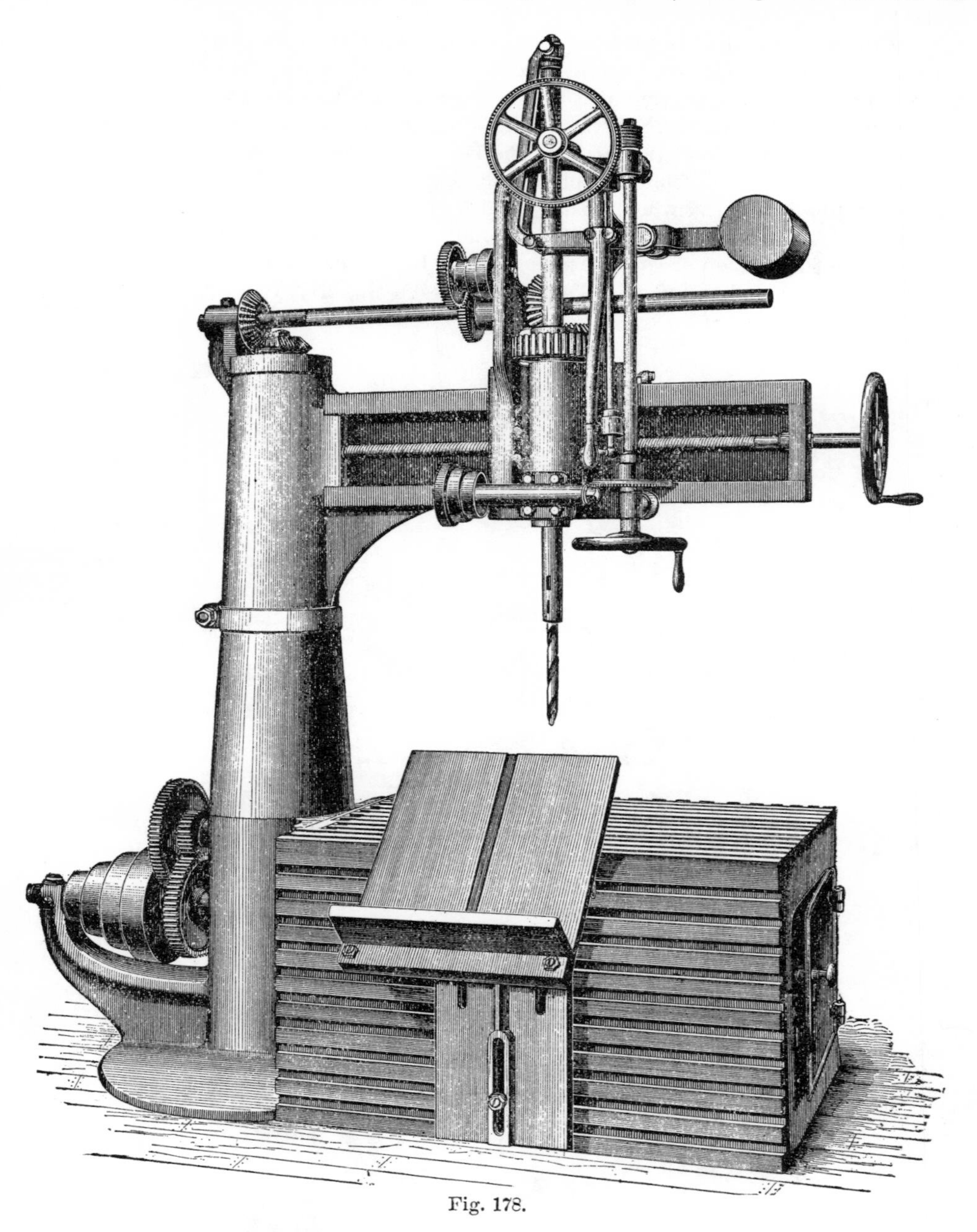

Fig. 178.

under a heavy cut. The arm is raised and lowered by power from the lower shaft. The feed is by a screw-gear, and the carriage traverses by a worm on a diagonal shaft taking into a rack. This cut and several of the others illustrate a form of table which has many advantages. Work may be secured to either top or side, and the interior may be used as a tool-closet.

Fig. 181 illustrated a similar adjustable double-faced table for a vertical radial drill. The spindle is carried at the lower end in a bearing on a slide, which is guided and receives the downward feed. The spindle itself, therefore, does not overhang its supports so far when fed out. The feed is by cone-pulleys from the spindle, with an axial spline device for altering or disengaging the power-feed. This has been utilized in an appliance for gauging

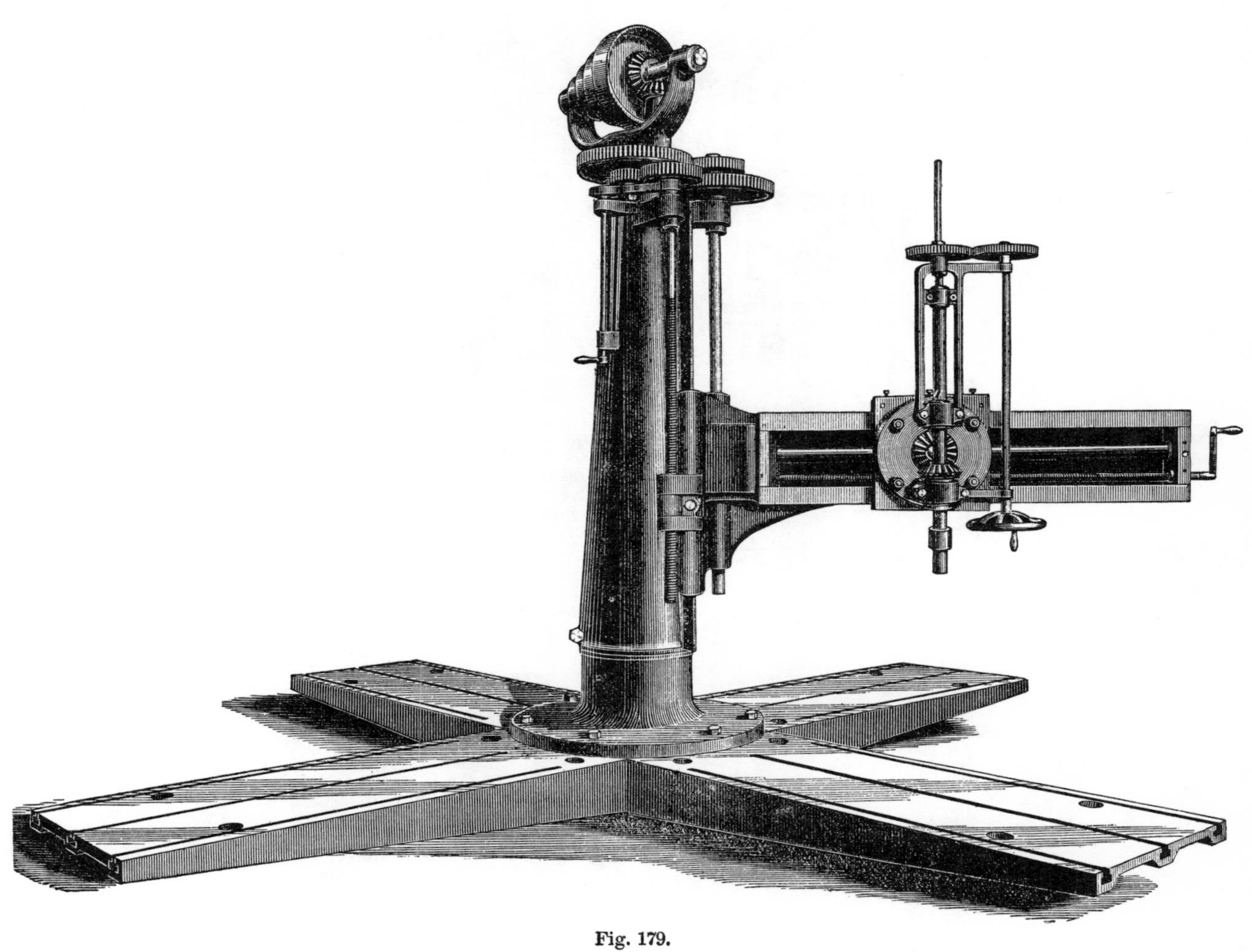

Fig. 179.

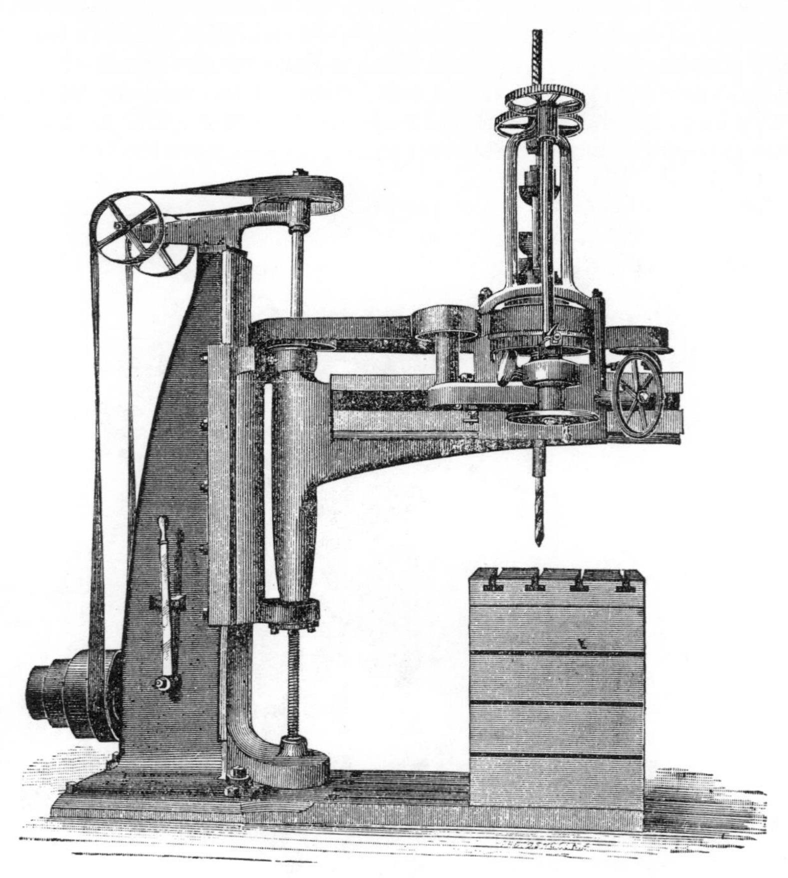

Fig. 180.

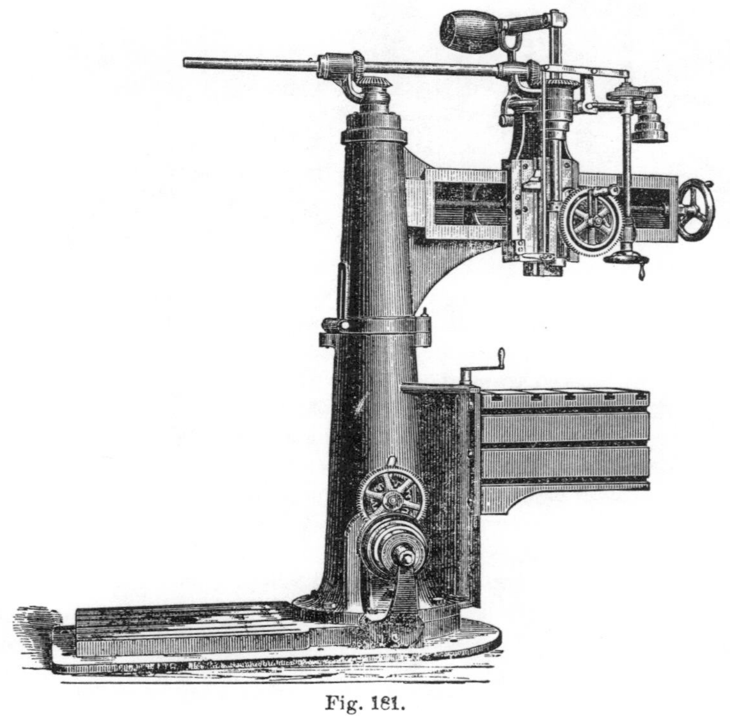

Fig. 181.

and tripping the feed for holes of uniform depth. The spline-rod is attached to a horizontal lever. A dog on the slide strikes a tripping-lever and disengages the feed-spline when the depth has been reached for which it was set. The hand-feed is engaged with the power worm-wheel by an annular friction-clutch.

Fig. 182 illustrates an improved universal radial drill, where all the motions are by power. The crane may revolve around the stump and rise and fall, and the feeds are by power. The jib may also turn around its own axis for oblique work, and the spindle may swivel to any angle. The engagement of the power motions is by hollow shafts and splines.

Belonging to the class of radial drills is the portable drill illustrated by Fig. 183. A short hollow post carries the column of the drill, which can thereby swivel to any radius by worm-wheel and tangent-screw. A long slide feeds the point of the drill in and out on the radius. The spindle-frame is held in a spherical clamp on a ball surface, by which the spindle can be set to drill at any angle up to 30° in any plane. A second sleeve,

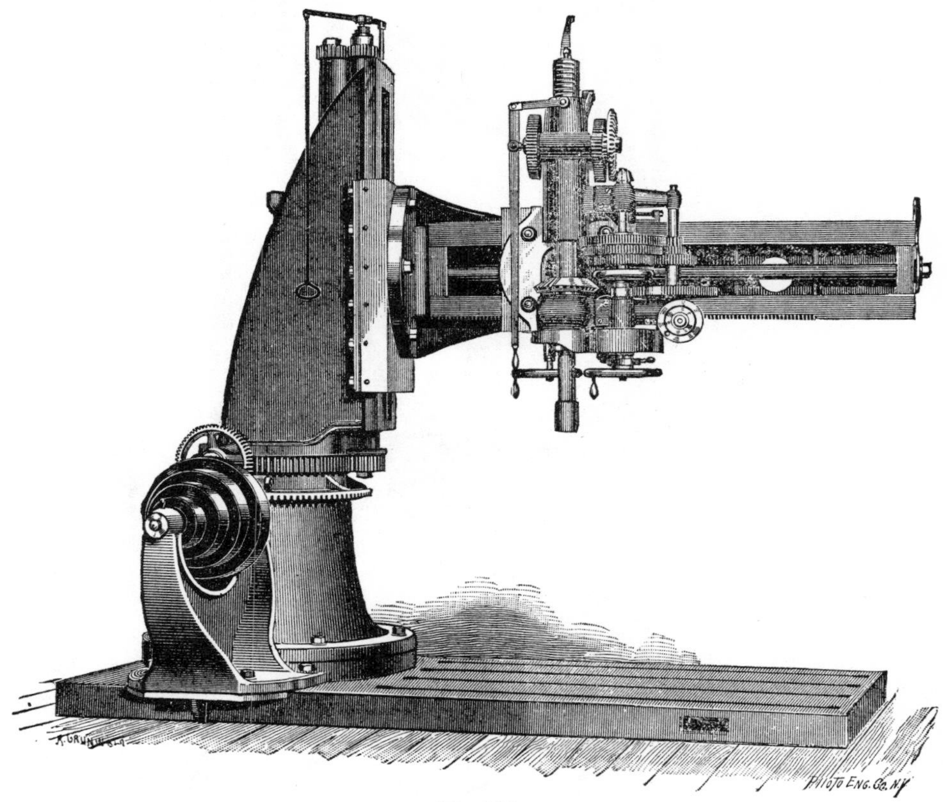

Fig. 182.

on the hollow post, will take the short column horizontally and give the same latitude of motions from horizontal plane. Power is transmitted to a cone of grooved pulleys by a round rope of Italian hemp, which passes over a guide-pulley at the counter-shaft and under another which is free and weighted to maintain the tension on the rope. The overhead guide-pulley is swiveled so that its periphery is always in the plane through the center of the driver in whatever direction the drill may be or at whatever angle. The entire adjustability of the drill in any position over a large area to drill at nearly any angle peculiarly fits this tool for erecting large work. The drill can more easily be brought to the work than the work can be presented to the drill. Of a very similar type of construction are the drills and boring-machines intended for the erecting shop, which are driven from counter-shafts upon the walls of the shop through rods with universal joints. A universal joint at the counter-shaft and another at the tool are connected together by telescopic shafts made of gas-pipe, with collars and set-screws. The two joints neutralize each other's irregularity. Even better than this is the similar use of flexible shafting. Coils of wire wound alternately into spirals, right-handed and left-handed, will transmit the power from a counter-shaft at any angle, and the necessity for supporting the shaft is entirely avoided. This must be done with the telescopic jointed system.

Fig. 183.

§ 23.

SPECIAL FORMS.

Fig. 184 illustrates a form of drill especially designed for drilling and boring the holes for the pins in the eyes of bridge-links. To insure accuracy in length it is wise to bore both holes at once, so that all may be alike. The heads slide upon a bed, and are arranged right and left. The links enter under one head and pass out through the other. Horizontal driving-belts pass from the drums over guide-pulleys to the driving-shaft. When the two heads are upon a wrought-iron screw for adjustment in length of the links, any changes of temperature will affect the link and screw equally, and the heads will slide on the cast iron to keep the lengths of all links the same. In other forms of this tool the spindles are carried on a cross-rail, receiving separate motion and feed from splined shafts geared to cone-pulleys. A primary advantage of this double system is that, by holding the work between centers, two holes may be drilled exactly parallel to each other and perpendicular to the axis of the work; or by putting bushings in the table, such a machine may be used for parallel boring, as in finishing the brasses of connecting-rods when keyed up in the stub.

Fig. 185 shows a machine for drilling the holes for crank-pins in the driving-wheels of locomotive engines. These holes need to be on radii at exactly 90° on the two sides. While the wheels are held by shoes upon their

Fig. 184. Fig. 185.

tread, and so adjusted as to bring the axle in line with the centers of the machine, the two drilling-spindles move on ways which are in planes at right angles to each other, and can be set for any radius of crank from 5 to 13 inches. The feed of the spindle is automatic, and variable within wide limits.

Fig. 186.

Fig. 186 shows a machine for drilling and mortising the seats for keys and cotters. Each drill has a longitudinal traverse of 36 inches and a transverse adjustment and feed of 10 inches. The feed is self-operating in all directions, self-reversing by the clutch and bevel-gears on the shaft at the right head, and the depth of the slot may be limited by a stop. The jaws are self-centering by right-and-left screw, and have capacity for a 7-inch shaft.

Fig. 187 shows a machine specially adapted for drilling the holes for the set-screws of pulleys without piercing the face. The drill is driven by a train of gears incased in the projecting arm, and the pulley is held upon the adjustable mandrel below. The machine has a capacity for pulleys from 56 inches in diameter down to 12 inches, and can also be used to tap the holes for the screws. The different speeds for drilling and tapping are obtained by the two belt-pulleys, and the motion of the tap is reversed by the clutch lever in the head.

Fig. 187. Fig. 188.

Fig. 188 shows a drill for the ends of steel rails, that the bolts for the fish-plates may pass through the web. The drills are fed down by a power-feed, positive and unvariable, the return being rapid by hand. The slide is counter-weighted, and the slack of belts is taken up by an idle-shaft linked to the driving-shaft. The rail is clamped in a vise upon the bed of the tool. These tools attain a rapid cut by high speed and fine feed. They are usually used in pairs, one at each end of the rail.

For drilling a number of holes at exact distances apart great economy of time results from the use of multiple drills. Fig. 189 shows a gang of four. The spindles are driven from a splined shaft, and can be adjusted to any distance apart greater than 7½ inches. The spindles are self-feeding and counter-weighted, and may be readily changed in relative height to suit drills of unequal lengths. The saddle which carries the drills is adjustable by rack and pinion on a cross-slide, which is long enough for sheets of 8 feet in width. The table is stationary, and the spindles are fed down by double worm-gear.

In the machine of Fig. 190 the spindles are six in number, and have no vertical feed. The machine is designed for truck-frames, and the spindles are made extensible by socket-arbors secured into the sleeve of the spindle by set-screws. The table is fed against the drills by a pair of cams driven by the worm-wheel at the right, so that the

Fig. 189.

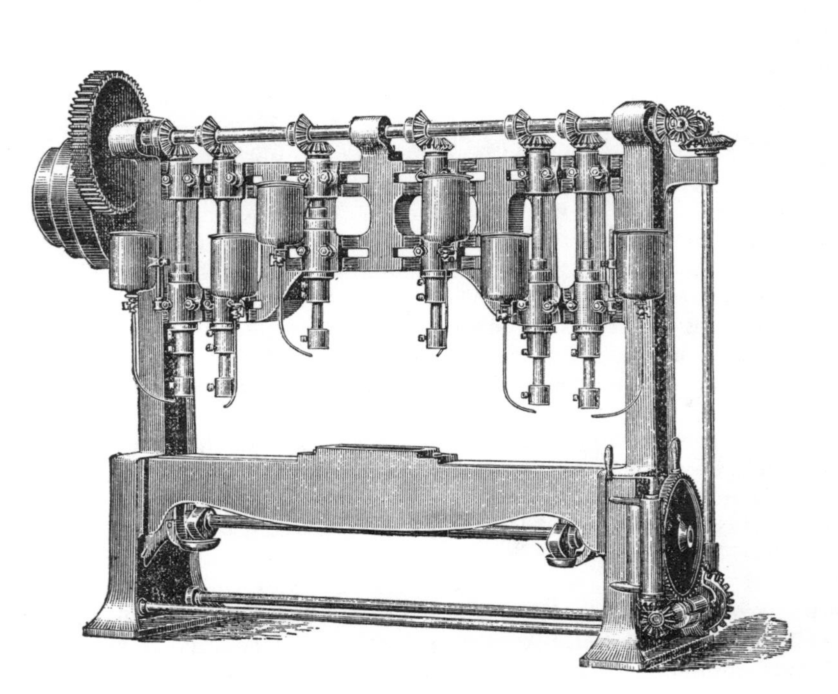

Fig. 190.

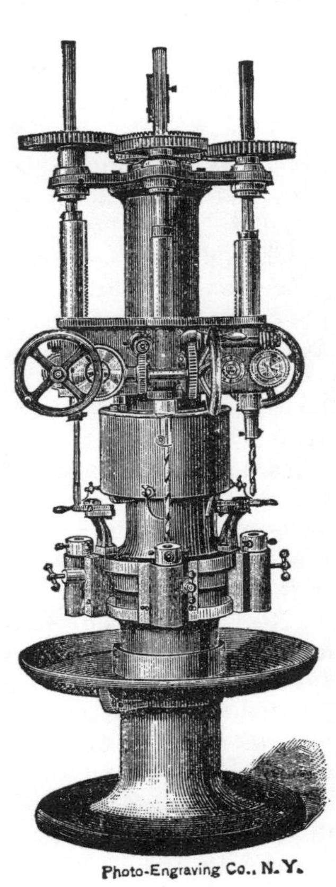

Fig. 191.

feed and return motions are automatic. Sometimes the spindles are driven by a many-threaded screw of steep pitch, meshing into a helical gear on the spindle. This permits the spindles to be brought very close together. On account of friction, this helical system only works well against small resistances.

For a different class of work, where the holes are to be drilled deep in small work, the type of gang-drill shown in Fig. 191 is approved. It will carry a starting-drill, a through-drill, an enlarging-drill, and a reamer, or four pieces of work may have the same operation performed on them at once. The feed is automatic, and one operator can attend to several machines.

Figs. 192 and 193 show the belted gang-drill in two forms. The pulleys on the spindles may be of different

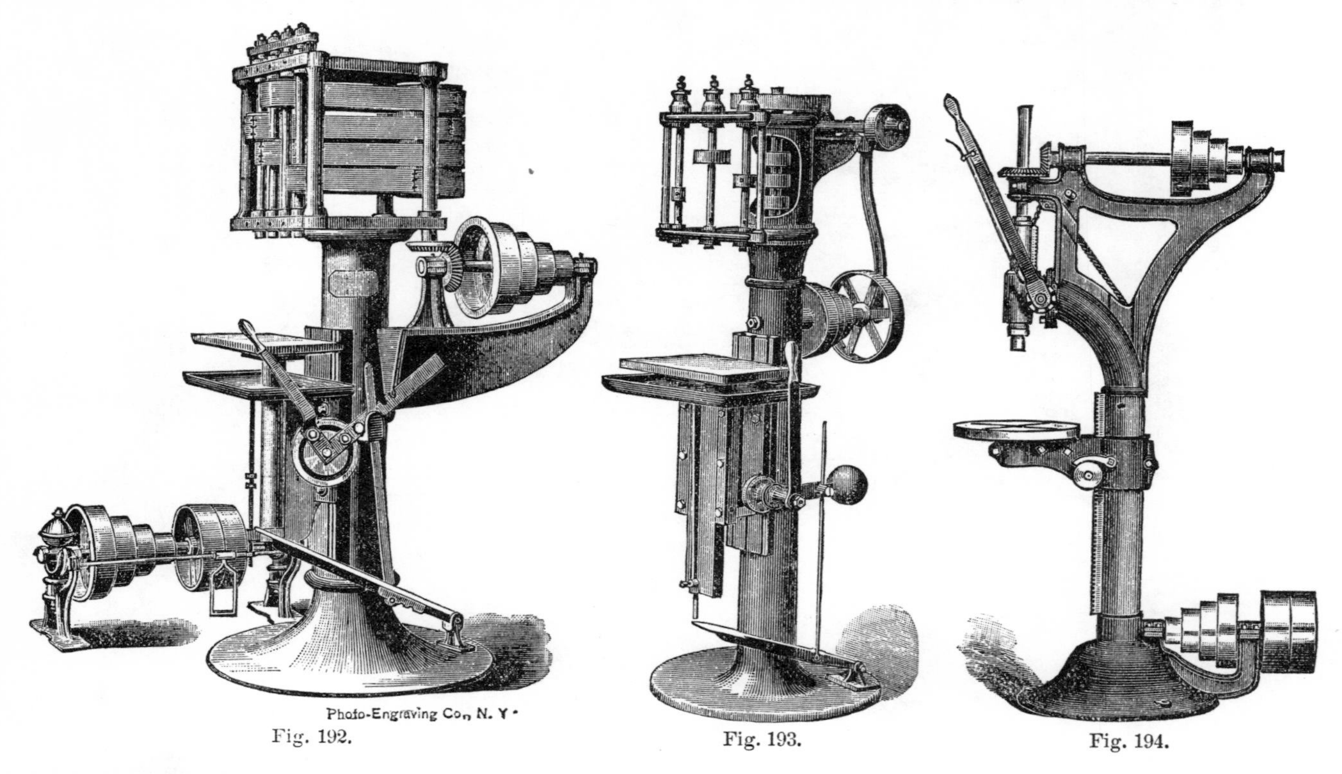

Fig. 192. Fig. 193. Fig. 194.

diameters if for different duties. The work is lifted against the drill by treadle or by hand-lever. The wear of the spindles is compensated for by take-up devices in the boxes, and the trouble caused by expansion of the spindles is avoided. The belts are made as long as possible.

Fig. 194 shows a type of drill approved for light work at high speeds. It makes a cheap design for a large class of manufactured articles.

Fig. 195 shows a tool for similar work arranged to have the work lift against the drill, which is belt-driven, and there is a stop device by nuts on a screw to gauge uniform depths.

Figs. 196 *a* and 196 *b* show a tool which has been approved in railroad and boiler shops on account of its limitless swing. The tool is called a suspension-drill, and is hung by the ring from the ceiling. Sometimes it is arranged so that the ring is on a carriage, which may traverse in two directions at right angles, making the adjustment of the drill-point more easy to the marks of the punch.

Fig. 197 shows a combination tool, drill, and slotter, which has found its use in certain shops. The slotter is disengaged by adjusting the wrist-pin into the center of motion and clamping the slide. The drill is fed by a screw from a worm on the spindle. It is disengaged by lifting the horizontal bevel-wheel out of gear by a milled head in the bracket.

Fig. 198 shows a special machine for drilling and countersinking centers for lathe work. The work is held by a scroll-chuck whose center coincides with that of the drill. The latter is fed forward by the ball-handle. Fig. 199 shows a similar tool, arranged vertically.

In all the tools which belong to this class of drills the workmanship in standard practice is of the best. The spindles are of hammered steel, the gears are cut, the important guiding surfaces are scraped to true planes. In the lower end of the spindle is made a taper socket, in which may be fitted a boring-bar or a secondary socket for drills. The sockets are most of them made with the Morse taper of $\frac{5}{8}$ of an inch to the foot. This is apparently displacing the so-called American taper of $\frac{9}{16}$ of an inch to the foot. At the top of the socket a slot is cut through the spindle, in order that a taper flat key driven through the slot may force out the drill without marring either spindle or drill, and the end of the drill taper is so milled as to prevent the drill from turning in the socket, and yet it is certain to "center" as the two conical surfaces come together. The old collet and set-screw is rapidly disappearing.

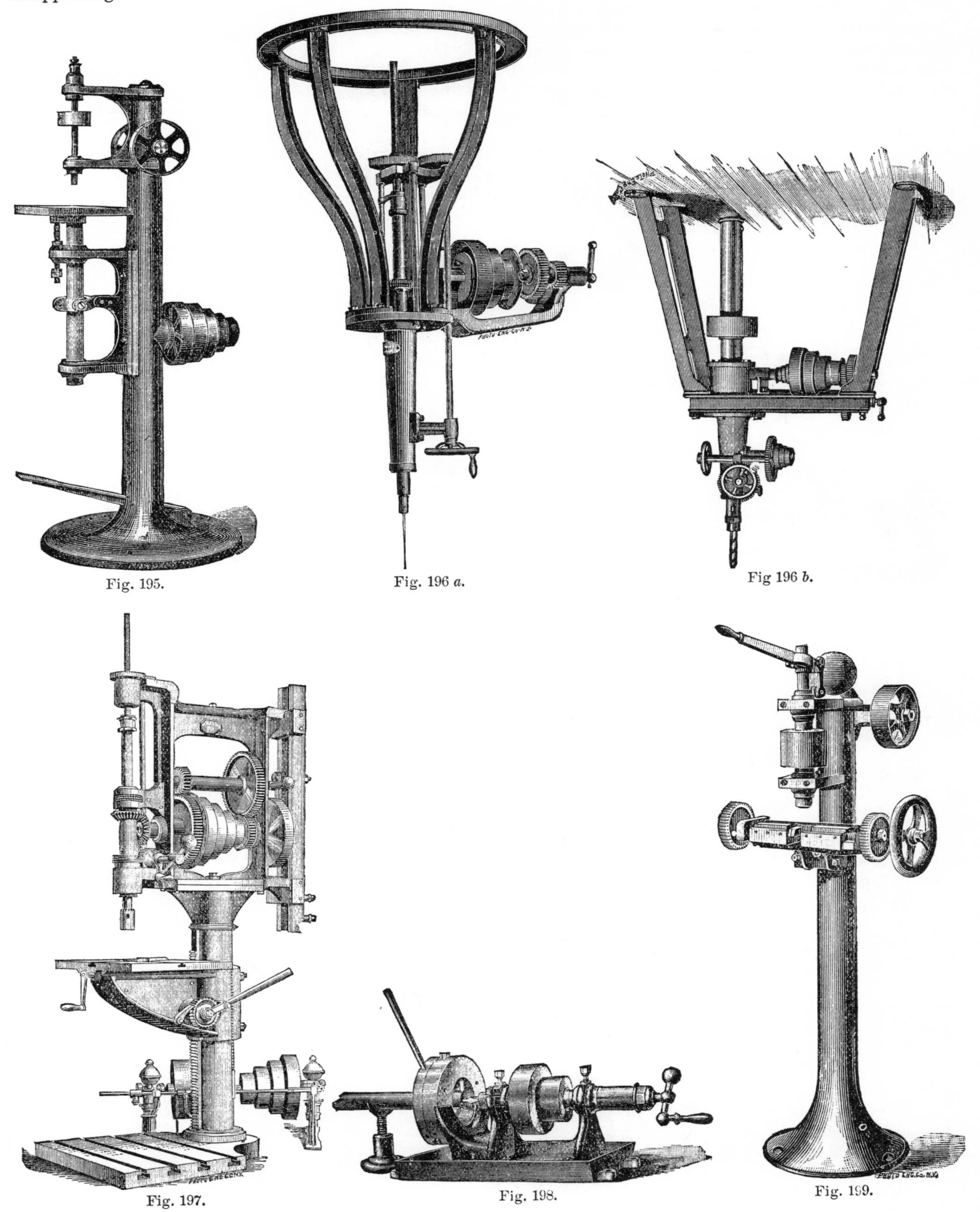

Fig. 195. Fig. 196 *a*. Fig 196 *b*.

Fig. 197. Fig. 198. Fig. 199.

§ 24.

BOLT-CUTTERS.

These tools for producing the screws on bolts might come perhaps under the head of the lathes. They have become, however, of so much importance as to be separate machines, and to form a class by themselves. They belong to two classes. The first includes those in which the work is held stationary and the dies revolve. The second class includes those in which the work revolves, while the dies are held stationary. Advanced practice rather favors the first class. The bolt-cutters may be again subdivided into the fixed die-machines which must be reversed to release the work, and the movable die-machines wherein the bolt is released by the opening of the dies, so that the machine need not be stopped. The latter system is preferred because the integrity of the thread is not endangered by running the die backward over the thread. Any chip from the cut getting into the relief of the die may tear away or mar several threads. The movable die system is also more rapid.

There are differences with respect to the number of chasers, and the position of the cutting-points upon the

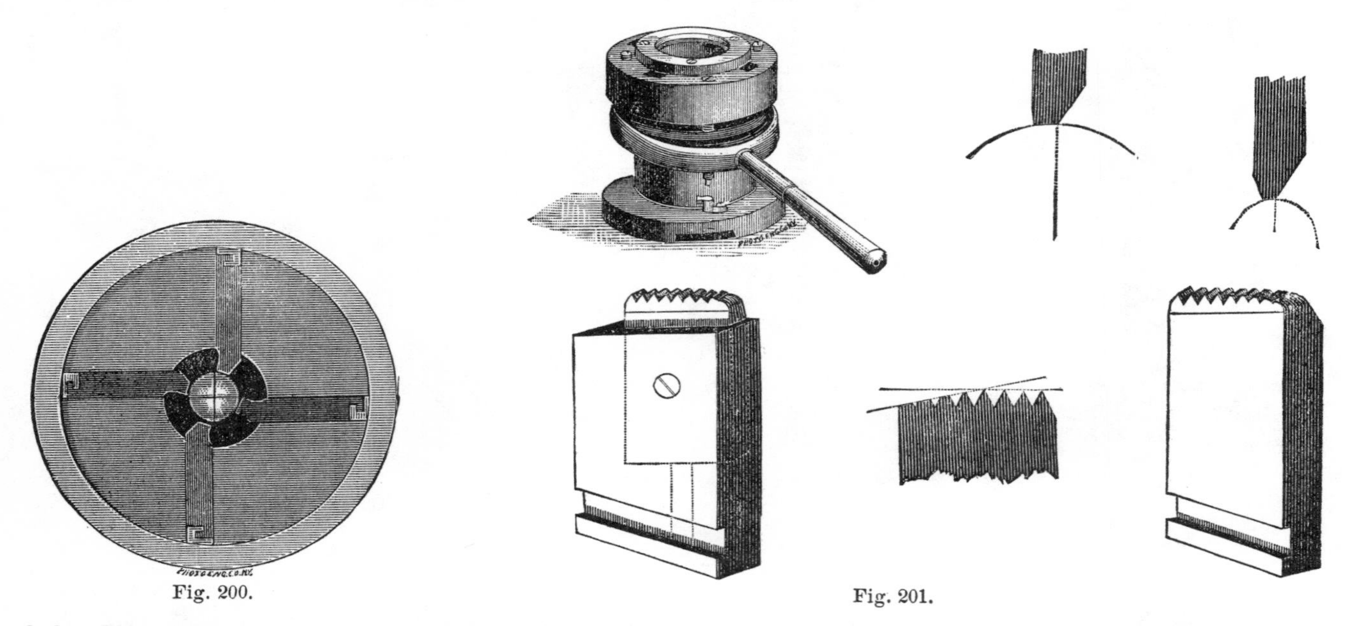

Fig. 200. Fig. 201.

bolt. Prevalent practice prefers four cutters, although three are approved in some quarters. Against the three jaws it is urged that the rod is never cylindrical, and that when the long diameter is on any one cutter, the other two are resisting near the short diameter. This permits the stock to recede from the one cutter, and the thread will be uneven and the nuts will bind.

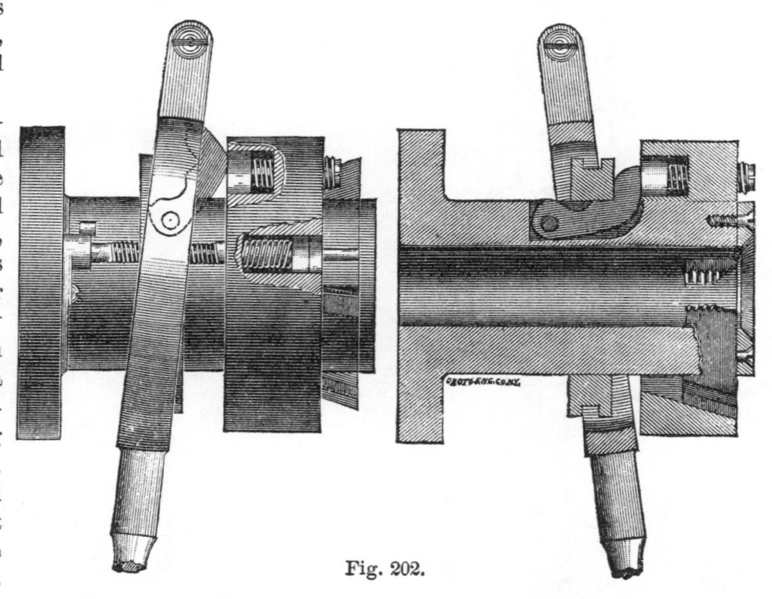

Fig. 202.

With respect to the position of the cutting-edge, the analogy of lathe practice has induced the system of Fig. 200. The cutting takes place at the ends of what corresponds to the horizontal diameter of a cylinder in the lathe. It is claimed, however, that when the cutter "leads" or cuts above the center the thread will be smoother than in the other case. On account of the play for adjustment of the jaws, a jaw nominally on the center line will often be really making a scraping cut below it. When this scraping occurs the edges tear the stock, instead of making a clean cut. Several good authorities, however, put the die on the center line, and nearly all favor the exact center for solid heads on account of lessened friction. When the dies are on the center line, the cutting or "hobbing" of the dies is done by a master-tap larger in diameter than the size called for, to secure the necessary relief at the heels of the cutters. When the cutters lead the center a smaller tap is necessary for the same purpose. The adjustable heads make this variation in size very easy while being cut.

Fig. 201 shows the hand-relief given to the tap, to give only the required amount of cutting-face, and also the relief for the entrance of the blank. The length of the cutting-face will vary with the speed and the severity of the work of the cutters. The same figure shows a case-die, in which the die proper is held in a holder. After being properly shaped the cutters are hardened, the threads being coated with soap to prevent scaling. The temper is drawn to a medium straw color, and the quenching is done in linseed oil or in water. The oil is thought to toughen the steel. While domestic steel has given results fully equal to those of imported grades, the tool-makers complain of the lack of uniformity and reliability which they encounter in its use. On this account only the imported product is preferred to the American at this date.

Fig. 202 illustrates one of the types of adjustable head in very general use. The dies fit in rectangular slots, by which radial motion alone is permitted. The dies have an oblique gain or mortise on one side, which fits a corresponding tenon in the external chucking-ring. When, therefore, the ring is moved forward the dies will close inward. When it is moved backward, the dies will open and release the bolt. The position of the heavy ring, and therefore the size of the thread cut, is determined by a small latch, which is held and released by the grooved ring pinned to the lever. This latch abuts against a screw in the heavy tenon-ring, which may be set at pleasure. The head is retracted by the long screws which pass through the tenon and grooved ring, thus uniting them together. The end of the long screw abuts against a stop, to prevent the rings from coming back too far. When this stop is swung out of the way, the dies are released, and can be exchanged for others. The shifting of the lever can be made automatic, so that the dies may be released when any desired depth of thread is reached. The entire machine is shown by Fig. 203.

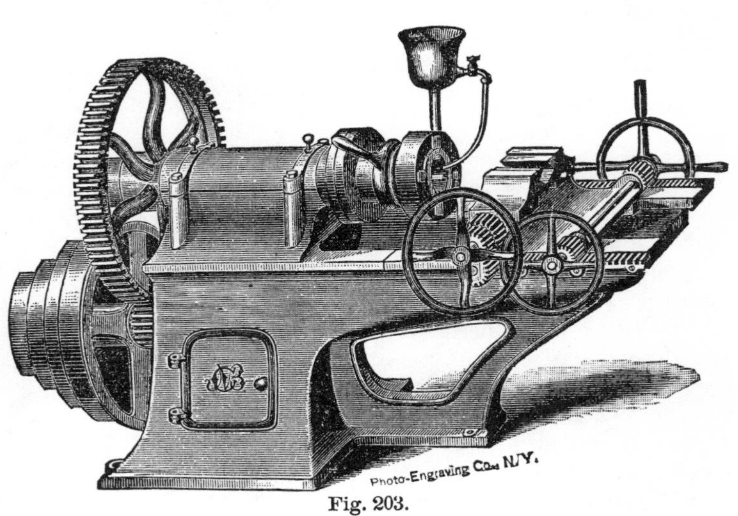

Fig. 203.

Fig. 204 shows a similar device for setting the jaws. The machine is entirely automatic. When

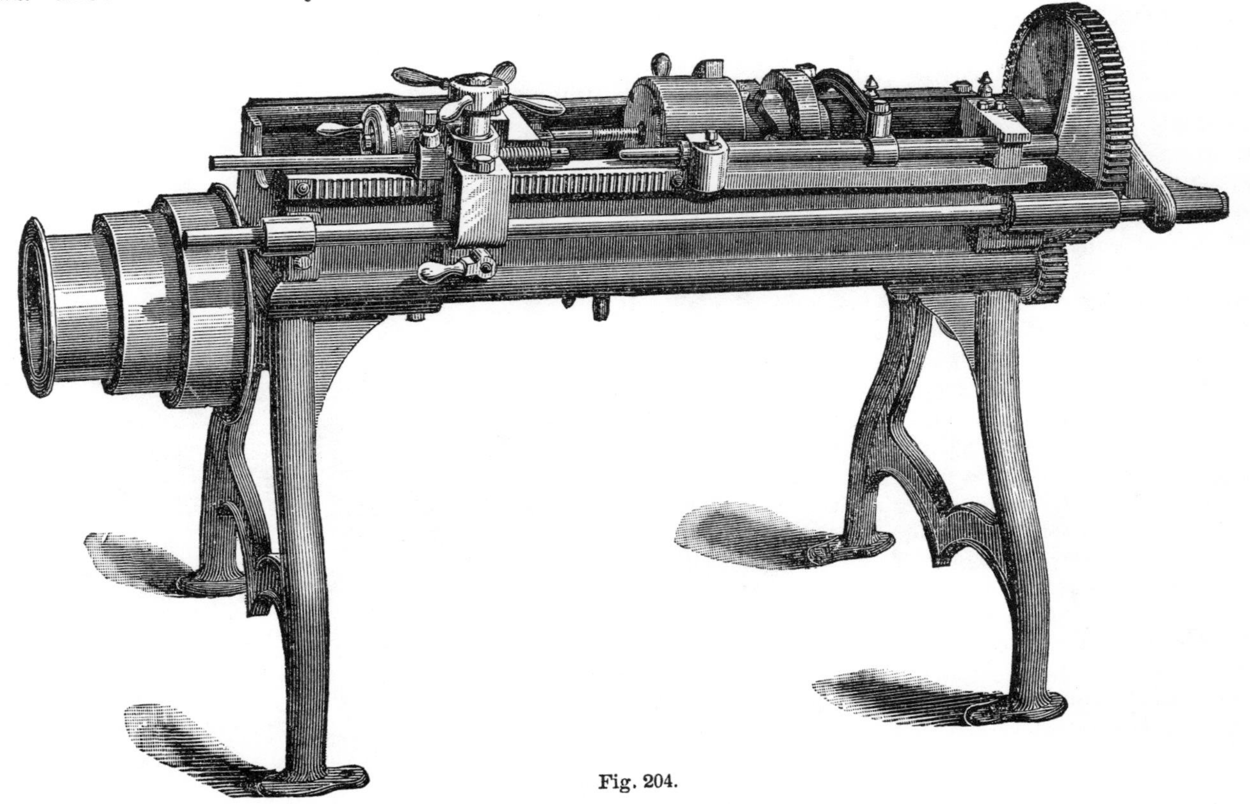
Fig. 204.

a latch is engaged with the ratchet-tooth on the head at the proper depth the outer ring is arrested and the flat groove on the inner sleeve retracts the keys on the jaws by virtue of its continued motion. At the same time the inclined plane on the large gear forces back the carriage and the finished bolt. The continued motion of the inner sleeve resets the jaws and locks them by the straight part of the groove. These tools are also arranged to hold the bolt between centers while being cut, in order to secure the same diameter of all threaded stock.

Fig. 205 shows another type of automatic machine, and Figs. 206 and 207 show its details. Three dies are held in radial slots in the head which is driven by the outer and larger gear-wheel M. This wheel is fitted loose on the hollow spindle B, and is secured to the latter by two bolts. These pass through the plate of the wheel and through circular slots in two arms, D and D′, which form part of the main spindle B. The position of M upon the spindle B is thus adjustable, and may be noted by a pointer, *d*, on the arm D, which moves over a scale upon M. The inner and smaller wheel, M′, is keyed to an outer sleeve, B′, which fits over B and carries a set of three cam-plates, *b*, upon the flange of the head. These cams are milled out on their inner edges to a spiral curve. These curved edges resist the radial motion outward of the dies when cutting, and it will be seen that the opening between the cutters will be determined by the relative position of the sleeve B′ and the driving-spindle B. If B′ were to revolve faster than B, the cutters would abut against a surface of *b*, which would get gradually farther from the center, and the dies would open. The wheel M′ is driven from the wheel M when the tool is cutting by projections E E upon their hubs. When these projections are in driving contact, any desired relation between the dies in B and the cam-plates upon B′ may be secured by bolts in the slotted arms D and the index pointer *d*. Any adjustment for wear, or any varied sizing of thread, large or small, may thus be effected. The large wheel M is driven from a pinion, F, keyed on the cone-pulley shaft. The wheel M′ meshes into a little larger pinion, F′, loose on the same shaft. A spiral spring, I, abutting against an adjustable collar, K, presses F′ against F, the adhesion being increased by a leather disk between them. When the spring is permitted to act, F will drive F′ by friction until the projections E upon the hubs come in contact, when the friction-disk will slip and B and B′ will move together. But F′ may be moved by the hand-lever H and the counterweight L so as to bring a male cone on it into a female cone which is fast in the leg of the machine; this arrests F, M′, and B′, while B still moves. Small spring cams, *c*, move out the dies in the head as they are relieved from the spiral of *b*, until the projections E on the hubs engage on the other side. The head then turns with the dies open until the lever H is latched back, when the spring I is permitted to act and the dies slowly close by the more rapid motion of M′ and B′. A rod in the axis of the cutter-head may be set to release the latch of H when any desired length of thread has been cut. This compact method of causing different relative speeds in the two large gear-wheels and utilizing the differential motion for moving the dies renders this a very notable machine.

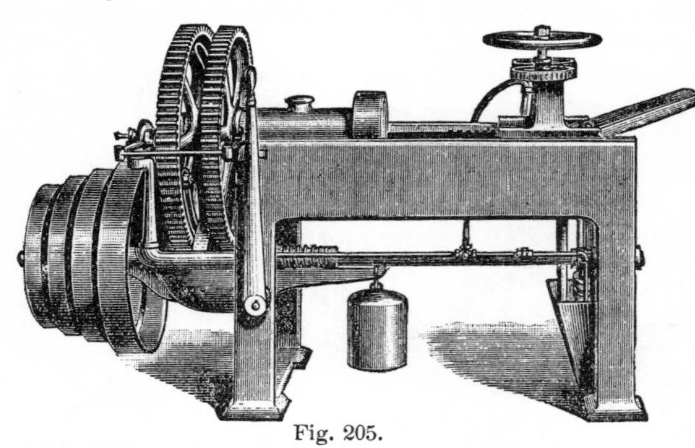
Fig. 205.

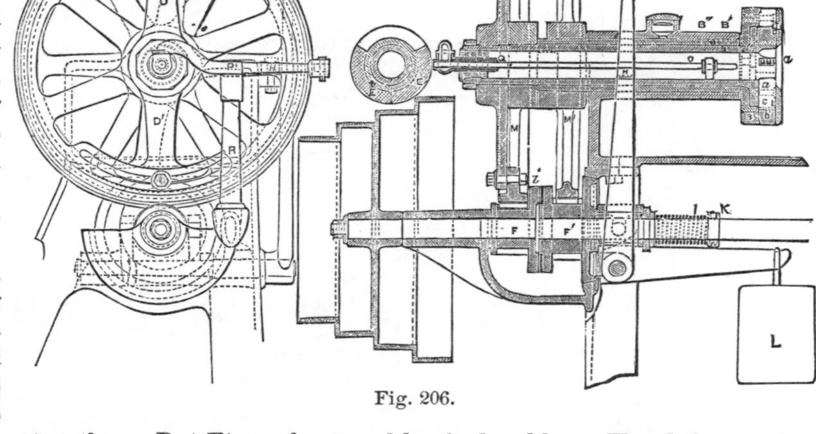

Fig. 206.

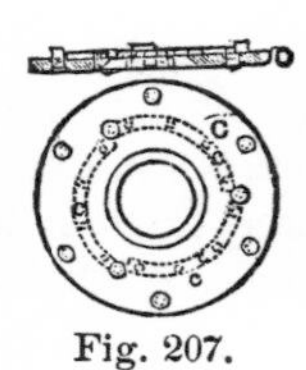
Fig. 207.

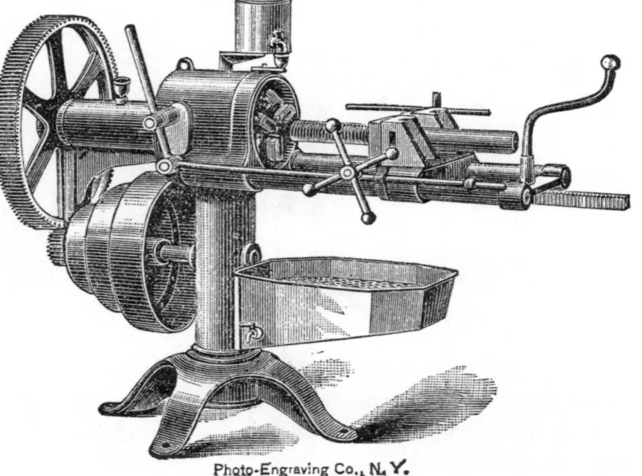

Fig. 208.

The tool shown in Fig. 208 illustrates another arrangement. Each of the cutters is carried in a species of holder made of a steel casting. The die is held in the holder by two set-screws on the side and one on the end. The holder has a turned stud near one end whose axis is parallel to that of the bolt to be cut. This stud fits into the head so that by the rotation of the holder around the stud the cutter-jaws approach or recede from the center. The holders are forced and held to their cut by a pin with inclined end, which moves parallel to the axis of the head and bears upon the back of the holder. The motion away from the cut is effected by stiff springs. These holding-pins are attached to a sleeve, which is moved forward by a spiral spring, and is moved backward when a pin is

Fig. 209.

released by a latch and drops into an inclined groove in the sleeve. This latch is moved by the bolt being cut, so that any desired length of thread may be produced. The bolt-cutters of Figs. 209 and 210 show the standard New England form of this type of machine.

Fig. 210.

Fig. 211 shows one of the largest machines of this class ever made, designed to cut the threads on 6-inch rolled iron. It was first built for the heavy bolt and turn-buckle work in the pumping and hoisting plants in deep mining in the state of Nevada. The machine weighs 10 tons, the large gear is 5 feet in diameter, and the 6-inch tap alone weighs 200 pounds. The same builders make smaller machines, presenting the same advantages as the other designs.

All these machines are fitted with self-centering jaw vises for holding the stock (Fig. 215). In one type the vise is geared differentially, giving great power. Usually the jaws are worked by screws only, either right-and-left handed, or else geared together. They are fed forward to the jaws by a rack and pinion and hand-wheel, or else by a lever. The designs and motions of the vises are shown in the cuts.

Fig. 211.

For bolt-cutters of the second class, where the bolt revolves and the die is stationary, a solid die is used. One of the types is shown by Fig. 212 *a* and *b*. The cutting-chasers are inserted in an iron collet, encircled by a wrought-

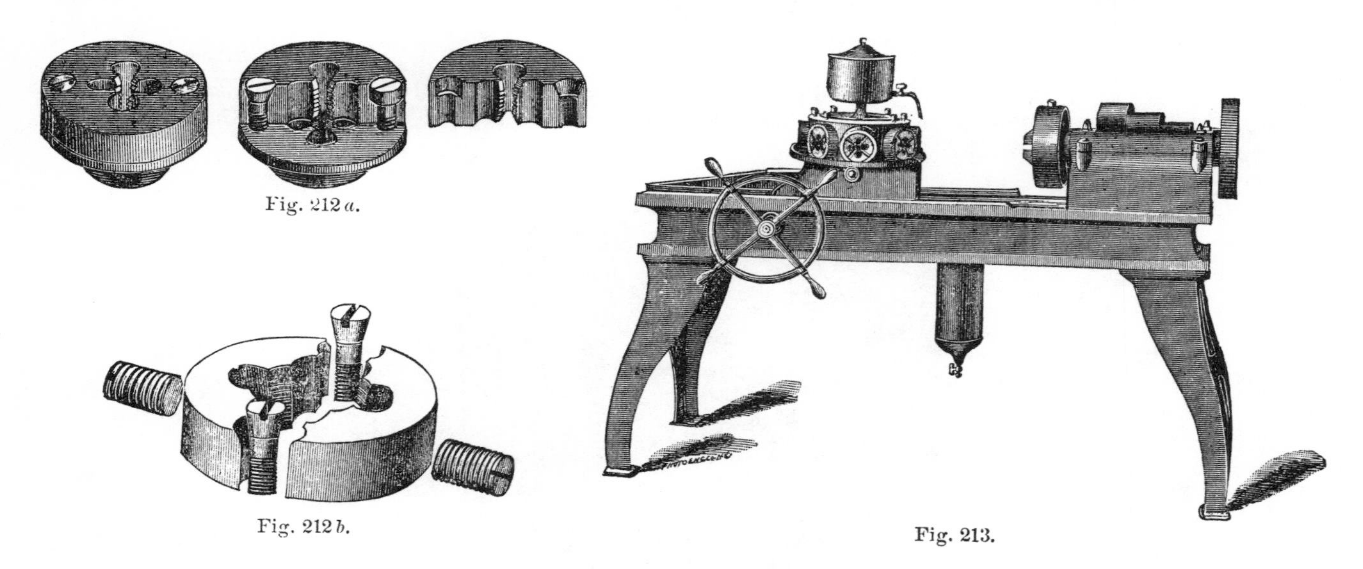

Fig. 212 *a*.

Fig. 212 *b*.

Fig. 213.

iron ring, beveled on the inside. The chasers are beveled to fit the ring, and the latter is secured to the central flange of the collet by adjusting- and distance-screws. An adjustment of $\frac{1}{32}$ of an inch or more may be made in the cutting size of each die. The collet is split, and the opening may be lessened by slacking off the conical screws.

Figs. 213 and 214 show the types of the entire machine. A number of dies are held in a turret-head, and are fed against the revolving bolt by the hand-wheel, pinion, and rack. In Fig. 214 a slide is fitted with sockets for various sizes of nuts. The taps will be held in the jaw of the head (Fig. 215).

A type of movable jaw-head for cutters of this class is shown by Fig. 216. The cutters fit into chuck-plates, which have spiral grooves in their back. The size of the thread will be determined by the position of the stop in the curved slot at top. The blank is released by the revolution of the holder by the hand-lever shown. For tapping-nuts any of the machines illustrated may be applied directly by the simplest inversion, or by replacing the cutting-jaws by a pair adapted for holding a tap.

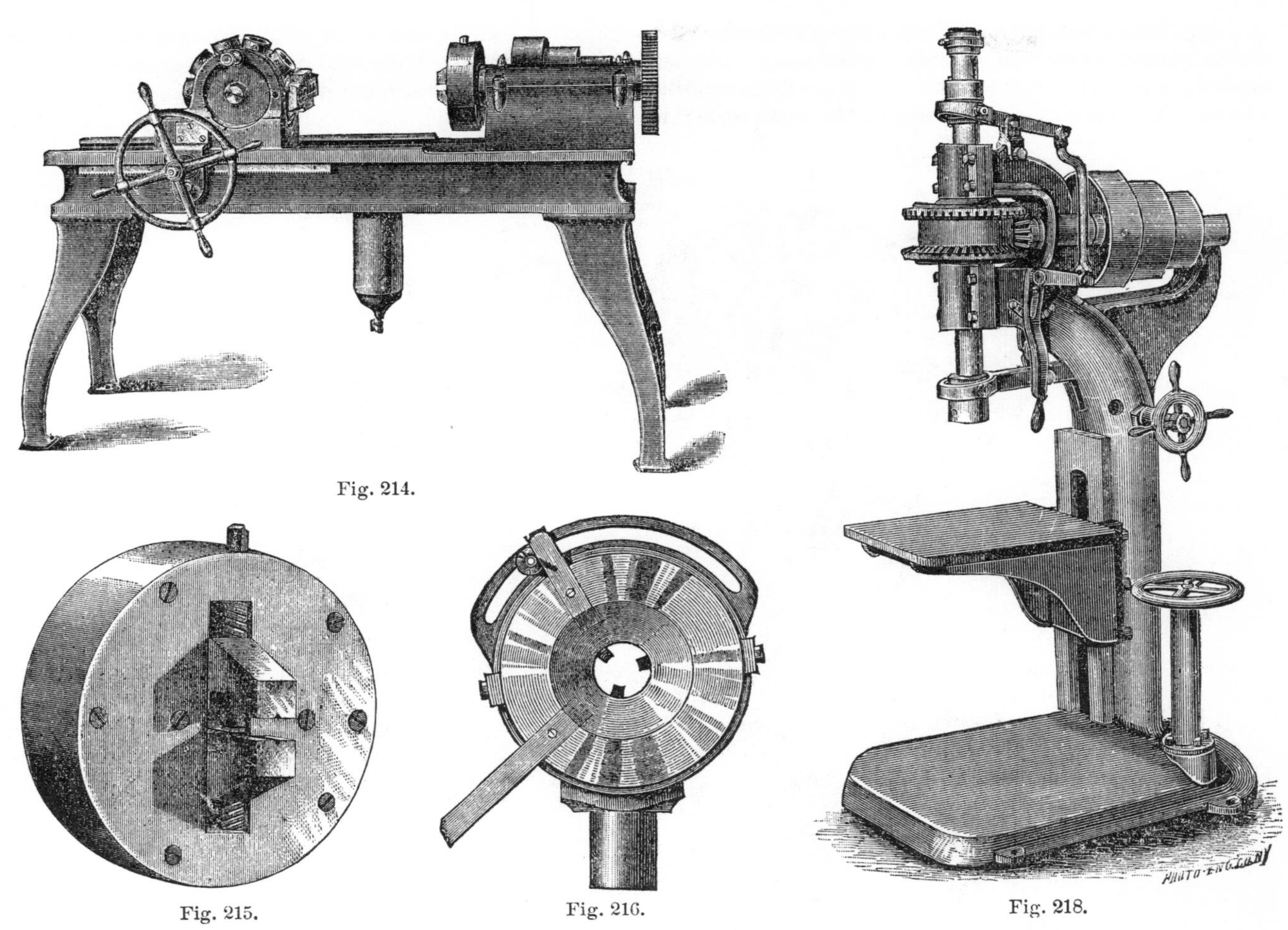

Fig. 214.

Fig. 215. Fig. 216. Fig. 218.

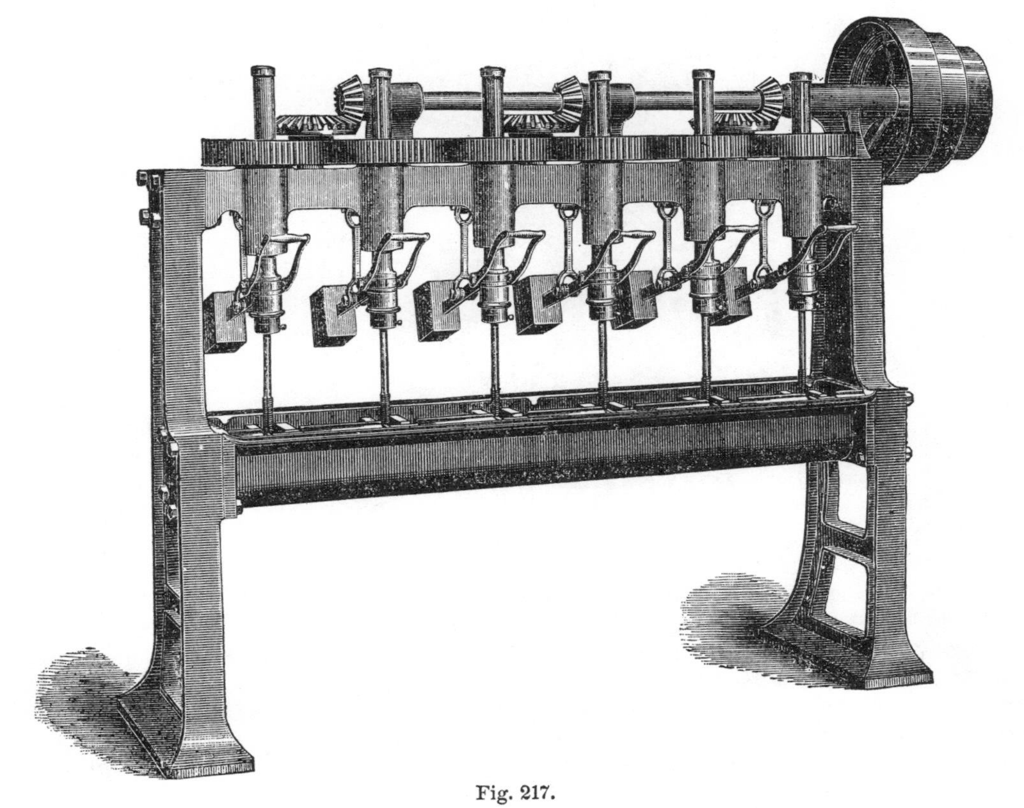

Fig. 217.

Fig. 217 illustrates a multiple vertical machine of six spindles. The spindles are counterpoised, and the nuts are immersed in oil while being tapped, and slide into their fit in the holders. The vertical tappers have the advantage of washing away the chips from the cutting-edges. On the other hand, in the tank-machines the tap may revolve in a film of oil on the surface of water. The water cools the tap, and the oil relieves the friction. The

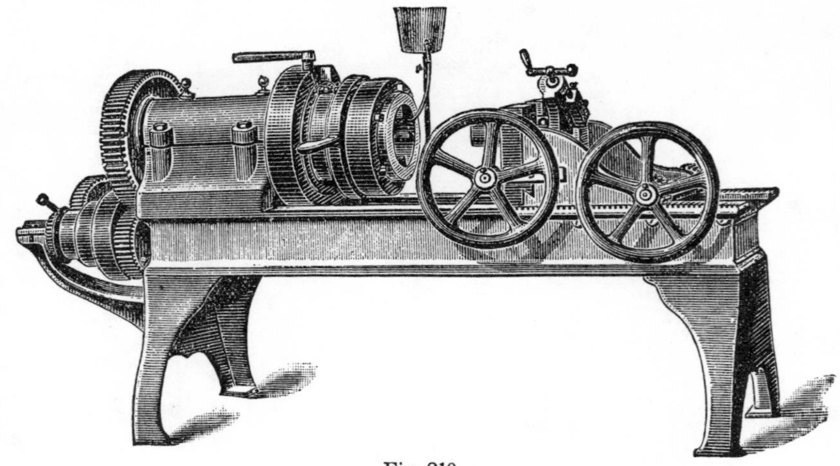

Fig. 219.

mineral oils do not answer for these purposes. Animal oils must be used, or a soda water, or an alkali mixture, made up of 10 pounds of carbonate of soda, 4 gallons of whale oil, 3 gallons of lard oil, and 40 gallons of water. These lubricant mixtures are either held in cans and delivered from a long spout at the cutting-point, or else are pumped on the work in excess to wash away the chips. The spent oil is strained into a reservoir and used over and over again, whence results a notable economy.

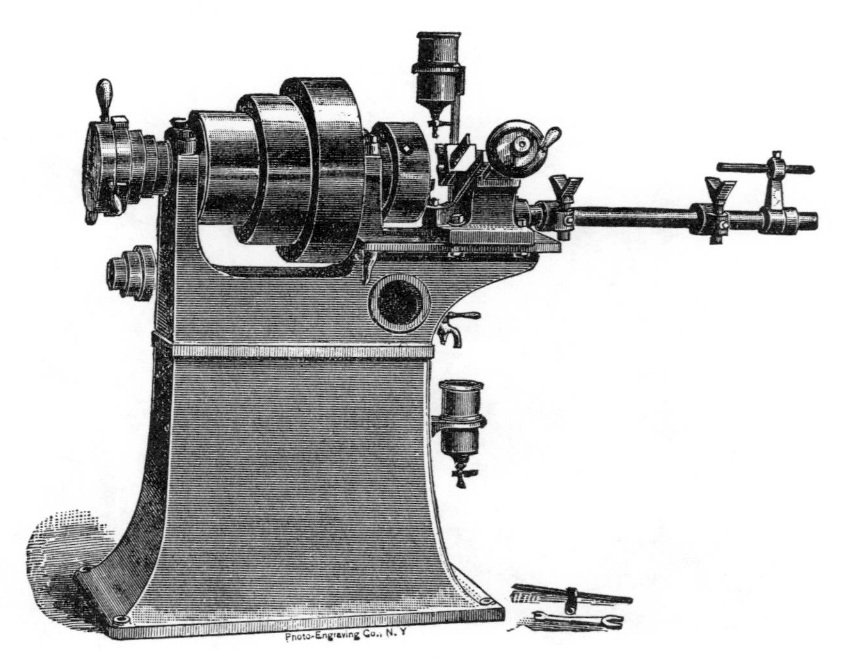

Fig. 220.

Fig. 218 illustrates a machine for tapping general work in cast iron, where the work will be run dry. The spindle is driven in one direction or in the other by a clutch between the horizontal bevel-wheels, which is operated by the lever. The spindle is fed down by hand, and the table is adjusted by screw and hand-wheel.

The machines for threading pipe differ in no essential respects from the bolt-cutters. The smaller sizes are usually worked with solid dies, the pipe being held in jaws in the head and passing through the hollow spindle. The larger sizes use adjustable dies in a revolving head (Fig. 219). Where the pipe is held stationary the required length may be cut by fed cutters in the head. Where the pipe revolves, the lengths must be cut either by a cutting-off tool, on a rest, or else in a separate machine. This latter class of machine is known as a cutting-off lathe, and types are illustrated by Figs. 220 and 221. The spindle is hollow, with a jaw at one end and a bushing, or, better,

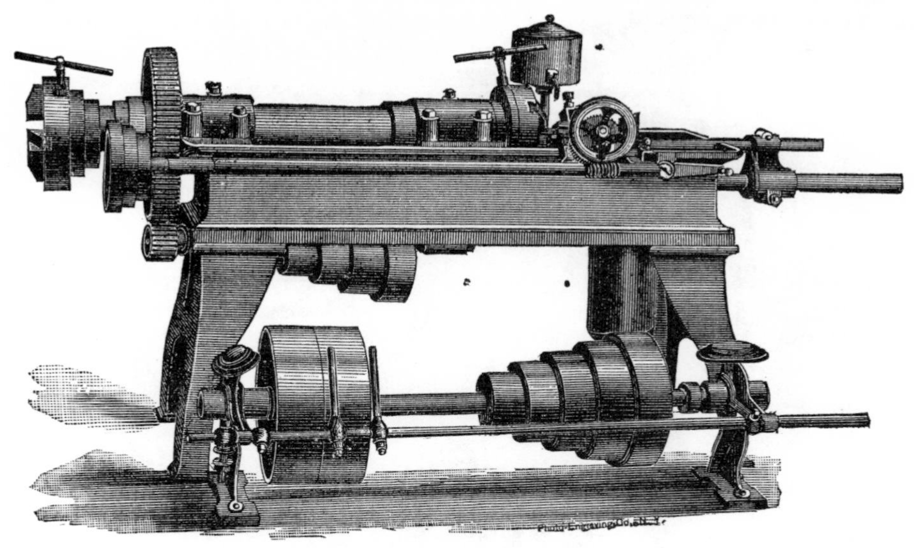

Fig. 221.

a self-centering chuck, at the other. The tool is fed obliquely downward by hand and by power, the required length being gauged by a stop. The tool may be forged of such a shape as to be efficient until it is ground so short as to become useless. Tools in holders are frequently used.

§ 25.

SCREW-MACHINES.

For making machine- or set-screws from the bar which has the shape for the head, a screw-machine is required. This may have several forms. For large work, a machine of the type of Figs. 222 and 223 would be used. The

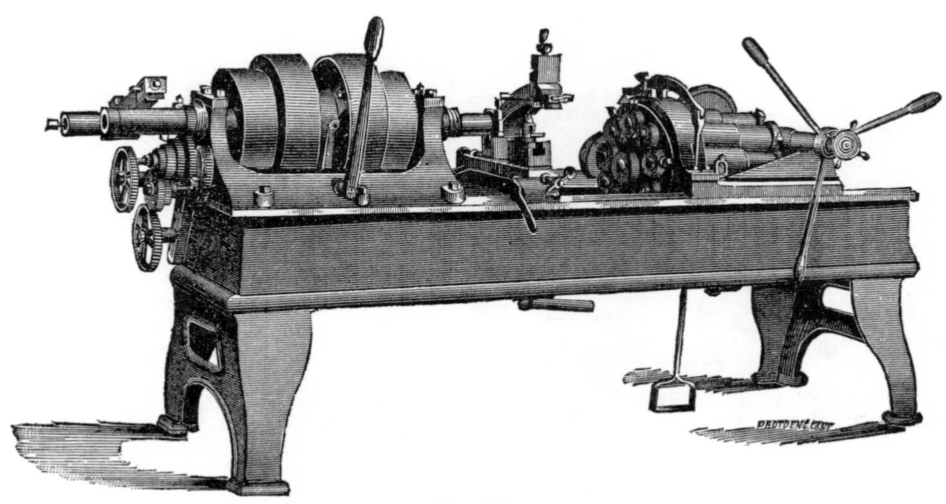

Fig. 222.

spindle is hollow and receives the rods. The tail-head carries a number of spindles, each of which is adapted for one operation on the screws. The tools are fed forward by rack and pinion by the levers, and the one in operation is held from motion by a pin on the treadle-lever. Larger screws will be chased by the slide-rest and hobs; smaller ones will be cut by dies in one of the spindles.

Fig. 224 shows a similar arrangement of tools. The linear motion is assured by the slotted disk on the tail-disk spindle, and an adjustable stop controls the lengths. Tools of this type may use tool-holders with detachable cutters for sizing, etc., thus avoiding the expense of hollow mills.

Fig. 225 shows the very usual application of the turret-head for this class of work, with a chasing-rest.

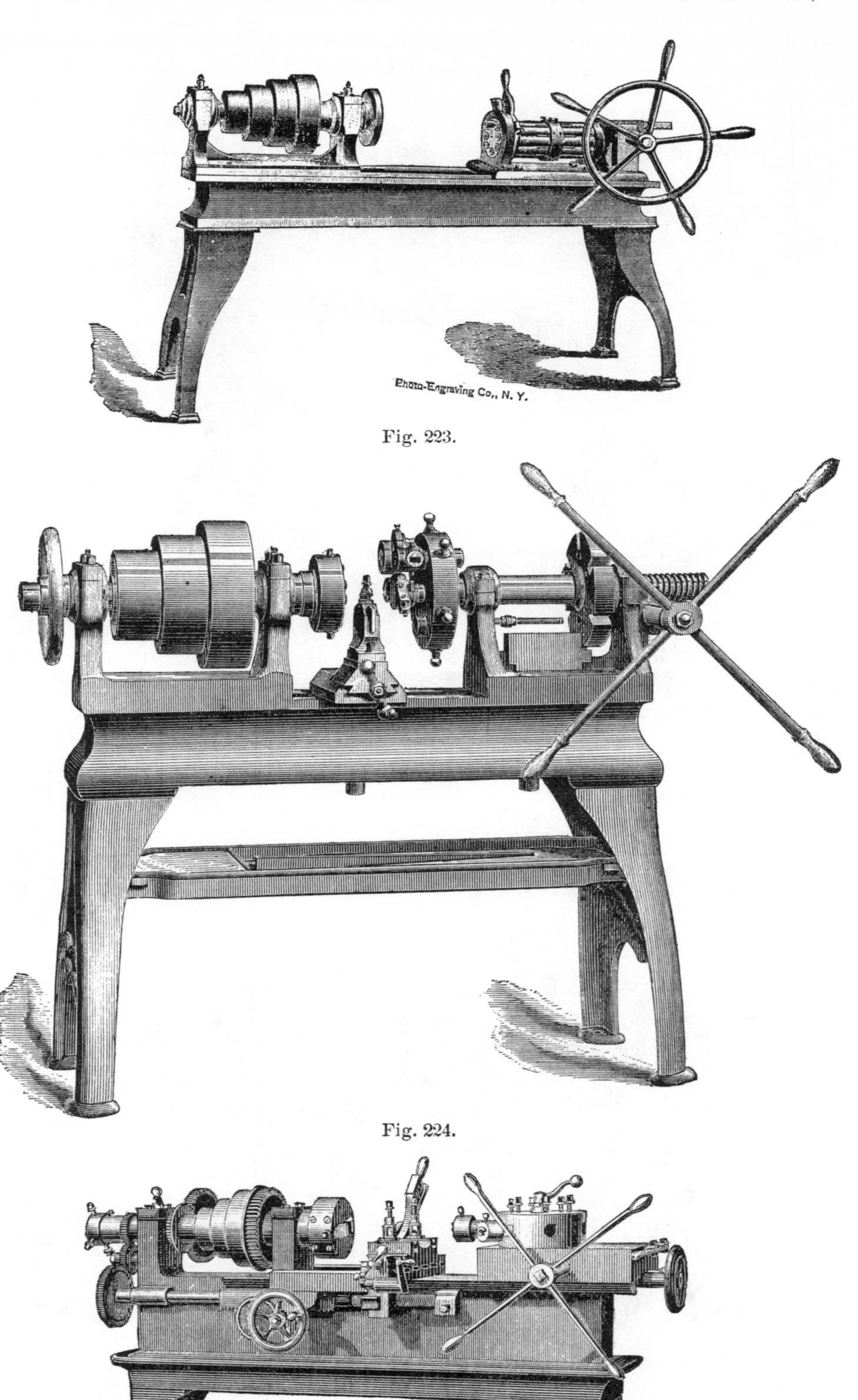

Fig. 223.

Fig. 224.

Fig. 225.

Fig. 226 illustrates the smaller machines without chasing-head the slide-rest being used for sizing and cutting off only.

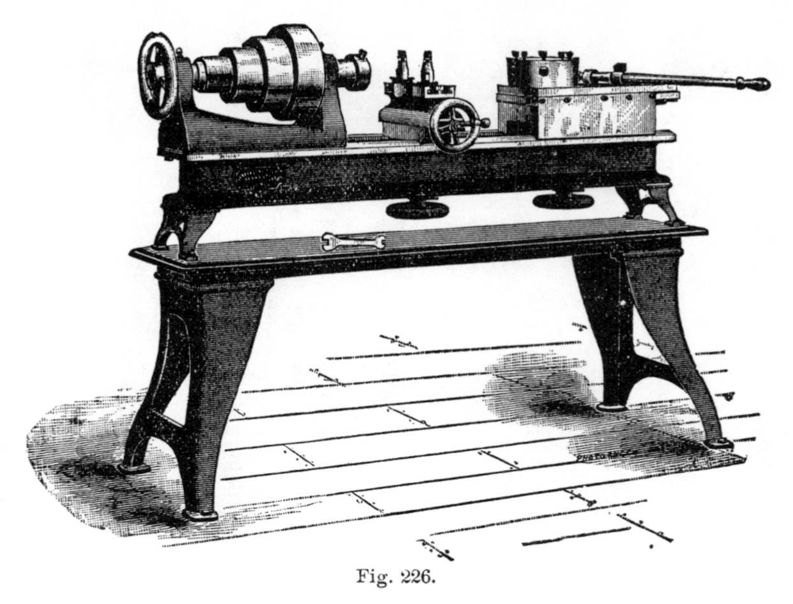

Fig. 226.

Fig. 227 shows the detail of this rest, giving the stop and gauge adjustment at the left, and Fig. 228 illustrates types of tools and holders. Machines of this class are capable of doing a great variety of work with very close accuracy and at high speed. They are especially adapted for finer grades of work, and when so applied will operate to a margin of error within $\frac{2}{1000}$ of an inch.

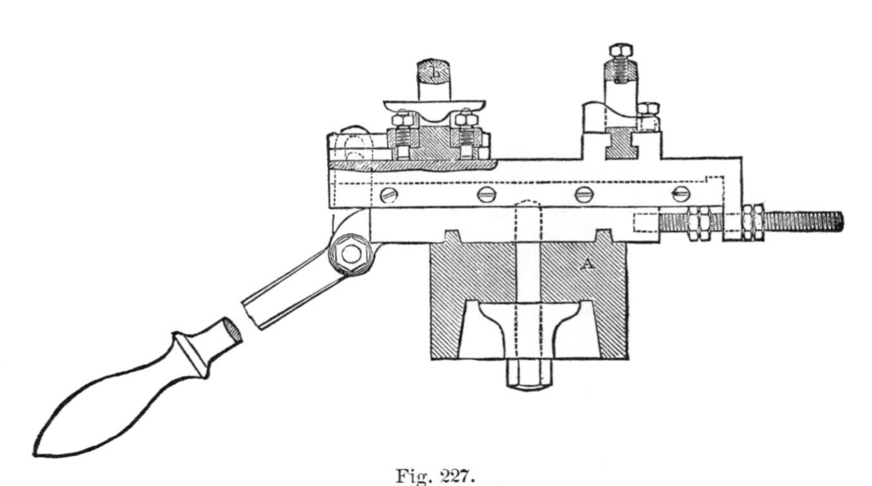

Fig. 227.

Fig. 229 illustrates specimen products of such a machine.

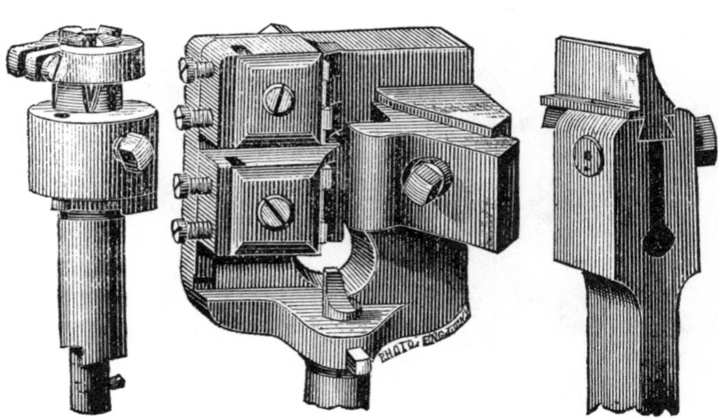

Fig. 228.

Fig. 230 illustrates a type of screw-machine, designed to give better support to the turret. The turret swings on two horizontal supported journals, instead of on one overhanging stud. The tendency to wear the turret loose upon its supports is thereby reduced. Several of its other excellencies are visible from the cut.

The smaller screw-machines are usually equipped to produce the sharp V-thread, which remains in very general use at distances from the centers of enterprise. The larger tools cut the flattened V-threads of the American standard unless specially ordered otherwise. Pipe-threads are uniform all over, and consist of a sharp thread cut with a taper of $\frac{3}{4}$ of an inch to the foot.

Fig. 229.

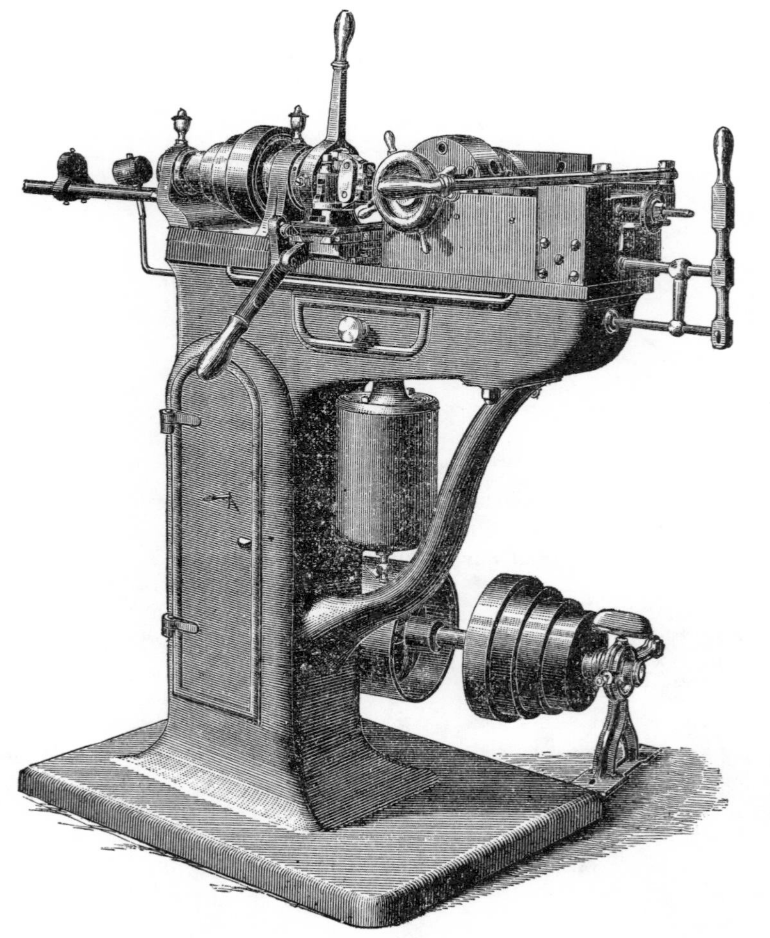

Fig. 230.

§ 26.

PARING-TOOLS WITH LINEAR MOTIONS—PLANERS.

The tools with rectilinear motions of work or of the cutter are especially adapted for producing plane or flat surfaces. The shaper and slotter are adapted for smaller work, or for work where the tool traverse need only be short, and they will readily work out curved profiles by cutting along their elements. But the planer is especially applicable for the production of large or long surfaces which must approach true planes.

The planer will consist of a table or platen moving backward and forward upon ways in a bed-casting. This table moves below a cross-head, which is borne upon two uprights, bolted to the bed-casting. The tool is secured to a slide upon this cross-head, and receives feed-motions in different directions. The gear for driving and feeding are the points in which there is the greatest divergence in the practice of to-day.

There are several reasons for making the table and the work move under the tool, which is stationary, except for its feed-motions. If the tool had to travel any distance, it would be very difficult to produce true horizontal planes. The overhang of the tool, varying at different points, would cause the chip to be always lighter when the slide was farthest out. Beside, the freedom of the slide for ease of motion would cause errors. By reversing this system the tool has its lost motion a constant, for the play of feed is the same at all points of the surface. Moreover, the weight of the table and work acts in the same direction as the strain of the cut, all being downward upon the ways of the bed. The play for motion is therefore resisted by the constant weight of the table and work, and there can be no yielding of the support for the work. If, therefore, the ways be true, and the upright and cross-head are stiff enough, true planes will be produced by this system. There is less gained by this form of tool when planing vertical surfaces. But its capacity for this class of work is small on the medium sizes, on account of the proper support of the tool. When these smaller machines are called on to do extensive vertical surfacing it is not unusual to invert their system and secure the work to a floor-plate, while the tool-holder is bolted to the bed,

Fig. 231.

and thus reciprocates. The larger machines have vertical surfacing holders upon their uprights. For the convenient holding of work the tables or platens are cast with a large number of **T**-holes. **T**-slots are often planed in the top in addition. Upon the under side of the table are two longitudinal **V**-guides, planed and scraped, truly parallel. These **V**'s rest in corresponding ways in the bed, and guide the motion of the table in a true straight line. The table is often cast with the top side up, in order that any blow-holes or defects may come in the upper side, so as to secure the soundness of the **V**'s. The trough-shape of the lower **V**'s enables them to retain the oil necessary for their lubrication. This could not be done were the arrangement of the **V**'s reversed. To insure the lubrication of all the bearing-surface of the guides, curved channels are chipped out from the faces, running from the bottom of the **V** to near the top. By this means the oil is carried to those places from which it would naturally drain off. It has been suggested to use flat, thin disks, which might turn in counterbores in the ways and effect the same purpose. To catch the oil which would be displaced from the ends of the **V**'s a cell or pocket is put at the ends of the troughs, and one designer planes a bead on a flat at the top of the troughs to prevent loss of oil over the sides. An objection to the use of the two **V**'s results from the difficulty in securing perfect parallelism of the four planes of the guides throughout their whole length, or of retaining that parallelism where the surfaces wear. If there is any difference in the hardness of different parts of the bed and table castings, the wear at different places will be uneven. If this wear be on one side of the **V**'s, the table will crowd over and produce curves on vertical cuts. If on both sides, the table will either dip or wind, producing errors of horizontal surface. To avoid the tendency of the bed to creep and bear a little harder on one side of the **V** or the other one designer uses one flat and one **V** groove. The bearing area of the two is calculated carefully to compensate for the different angles of resistance to the downward pressure (Fig. 231). A form of planer with two flat shears offers certain points worth noting. The surfaces for wear and bearing are large and are easily made true. Side-play is prevented by adjustable gibs. Special oiling devices by flanged rollers counter-weighted so as to lift oil against the under sides of the slides prevent dry seizure of surfaces, and they promise excellent results of exactness and durability.

The bed of large planers will rest directly on the foundation, which will oppose any flexure from the strain of the weight or the cut. On the smaller sizes the bed must be made deep enough so as not to sag between the legs or supports which lift it from the floor. There has been considerable improvement in this respect in the newer designs. A very excellent arrangement is to lessen the span between the legs by making them columnar and hollow, to serve as tool-closets. The ends of the troughs are strongly bracketed out beyond the legs for the same

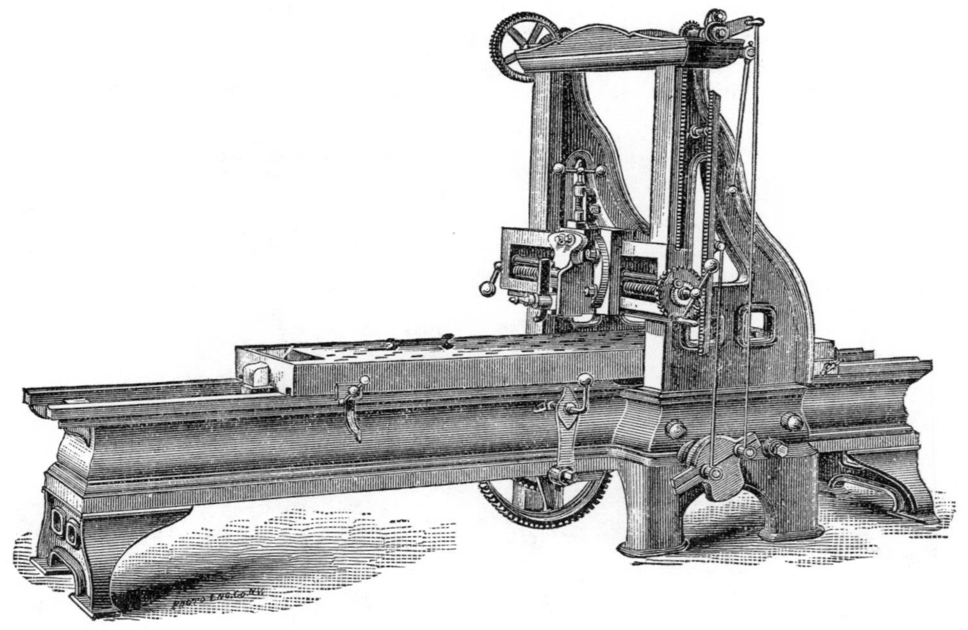

Fig. 232.

object, since the heaviest strain will always be upon the length between supports, and by the use of brackets the legs come nearer together, with a given length of trough. The bed must also be longer than the table, for while it is not necessary that it be twice as long, yet there must be no tendency for the table to tip when loaded at one end. By making the table itself deep the pressure is distributed more uniformly, and the tendency to spring is diminished. The uprights or cheeks have to resist a strain tending to bend them backward by pressure against the cross-head. This pressure will have the greatest leverage when the cross-head is near their top, and therefore the uprights will be of greatest depth and section near the bottom. There has also been great improvement in the design of these uprights with regard to stiffness. The amount of metal and its disposition is much more judicious than in the earlier forms. Openings are made in the cheeks for lightness of their web, considered as a girder, and to enable the operator to look through them at the work. The uprights are bolted very firmly to faced surfaces upon the sides of the bed. They are united by a strong girt at the top. In older practice this was an entablature bolted to the top of the sides. In modern designs the girt is cast as part of the uprights, or bolted to their sides, and is curved horizontally to act as an arched brace, to stiffen further the uprights and distribute an unsymmetrical pressure more equally on both. The uprights are put a little behind the middle of the length of the bed, in order that in front of them may be a clear space for securing and examining work. They are faced on the front side for the bearing of the cross-head, and upon some rear surface to admit of clamping the cross-head by a gib. This clamping surface may be either an outside flange or one made by a slot down the face, which divides the bearing surface into two parts. The cross-head is upheld and adjusted by two screws, which are coupled together by a horizontal cross-shaft overhead through pairs of bevel-gears. By turning the horizontal shaft by a crank- or hand-wheel the two ends of the cross-head are raised equally at once, and require no repeated adjustment. In the larger tools this cross-shaft is driven by power, usually by a belt-wheel. Since the weight of the cross-head and attachments are opposed to the strain of the cut the screws can be used to reinforce the clamps. After the head is secured in place by the clamping-bolts, an attempt to screw down the screws will take up all lost motion and give extra points of resistance. On account of the necessary play in the number of joints, it is not generally thought judicious to attempt to feed downward by the adjusting-screws. It has been done (Fig. 232), but recent practice

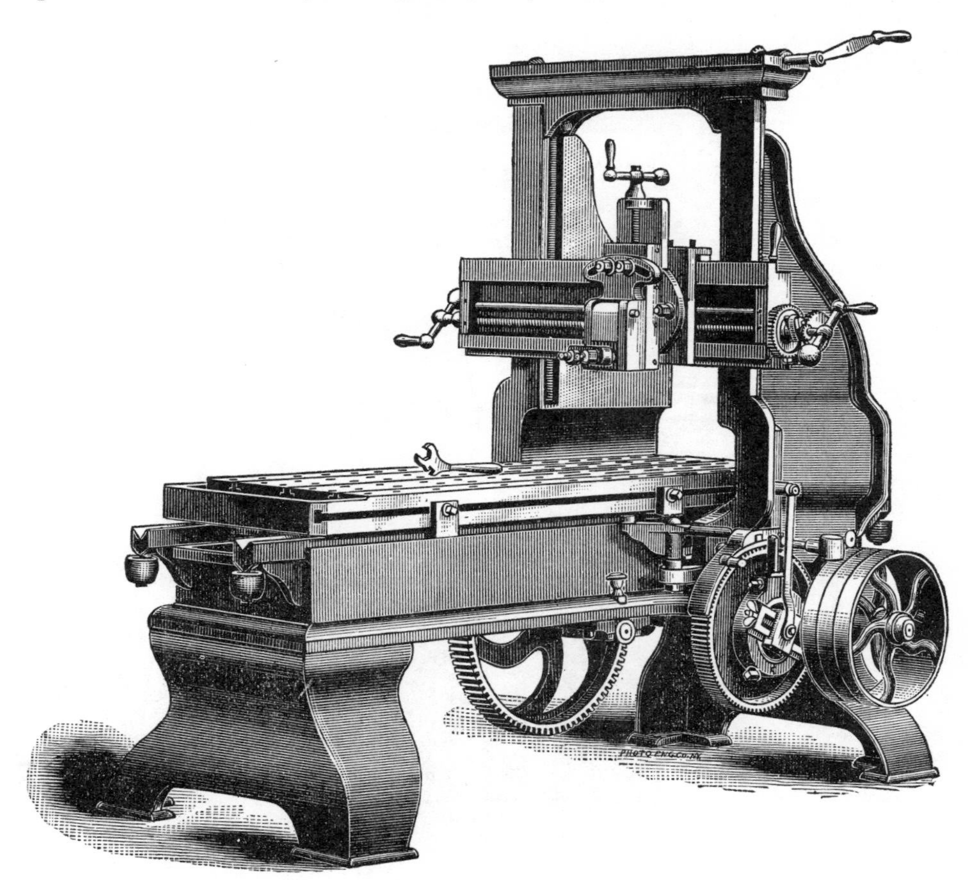

Fig. 233.

prefers to clamp the cross-head, and give all the vertical feeding at the slide to the tool-point and apron. The clamping is usually effected by two bolts at each cheek, which tighten a gib or plate, clasping the faced guide surface of the upright. The lifting-screws are carried either inside the uprights when they are of box-form, or outside of them at the back or sides. In the former case the projecting lugs which form the nuts pass through slots in the upright and serve as guiding-slides. In the latter arrangement the nuts are often separate and are bolted on to the back of the head. The uprights are often arranged so as to carry extra tool-holders (Fig. 248) for vertical surfacing.

The cross-head itself must be straight. It is very often strengthened against flexure sidewise between the uprights by stiffening-ribs at the back (Fig. 235). To lighten the web of its depth, holes are often cored out in the casting in the central part. Since it is designed to carry the slide or saddle which holds the tool stiffly and yet permit the feed-motions, there must be a track or shear planed on the front surface, in order that the saddle may be gibbed to it. These shears appear in three different forms. The upper part is made square, to resist the pressure due to the weight of the saddle (Fig. 233). This embraces the square on the top and front and rear, the top and rear bearing being gibbed to take up wear and lost motion. The under side of the shear is planed to a **V**, sloping inward and upward. In the second form both upper and lower surfaces are inclined inward, and the third form has the upper and lower **V** parallel, the lower face in all cases sloping upward and inward. The first form is by far the most prevalent, though some very excellent designs retain the second. The squared surfaces oppose the strain on them by normal resistances, and therefore move more easily than where there may be a wedging action.

The lower **V** resists the upward oblique strain of the cut, and prevents any jarring by its shape. The gibs are adjustable by screws bearing against them in shallow counterbores, or else they are tapered, and adjustable by screws and jam-nuts.

The front of the track is flat and of sufficient breadth to resist the horizontal pressure. What surface is not required between the top and bottom rail is cut away, and accommodates the rod and screw for the feed-motions of the saddle and apron (Figs. 234 and 235). The saddle fits upon the track on the cross-head, and has a horizontal motion upon it. The saddle is either rectangular, as in the cut, or in more recent practice has wings at the top for increasing the length of bearing surface, thus diminishing wear. Into the back of this saddle is secured a brass nut, through which passes the feed-screw. This screw usually runs near the bottom of the hollow of the rail, and its rotation in either direction will accordingly carry the whole saddle across the table. The front of this saddle-plate is finished off with a boss and a circular **T**-slot, into which bolts may fit, by which a swivel-plate may be

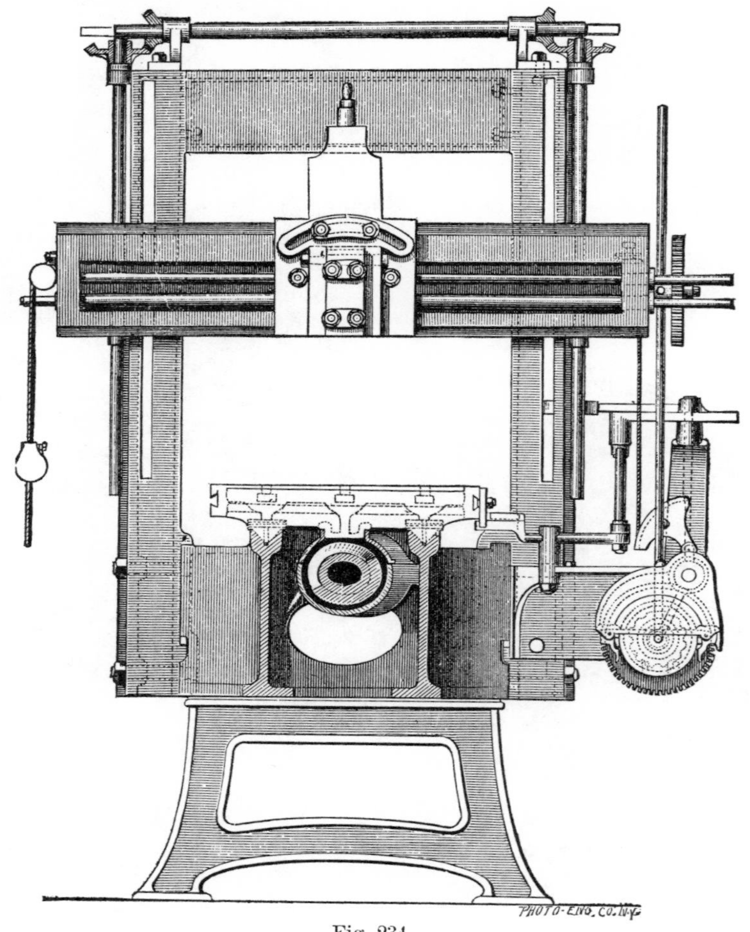

Fig. 234.

secured in any angular position. This swivel-plate carries a second flat shear, planed on its edges to a **V**, sloping inward. Upon this guide is gibbed a slide, to which the tool is secured. The slide is fed along the guide at whatever angle it may be by a screw with ball-handle or hand-wheel. To produce this vertical or angular feed of the tool-slide is the object of a splined shaft which lies along the hollow of the cross-head above the screw. This shaft carries a bevel-gear which drives a short idle shaft of bevel-gear in the axis of the swivel-plate. The third gear turns a fourth upon the axis of the downward feed-screw, so that rotation of the splined shaft will turn the screw of the feed at whatever angle the latter may stand. The fourth gear will roll around the circumference of the third when the swivel-plate is adjusted. The fourth gear may be splined to the angular feed-screw, or it may be made to serve as the nut for the latter. In this latter arrangement, when the automatic feed is in use, the screw must be locked either by a friction-clamp or by a locking-pin. When fed directly, the friction of the splined horizontal shaft is the dependence for holding the nut. In the former arrangement it is not expected that the direct feed will be much used. In fact it is not. Very often in large tools the top of the saddle is out of reach, and in smaller ones the end of the cross-head is more accessible without reaching over the work. The ends of the screw and the splined shaft are squared to receive crank or ball-handle when feeding by hand.

The power-feeds are intermittent, as they should be. The cutter, after being set, makes a stroke with the feed at rest, thus cutting always in lines parallel to the guiding V's. The feed-shafts are fitted at their ends nearest the operator to receive a loose gear. This gear carries a pawl or dog, which may turn a slip-gear in one direction or the other. Motion is imparted to the loose gear through a small angle from a slotted crank, the variation in the amount of feed being caused by greater or less length of crank. A link from the adjustable pin of this crank gives

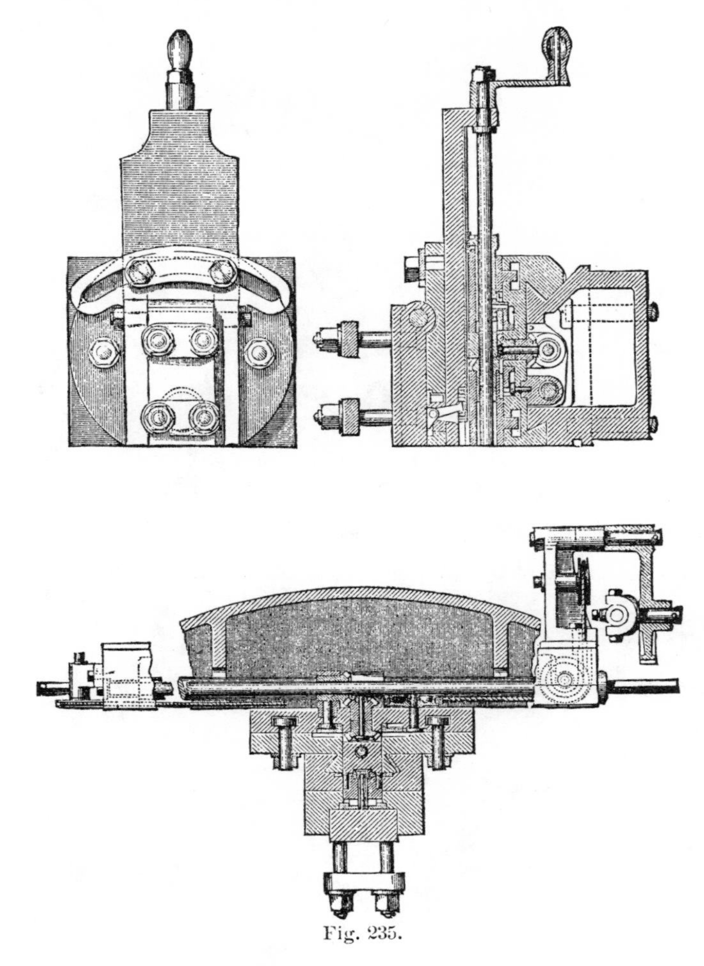

Fig. 235.

an alternating motion either to a rack, which thus turns the loose gear, or else to a sector, which acts similarly. The reason for the use of the rack is that thereby the cross-head may be at any elevation and yet the feed mechanism will be always in gear without adjustment from the operator. Where the sector or its equivalent is used, the link which moves it is clamped to it by a short set-screw, which must be loosened when the cross-head is to be reset.

In the type shown in Fig. 236 the adjustment for height is permitted by the vertical shaft with a spline. Motion is imparted to it by partial bevel-gears. The reason for using geared transmissions is that if jointed linkages were used the leverage of the ratchet would be continually varying, and a coarse feed would be impossible with a compact arrangement and short levers. The slotted crank, from which motion is received for the actuation of the pawl, should be made as part of a wrist-plate, so that the pin in the slot may be on either side of the center of motion. This is necessary, because the stroke of the link in which the pawl slips over the teeth of the wheel must always be made at the end of a cutting traverse of the bed. Otherwise, before the return of the bed under the tool the feed for the ensuing cut would have been made, and great wear of the cutting-edge would ensue. Hence the acting stroke of the feed must be on the lifting or falling stroke of the dog according as the feed of the tool is in one direction or the other. There are but few tools which do not permit this adjustment.

This alternating motion for the feeds is either received directly from the driving mechanism or from some of the levers which control it and make it automatic.

The earlier driving mechanism consisted of a screw in the middle of the bed, whose long nut was made part of the table. The screw was square-threaded, of quite steep pitch, and was turned at one end by bevel-gears from a transverse shaft. These gears had to be small, in order that the rear end of the table might pass over them when planing long work. To effect the quick return of the table on the stroke when the tool was not cutting the screw carried two bevel-wheels of different diameters, driven by two others of corresponding diameters, whose axes coincided with that of the transverse shaft and were on different sides of the axis of the screw. Of these latter bevel-wheels one was keyed to the transverse shaft, and turned the wheel of largest diameter on the screw. This was driven by the outer belt-wheel of three equal wheels, which was keyed also to the transverse shaft. The

Fig. 236.

other bevel-wheel geared into the smaller wheel on the screw, and instead of being fast on the transverse shaft was secured to a sleeve, turning freely upon the shaft. To the sleeve was also secured the inner belt-wheel, while the intermediate third wheel was loose. It will be seen that while the driving-belt was on the outer wheel the screw would turn slowly with leverage for the cut. When the belt was shifted to the inner wheel, the screw would turn faster and with less leverage in the opposite direction, thus producing the quick return. The idle loose wheel is necessary that the belt may not be upon two pulleys at once which move in opposite directions. The shifting of the one belt from one pulley to the other was effected (and still is) by a pair of dogs or chocks, which bolt at any point in a T-slot planed in the side of the bed. These dogs strike an arm, which gives the transverse motion to the shifter-eyes by a bell-crank. The inertia of the moving bed, coupled with the high speed of the belts, renders the stalling of the machine with the belt on the loose pulley practically impossible. In place of the screw of the earlier types modern practice approves a rack in the middle of the table, driven by a spur pinion. This rack, in the best practice, is cut out of the solid. In the smaller tools it is a plain rack with linear teeth. Some of the larger use a rack and pinion with V-teeth. The object of this is to gain the advantage of strength which comes from large circular pitch, while securing the smoothness of motion which comes from smaller circular pitch and greater numbers of teeth. Something of the smoothness of helical gearing is obtained without the sidewise thrust which they produce. Any sidling is counteracted by the convergence of the lines of each tooth. The pinion which drives the rack is driven by a train of gearing from belt-wheels. This train will differ according as one or two driving-belts are used in any one type of arrangement, and they will also differ in the arrangement. The most usual arrangement consists in a train of spur-gears, by which the velocity is reduced from that of the belt-wheels. The gears are heavy and are cut. Some are using steel castings for this train. The disadvantage of this system is that the long dimension of the tool is at right angles to the line shafting of the shop, while all the

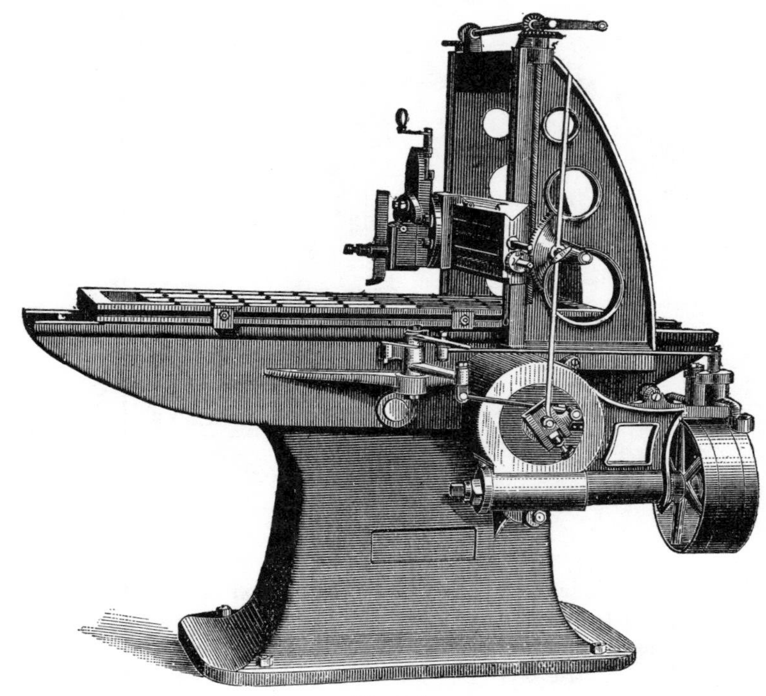

Fig. 237.

lathes are parallel to it. Hence the planers of this type are wasteful of room in a crowded shop. To counteract this difficulty the first transmission from the pulleys has been made by bevel-wheels, the other gearing being the

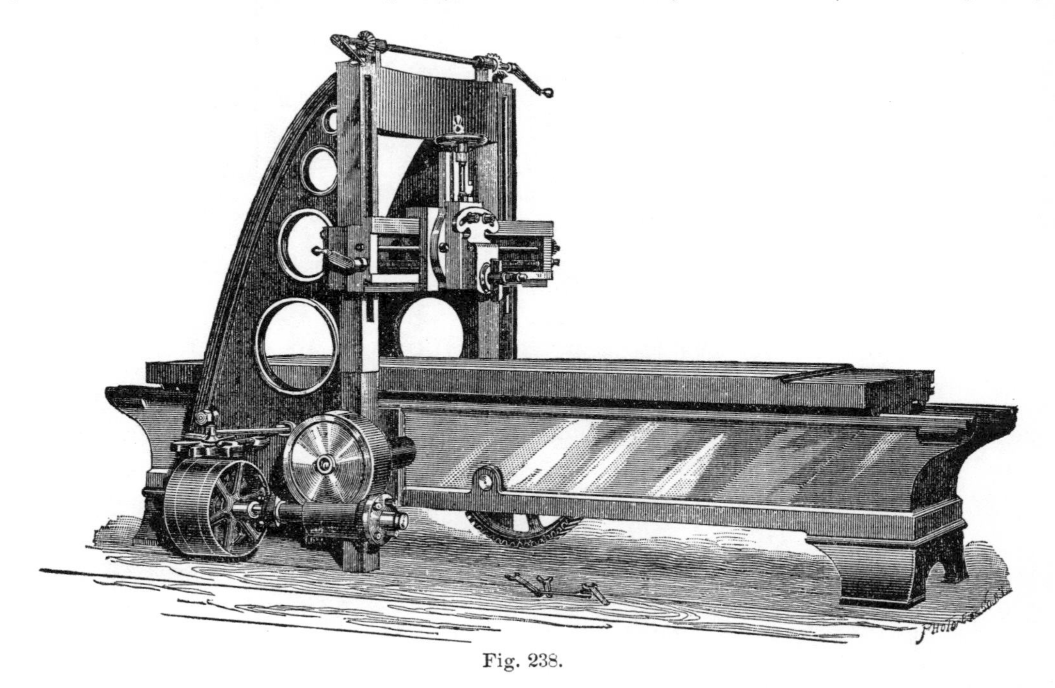

Fig. 238.

same (Fig. 236). This brings the planers parallel to the lathes. Another arrangement uses a worm and wheel at the first corner (Figs. 237 and 238). In still another the rack is driven by a worm of four threads, which has been called a "spiral pinion", and gears the worm-shaft to the belt-wheels parallel to the bed by a pair of bevel-gears of great difference of diameter (Fig. 239). This arrangement is inferior to the one just preceding, in that

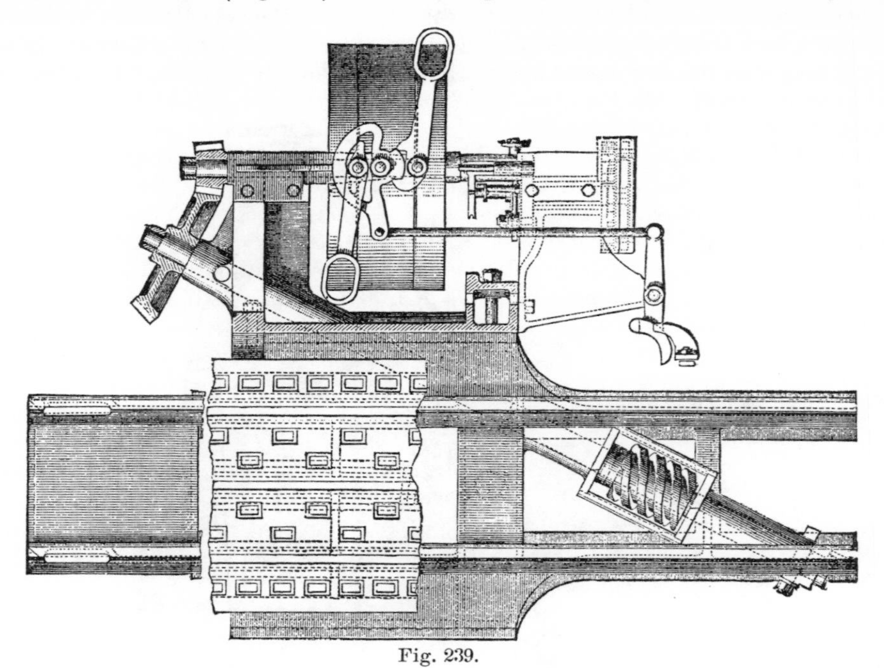

Fig. 239.

the rapid reduction of speed due to the worm takes place after the toothed gears, instead of before. The slower the gears revolve the less noise, chatter, and wear. To accomplish the quick return on the inoperative stroke of the table with two belts is comparatively simple. The usual ratio of quick return is about as one is to two; the return is twice as fast as the cutting traverse. Upon the counter-shaft above the tool are two pulleys whose

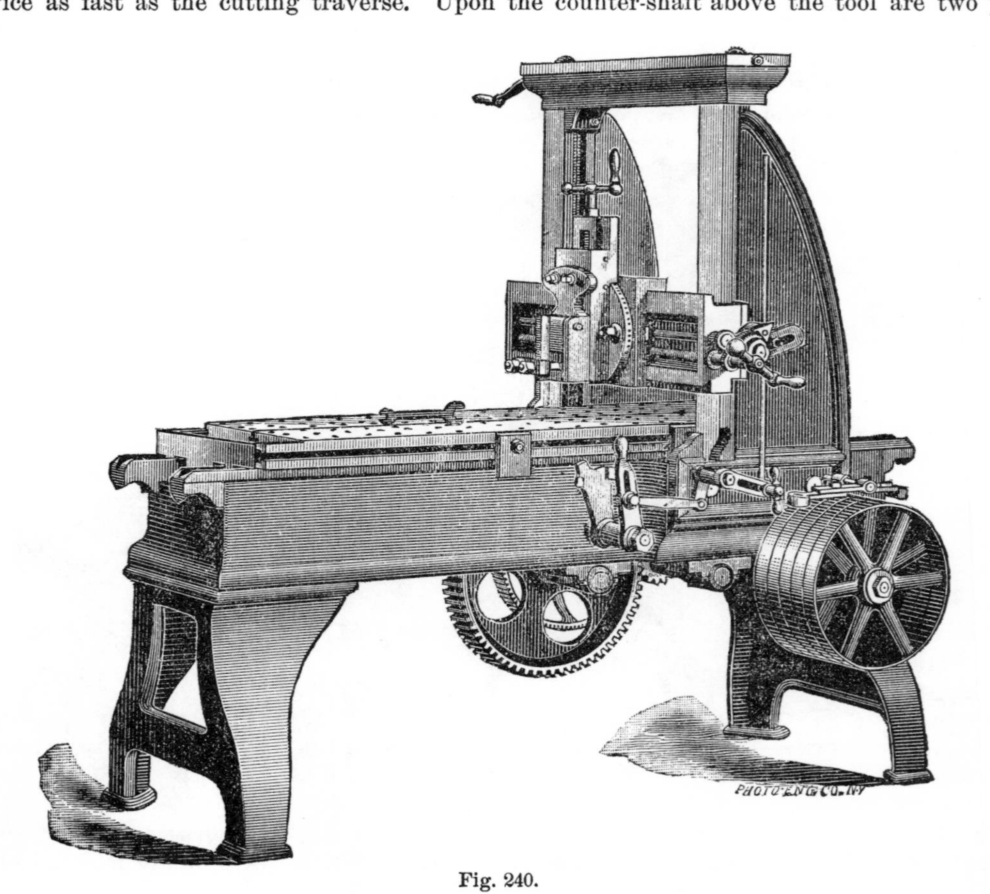

Fig. 240.

diameters are as one is to two. From the smaller one comes the belt for the forward stroke to the pulleys on the machine, while from the larger comes the belt for the return. This belt is crossed or open, according as the other is open or crossed, as determined by the shafting of the shop. The pulleys on the machine are of the same diameter usually. Where both belts are shifted at once, as in some of the smaller planers (Fig. 240), there must be five of them, the two outside and the middle one being loose. This has the advantage that the tool may be stopped without arresting the counter-shaft. On the other hand, the motion of the belt-shifters must be greater. When one belt is shifted upon the loose pulley before the other is shifted upon the fast pulley, as in the newer and better practice, but three pulleys are needed. A wide fast pulley turns between two narrower loose ones. The shifters prevent both belts from getting at once on the driving-pulley, and the shrieking of the belts as they slip in arresting the motion of the train is, to a great measure, avoided. One design has pulleys of different diameters on the machine, by which system four will be required, the two inner pulleys being loose. The system of two belts has an advantage over that using but one belt, in that the train of gearing under the machine is made simpler. Where but one belt is used, the outer wheel will be on a shaft connected to the rack-pinion by a train of gears consisting of an even number of wheels, with large reduction of velocity. The inner wheel will turn loose on the first shaft, and will be connected to the rack-pinion by a train with less reduction of speed and containing an odd number of wheels. When, therefore, there is an odd or an even number of shafts between the belt and the rack the one belt will move the table forward or backward. A loose pulley must separate the other two; therefore the tool may be arrested without stopping the counter-shaft. But the shifting-motion must be ample. Sometimes, to prevent very wide shifting of wide belts on larger tools on this system, two narrow belts were used, four pulleys were required, and each belt was shifted over only one-half the width of the wider belt which would have been required. One form of planer was made in which the reversal and quick return was effected by using external spur-gear from the inner wheel and internal gear from the outer. The internal gear moved the table in the opposite direction from that due to the external, and the speed was changed by the ratio of diameters.

For shifting the two belts in that system at once simple eyes or forks embracing the belts are secured to the rod which receives the cross-motion. For shifting them in succession a variety of devices are in use.

Fig. 239 illustrates one system in plan. There must be a separate shifter for each belt. These are pivoted near the end which is farthest from the belt-eye, in order that a small motion of the shifter-lever may move the belt over a larger distance. The link from the lever, which is moved by the dogs on the table, is attached to a lever vibrating horizontally around a fulcrum-pin. This lever has a tooth shaped on one side, which engages in a space formed in the side of one shifter. This tooth is so shaped as to move the shifter, and after escaping the corner of the space to lock the arm from moving. On the other side of the fulcrum is milled out an internal tooth or hollow cam, which acts upon tooth-like projections upon the other shifter. These profiles are so located with reference to each other that on both forward and backward stroke the belt which has just been in action shall be shifted first upon the loose pulley. Otherwise, large belt-motion would be required.

Another device is shown by Fig. 241. It depends on the principle of crank-motion that the piston moves most rapidly when the crank is at right angles to the axis of the rod. The two shifters are connected by links to pins on a horizontal wrist-plate which are on radii about 90° apart. The wrist-plate receives a partial rotation from the shifter-dogs, and always stops so that the pin connected to the belt which is driving shall stop with its radius perpendicular to the link to the shifter of that belt. By this expedient, for any angular motion of the wrist, the driving-belt will be shifted farthest at first, and may be off the fast pulley before the other is moved on.

Another device has a vertical pin upon the tail of each shifter, which is moved by a groove in the lever from the shifting-dog. This groove is so designed that the pins shall be moved successively upon each reciprocation of the lever (Fig. 245).

In another design a slide receives a motion greater than that required to move the shifters. Truncated pyramids on each side of the slide engage with the double rocking tails of the shifters. The excess of motion of the slide causes the motion of the shifters to be successive, and the upper bases of the projections lock the tails of the latter. In another device the sliding-plate from the dogs has two inclined grooves in it, which operate pins on the shifters.

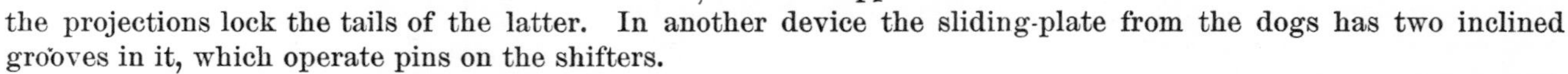

Fig. 241.

The planer shown in Fig. 242 adopts a principle different from any of the foregoing. There are two pulleys loose on the spindle. The middle wheel is a double-friction clutch, which may be engaged with either wheel by a slight longitudinal motion, so that the arbor will be turned either by the open or the crossed belt and at the suitable speed. The clutch is moved by a pin on a sleeve upon which turns the inner belt-wheel. This pin receives its motion from a slot cut diagonally in a short sleeve. This sleeve is rotated on its axis by the table dogs, which rotation causes the pin to slide up or down the incline and to throw the clutch in one direction or in the other. This arrangement causes the reversal to be very quiet and instantaneous.

To insure that the shifting devices shall receive equal motion on both strokes of the table the two dogs are often made to strike the levers at different points. The table has less momentum on the cutting-stroke than on the return, since it is moving more slowly. Hence the dog for the motion on this stroke is often made longer, so

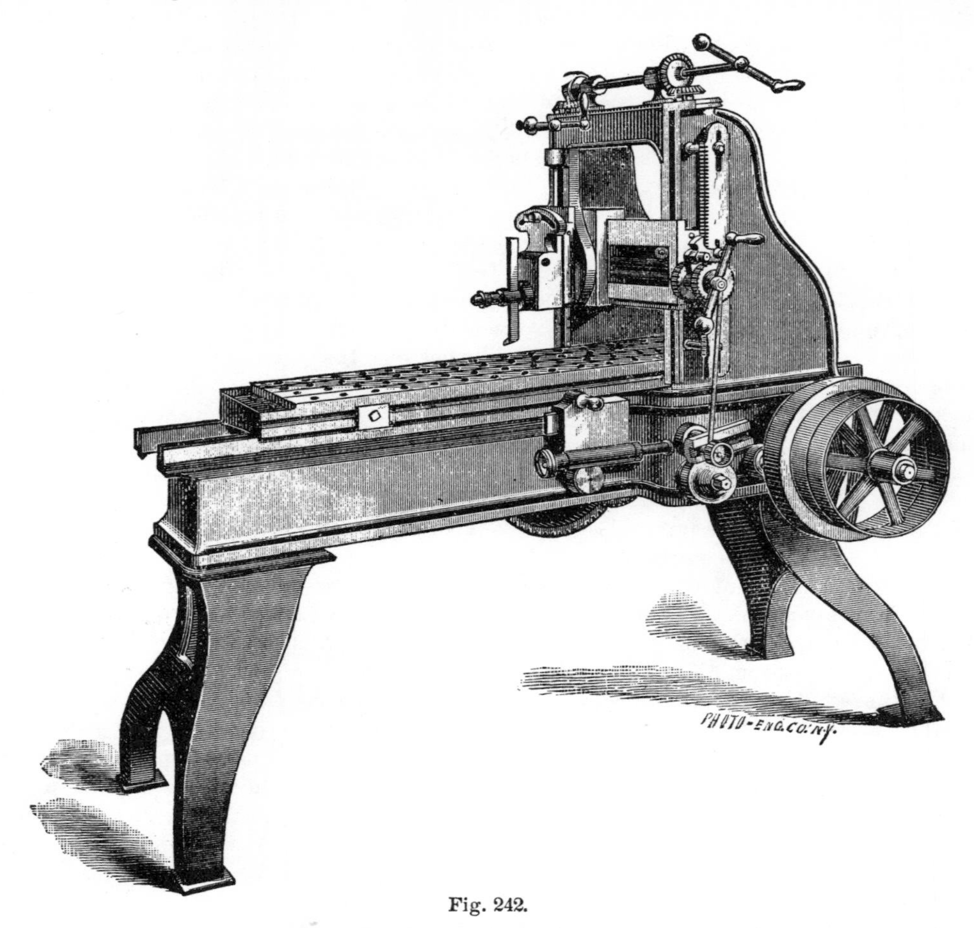

Fig. 242.

as to strike the shifting-lever nearer the center of motion. This will give the same ultimate motion as when the shorter dog of the return traverse moves a greater distance nearer the end. The end of the lever which is moved by the dogs is often arranged with a spring latch-gear, so that the latch may be sprung out of the path of the dog and permit the table to traverse farther than the limit for which the dogs are set (Figs. 237 and 243).

Without this convenience it is necessary to unscrew the dogs when the operator wishes to examine the work in front of the cross-head and tool and to set them anew when the cuts are to be resumed. The shifting-levers have usually a handle for their convenient manipulation by hand.

To obtain the single reciprocating motion required for the feed-motions in all directions is a simple problem. It is solved in two general ways. The motion is either taken directly from the levers which are moved by the table-dogs, or else it is taken from the train of driving-gears by a frictional device. This latter system is perhaps more general than the other, but it may be questioned whether it is preferred for any very cogent reason on small tools. The shifting-dogs and levers should be stout enough for their own duty, to be able to withstand the slight extra strains for feeding. The feed has only to overcome the friction of parts, since there is no cutting strain on the tool when the feed is given, and therefore the shifting-motion may be multiplied, if desirable, to have a capacity for a coarse feed for finishing. When the feed is taken from the train one of the arbors (usually the second) is prolonged outside the bed. Upon this arbor is secured a cast-iron disk, and a second disk compresses a loose washer of leather against it with any desired pressure. This pressure is made adjustable by a screw and nut. The second disk is loose on the arbor, and carries on its face the slotted crank, from whose pin the reciprocating link passes to the ratchet-gear. This loose disk is caused to revolve by friction of the leather, between stops, which permit the crank to make one-half of a revolution at each change of direction in the motion of the train. This also insures that the feed shall be given before the cut begins, and any desired power of feed may be secured by the frictional compression of the leather. The disadvantage of this form lies in the slipping of the disks while the movable one is held against the stops. This consumes a little power, and wears the disks.

Another form (Fig. 245) uses the friction due to compression of a wrought-iron split ring on the periphery of a disk. The ring is split, and is compressed by adjustable springs on the outside. An elliptical pin is fitted in the

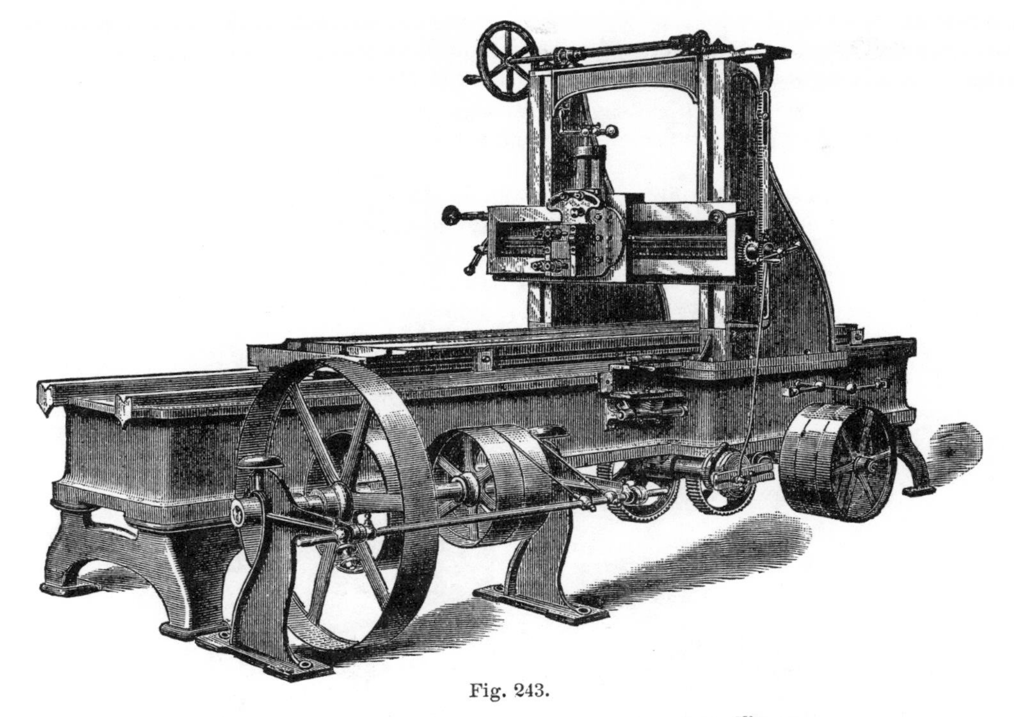

Fig. 243.

Fig. 244.

split of the ring, which is of such dimensions that the long diameter shall be sufficient to open the split and release the ring. The short diameter of the pin is enough less to permit the ring to close and establish the friction when the former is turned less than one-half around. It will be sufficient to cause the stops to turn this pin partially when the feed is made. The friction will be in a great measure released as soon as the stops are reached. A similar type is shown by Fig. 233. The friction will be engaged by the spring of the ring, when a stop no longer opposes it.

The device of Fig. 246 uses friction only to engage the pawls at each change of motion. A positive motion of the crank-disk is kept up by the ratchet-wheel until the pawl is disengaged by a positive stop. The ratchet-wheel is revolved by a pinion on the front end of the pulley-shaft.

In the planer shown in Fig. 236 the feed-motion is positive from the train, without the necessity of friction devices. A pinion on the second arbor of the train turns a half-wheel. The pinion and wheel may be toothed, or

Fig. 245.

in newer practice are made of V-friction faces. The semicircle of the wheel is counter-weighted, to preserve its equilibrium. The face of the pinion is broader than that of the wheel. The last three-fourths of an inch of the face of the latter at the two ends of the semicircumference is arranged so as to be effective at the *beginning* of the half revolution, but inoperative at the end. This is accomplished by making this last fraction of the face at each end to be the end of a dog, which swings from a stud on the plate of the wheel and abuts in one direction against a stop. When the pinion on the train reverses, the dog engages with it, and by pulling against the stop the face is drawn into gear. At the end of the half revolution the dog clicks idly over the pinion, until its

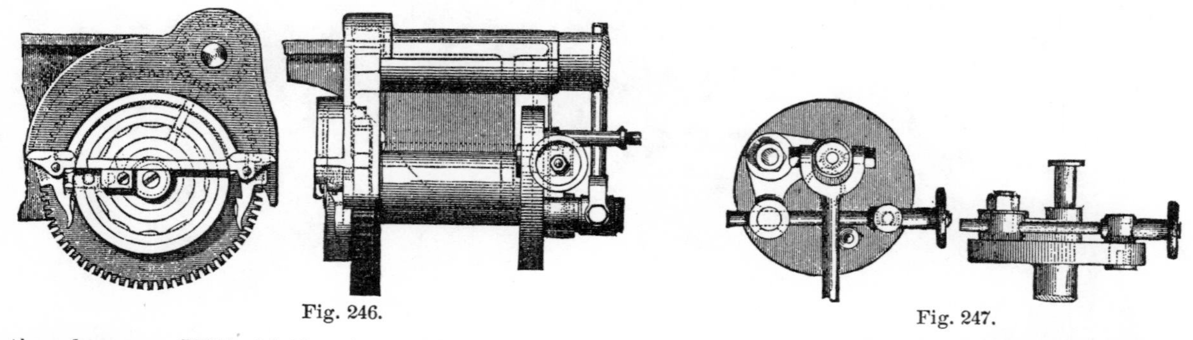

Fig. 246. Fig. 247.

direction changes. With friction faces this clicking is noiseless. For the adjustment of the amount of the feed, while the tool is in motion, the pin on the wrist-plate is either clamped by a hand-nut or else is upon a screw. By turning this screw the pin traverses in the slot, and by it may be held at any distance from the center.

A very ingenious device for this object is illustrated by Fig. 247. The milled head on the post will move the upper end of the pivoted bell-crank, by which the pin of the vertical link will be moved and clamped nearer or farther from the center of the motion of the disk.

Were the tool held rigidly at the slide-rest, the return of the work under it would scrape the cutting-edge from behind and dull it. Hence all tools, both light and heavy, have the tool secured to a swinging apron, hinged on a conical pin between cheeks on the slide. This permits the tool to swing outward upon the return of the work, and where the tool and apron are light this arrangement is sufficient. On larger machines, with heavy cutter and

Fig. 248.

apron, the weight of the combination will be sufficient to press the edge with a grinding pressure against the work. It becomes necessary, therefore, to lift the apron and the tool by positive means. There are several methods of

Fig. 249.

effecting this, but all use a cord over pulleys pulled by the feed-levers and kept taut by a weight. The feed-lever pulls on the cord and turns a spiral washer under the apron. The rise of the inclined plane against a twin washer in the bottom of the apron throws the tool forward and up. When the feed-lever reverses, the weight rotates the washer back into its first position. A second arrangement makes the cord lift a knee-lever against the apron by the rotation of a disk or washer with eccentric hole. Still another has a cam on the end of a vertically-oscillating lever. All accomplish the purpose about equally well.

Planers of very large size will have two slide-rests on the cross-head, and an extra rest upon one or both of the uprights (Figs. 248 and 249). An extra feed-rod will probably be required for the second rest on the cross-head, but the rests on the uprights are usually arranged for hand-feed only. These larger tools, being designed for work of great weight from which a heavy chip is to be taken at each cut, usually move more slowly than the lighter tools, and have more wheels in the train which drives the table. The feed also has to be powerful, and the cross-head and rests must be located by power.

Fig. 249 shows the device for lifting and lowering the cross-head by two bevel-wheels, which may be clutched to the shaft of the overhanging belt-wheel to produce motion in either direction. These larger tools are usually built with the rack with **V**-teeth. In these longer trains of gears there is more chance for back-lash in the teeth, which produces, with the elasticity of the belt, a disagreeable intermittance of the motion of the table, which is fatal to the exactness of some work. The design of Fig. 249 drives the table through one pair of gears and the worm which meshes into the rack. The smoothness of the worm-motion is noticeable, and the obliquity of the passage of the worm-shaft through the bed-casting prevents the weakening of the bed by its being cut open to admit of the

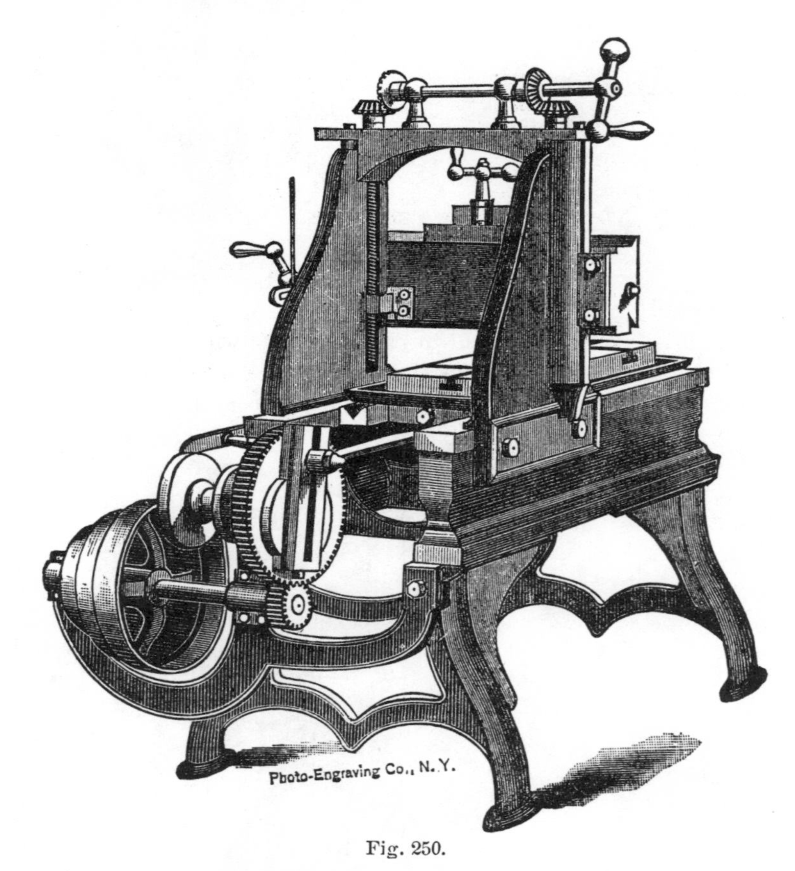

Fig. 250.

gear-train arbors. The rack-teeth are straight, but inclined at about 5° to prevent a tendency to sidewise motion. The thrust of the worm-shaft under the cut is borne by a step-bearing in the rear side of the bed, and that of the quick-return motion by hardened steel collars. The other features are common to the smaller designs of the same builders.

For small work, where the speed may be increased, a great deal of work can be satisfactorily done upon crank-planers. The bed stands high upon legs, and instead of being driven by screw or rack, it is reciprocated by a slotted crank on the cone-pulley shaft. The stroke is adjusted for length by the position of the crank-pin, and for speed by the cone-pulleys. This adjustment of speed is made necessary by the fact that without it the table would move over its travel in the same time, whether the stroke were long or short. This would make the cutting-speed to vary between too wide limits.

The crank is either of the ordinary form, or else of the Whitworth quick-return type, which is employed for shapers (Fig. 250). This latter device results in a saving of time. The tool is usually fed by power for horizontal traverse only, from a groove in a cam-plate. The design of Fig. 251, however, presents all the conveniences of the larger tools. The connecting-rod eye is held in a slot in the under side of the table in these tools, its position being adjustable by a screw in front.

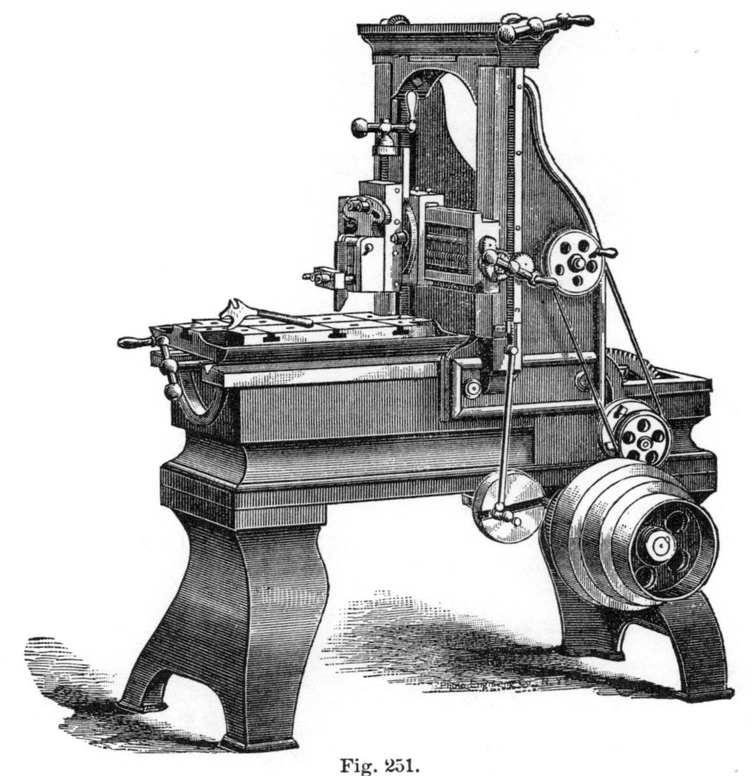

Fig. 251.

This class of machine is much used for brass work and the like, presenting some advantages over the ordinary type of planer, or the shaper, which it much resembles.

§ 27.

SPECIAL FORMS OF PLANER.

To save at least one-third of the time of planing operations as usually done, planers have been devised with two cross-heads. These are held upon two sets of uprights, which may be bolted in T-slots on the side of the bed. Both may be made adjustable (Fig. 252), or only one (Fig. 253). The former shows a novel device for feeding the

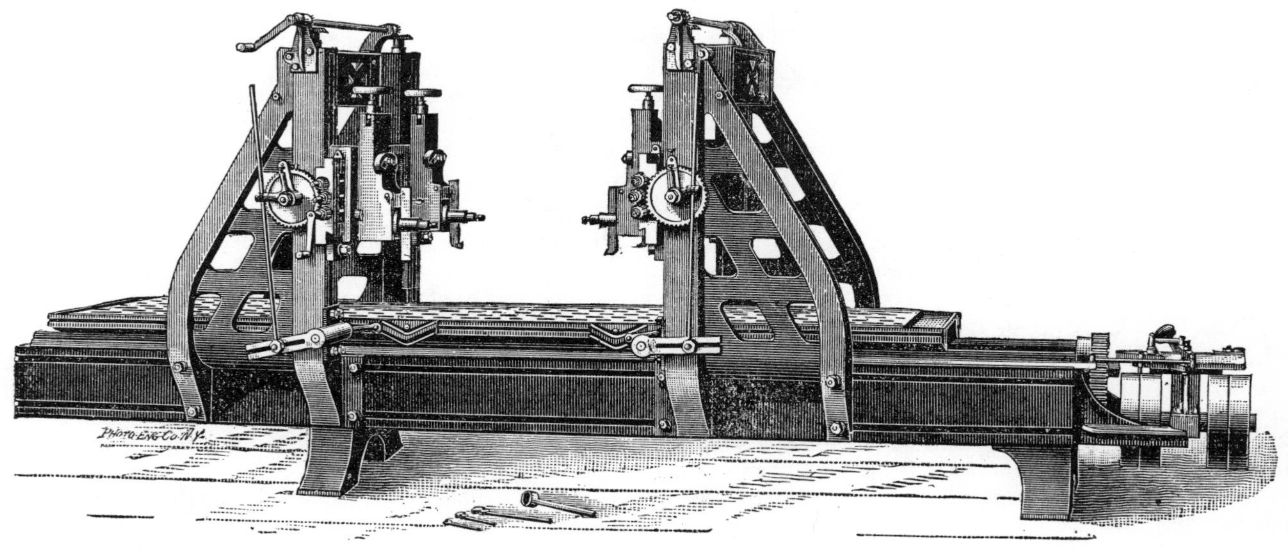

Fig. 252.

slides, and the two designs differ in the method of applying the principle of the screw for driving the bed. Each is driven by two belts. These tools are especially adapted for planing the stubs of engine-work or for other short surfaces upon long work. At least two articles can be finished at each end at once.

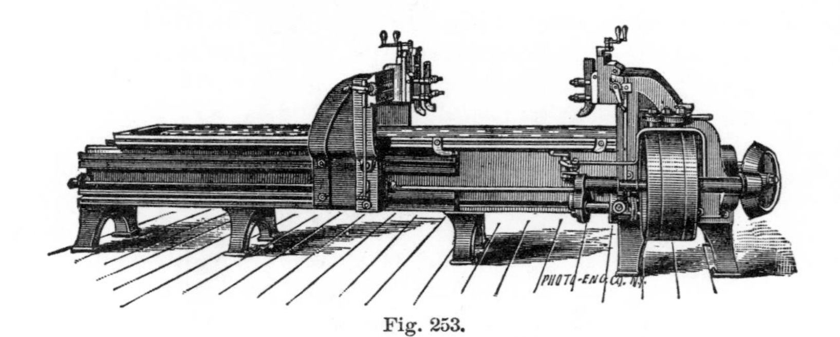

Fig. 253.

Figs. 254 and 255 show two types of machine for edge-planing of boiler- or ship-plate for calking. If not so treated the calking edge must be produced by hand-chipping, which is costly, and will not be so exact. The plate is held stationary by the long vise-jaw in Fig. 254, the two screws at the ends being worked together by the hand-

Fig. 254.

gear at the right. Bosses for set-screws are provided in the movable jaw, in case ship-plates are to be beveled after being curved. The other design clamps all work by the set-screws. The tool-carriage is fed by a long screw from open and crossed belts. It is intended to carry at least two tools, and sometimes three. Where two are used one cuts on one stroke and the other on the return. Where three are used, two cut on the forward stroke and the third makes a finishing cut upon the return. This latter has a stop provided, so that when the holes are arranged at first to be parallel with the future edge, all holes shall be at the same distance from that edge. These tools will plane plates 14 or 15 feet in length.

For special purposes attachments may be applied to any pattern of planer. One builder of large engines has applied a boring and facing attachment to his largest planer. By this means engine frames may be planed for the guides and trued at the cylinder ends with one chucking to the table. Locomotive-shops have applied false tops to the tables for planing the links of the reversing and cut-off gear on the Stephenson system. The link has a curvature due to the radius of the eccentric-rod. The link may be clamped to a vise which swings around a center in a line at right angles to the path of the tool, and at the proper distance from the center line of the slot. In another and simpler device a slotted bar bolts to the rear of the cross-head. It projects horizontally at an angle, and a slide on top of a post fits the slot in the bar, and gives the proper rotating motion to the false top.

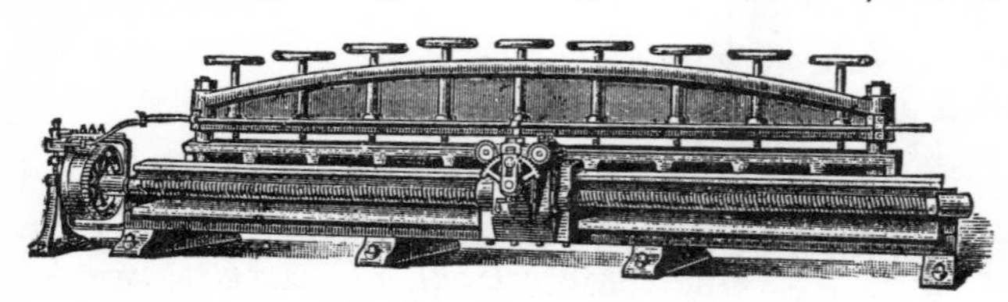

Fig. 255.

The frames and table of planers are often used for the foundation of other machines, working with rotary cutters, to which allusion will be made in the sequel. For some special work on locomotive-frames an unique planer has been made, with one upright at the working side as usual, but having the other end of the cross-head carried by an arched frame. This frame is made of open cast iron, in somewhat the form of an arch. The abutments are at the ends of the bed, so that wide work may overhang the table of a smaller planer at the farther side. There are but three or four of them in use.

§ 28.

SHAPERS.

The term shaper is applied to a tool in which the planer principle is inverted. The work is held and the tool traverses across it while feeding-motion is imparted to either or both. The tool is held at the end of a long slide, which receives a reciprocating motion usually from a connecting-rod and crank. This slide is guided by a track or shears, to which it is gibbed, and is made long to resist the increased strain when working on a long stroke with considerable overhang. The tool has a quick return in most cases, either by the Whitworth gear by two elliptical wheels or by two belts from wheels of different diameters.

The principle of the Whitworth gear is shown by Fig. 256. A gear-wheel, S, is driven by the small pinion. The crank-body P does not have the same center as S, but is eccentric to the latter. Its center is C. The center of S is made large enough for the center C to pass through it, as shown by the dotted line. The crank P is not connected to the face of S, but may slide upon it as it is compelled by their mutual eccentricity. The rotation of S, however, compels that of P by the pin in the face of the former which plays in and out in a slot in the tail of the latter. Hence, when the pin is farthest from the center C, the slide connected to R will move most slowly with

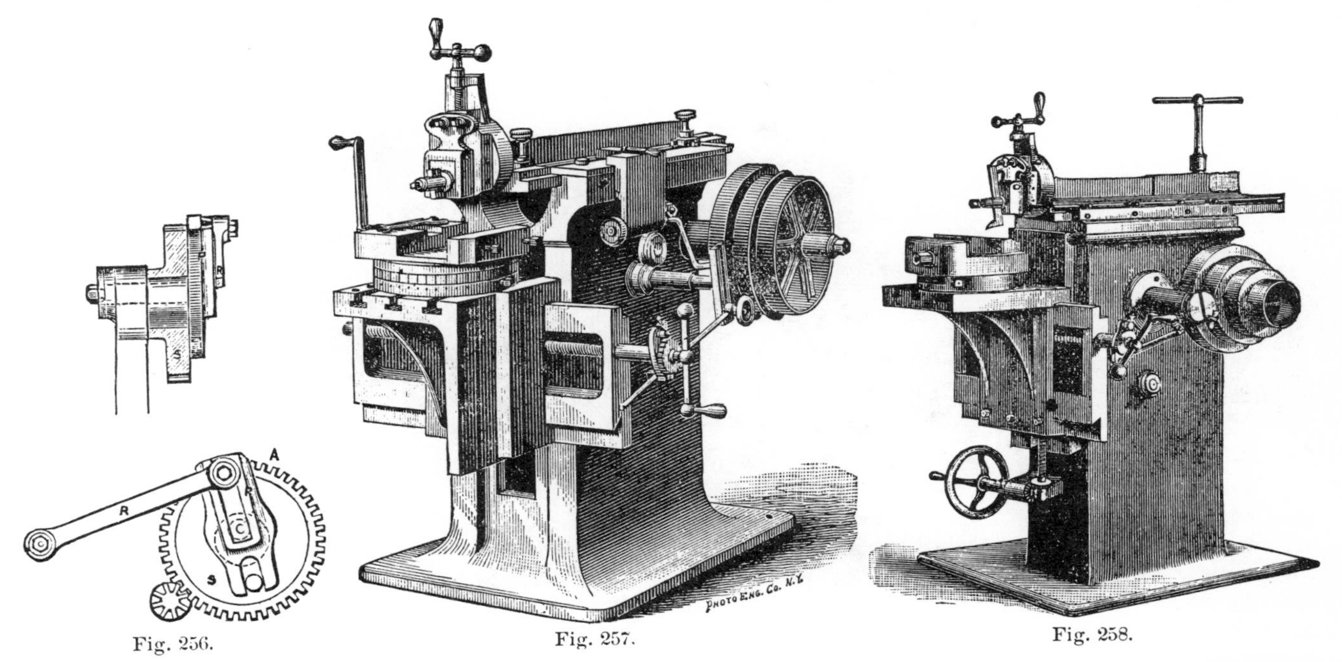

Fig. 256. Fig. 257. Fig. 258.

the greatest power. When the pin is nearest C the crank will turn most quickly, but with least force for the return stroke. The variation of stroke is accomplished by the slot in the crank-arm. To compensate for the higher speed of long cuts the small pinion is driven from cone-pulleys. In the elliptical-gear arrangement the wheels are horizontal, and turn around their two foci. The quick return will be effected when the long radius of the driver turns the short radius of the gear which carries the crank-pin.

The shaper shown in Fig. 257 has the tool-slide driven by a pinion which meshes into a rack upon its under side. The pinion is driven from either of two belt-wheels driven by open and crossed belts, to either of which it may be clutched by a double-friction cone, precisely as in the planer built by the same makers. This makes the tool the most direct inversion of the planer, and permits the length of stroke to be varied without stopping the machine. The position of the slide relative to the crank is made variable in the other forms by a long slot in the side of it. The pin for the free end of the connecting-rod may be clamped to any part of the slot.

The shaper appears in two forms, the pillar-shaper (Figs. 258 and 259), and the traveling-head shaper (Fig. 260). The pillar-shaper has the power-feed to the work given horizontally only. Vertical or angular feed is given by hand. The whole front has a vertical adjustment by screw and hand-wheel. In another form (Fig. 261), the slide is arranged vertically to secure stiffness from depth in the overhang. The table in this tool is made with a vertical face, to which work may also be bolted. The fly-wheel is preferred by some builders, in order to equalize the active and inactive strokes.

The older form of horizontal shaper belongs to the pillar class.

The shaper with traveling head is built for the larger services. The cone-pulley shaft is splined, and the head which carries the tool-slide carries also the driving-gear and crank. The whole head is fed by a screw along ways on the top of the frame (Fig. 260). The feed is by a pawl and levers, and it is so arranged that the feed shall always be given at the beginning of a cut, and not at the end or in the middle. There are two tables, to which an object may be clamped vertically or horizontally, or to which any vise or centers may be applied. There is also a mandrel

Fig. 259.

with cones for cylindrical work. The tables have a vertical feed-motion, and the tool may be fed vertically or at an angle, or may have a circular feed for concave or convex surfaces. The tool-feeds are given by hand.

Fig. 262 illustrates a similar tool, where the circular, vertical, or angular feed may be effected automatically. The stops give motion to the rod which is connected to a ratchet on the feed-screw by universal joints. The saddle, or head in this tool has quick hand-wheel traverse by the rack on the inside of its track. One of the tables is arranged to have a swivel top, interchangeable with the vise and centers. Fig. 263 shows a tool with similar capacities. Sometimes shapers are made with two heads upon one bed-plate to operate on both ends at once of long work, such as engine-rods and the like. These are called double-shaping machines.

Shaping-machines are especially applicable for small work, or for the finishing of small areas on large work. They are also adapted for finishing the curved surfaces of cranks or of levers with bosses upon them. They will also work rapidly on polygonal work, held in the centers. They do a variety of work which the planer could only do with less economy of time, and with less ease of management, beside requiring more power.

The fundamental principle of the shaper is often resorted to for work which is relatively very large as compared with the tools which are to operate on it. The work is bolted fast to the floor-plate or a bed-plate, and a tool is made to slide in front of the work and receives the proper feeds by hand. The tool may be held on a planer-bed which reciprocates at the side of a heavy casting.

A tool specially adapted for this class of work consists of two parallel rails which form the bed. Between them is a pit, in which may be laid the large work. The insides of the rails are fitted with inclined lugs and brackets, so that the work may be held and adjusted parallel to the shears on top of the rails. On the upper side of these

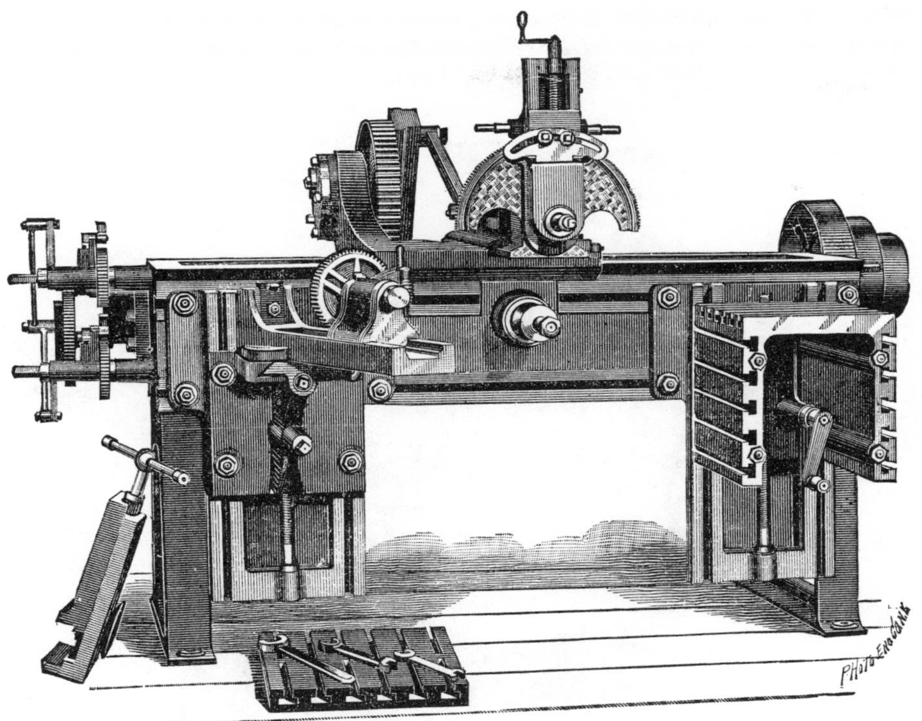

Fig. 260.

Fig. 261.

rails slides a stiff cross-rail spanning the pit and carrying shears and a saddle for holding tools. The cross-rail receives longitudinal motion along the rails by two screws between the shears of the primary rails driven by bevel-

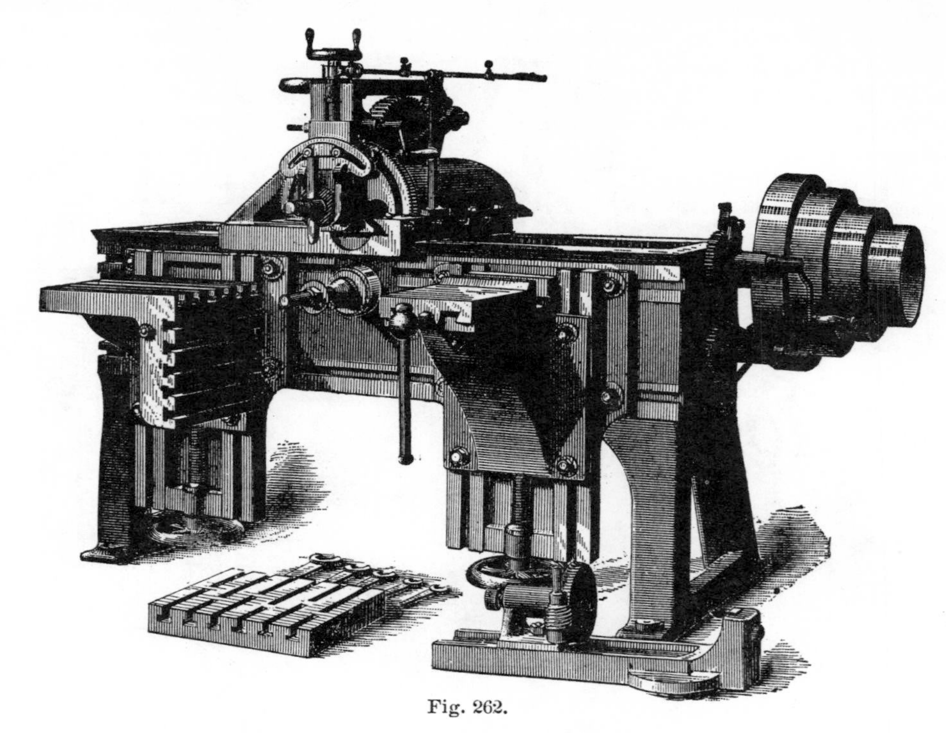

Fig. 262.

gear from the driving-shaft at the head. A very ingenious and simple form of holder keeps the horizontal screws from sagging, as the cross-rail nuts recede from the center, and so prevents jumping at the cut. This tool is particularly adapted for work upon heavy engine bed-plates.

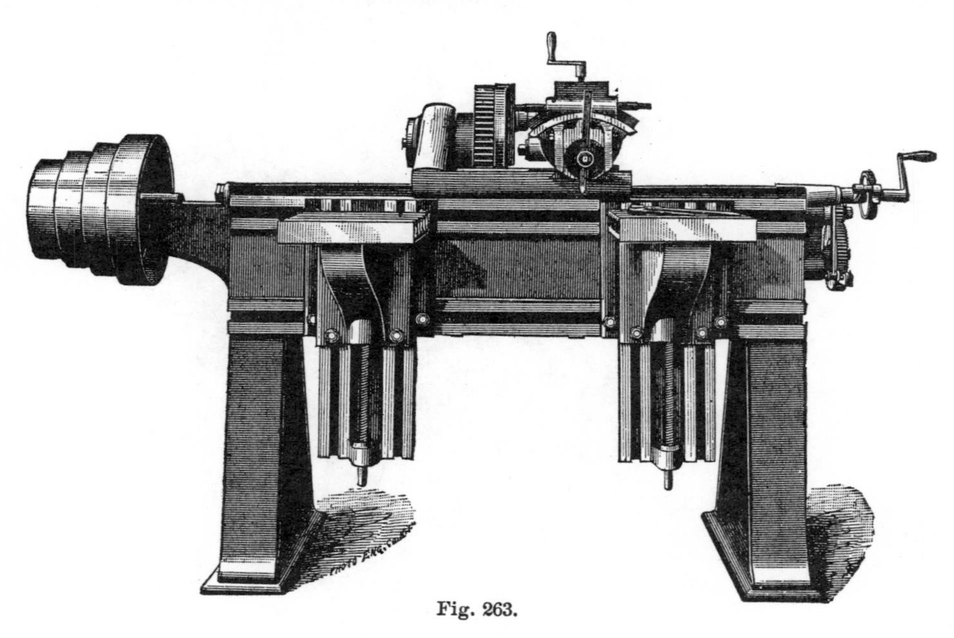

Fig. 263.

§ 29.

SLOTTERS.

The term slotting-machine is applied to a shaper with a vertical cutting-stroke. They are so often applied to the cutting of key-ways and similar vertical slots that their name has come from that one function.

The tool-slide is guided by the dovetail slides in front of the machine. In two designs these guides are adjustable, and may be brought down nearer the table to prevent any spring from the long overhang (Figs. 264 and 265). The reciprocation is derived from a slotted crank or wrist-plate, to which a quick-return motion is imparted by elliptical gear (Fig. 269) or by the Whitworth device. The slide-pin is adjustable in a slot, in which it may be clamped by a nut, or it may be carried upon a screw (Fig. 266). The tool illustrated has a convenient method for turning the adjusting-screw. The strain on the tool is in the direction of its length, consequently it needs to be clamped very firmly against the slide. This is accomplished in the smaller tools by means of two heavy set-screws. Not infrequently the cutting-edge is a simple "bit," carried in a large holder, which gives ample hold for the tool-screws. To avoid the dragging of the tool-point on the up-stroke, which its spring under the strain of the cut is certain to cause, the bit may be hinged in its slot in the holder, and fall away from the work when lifted. A

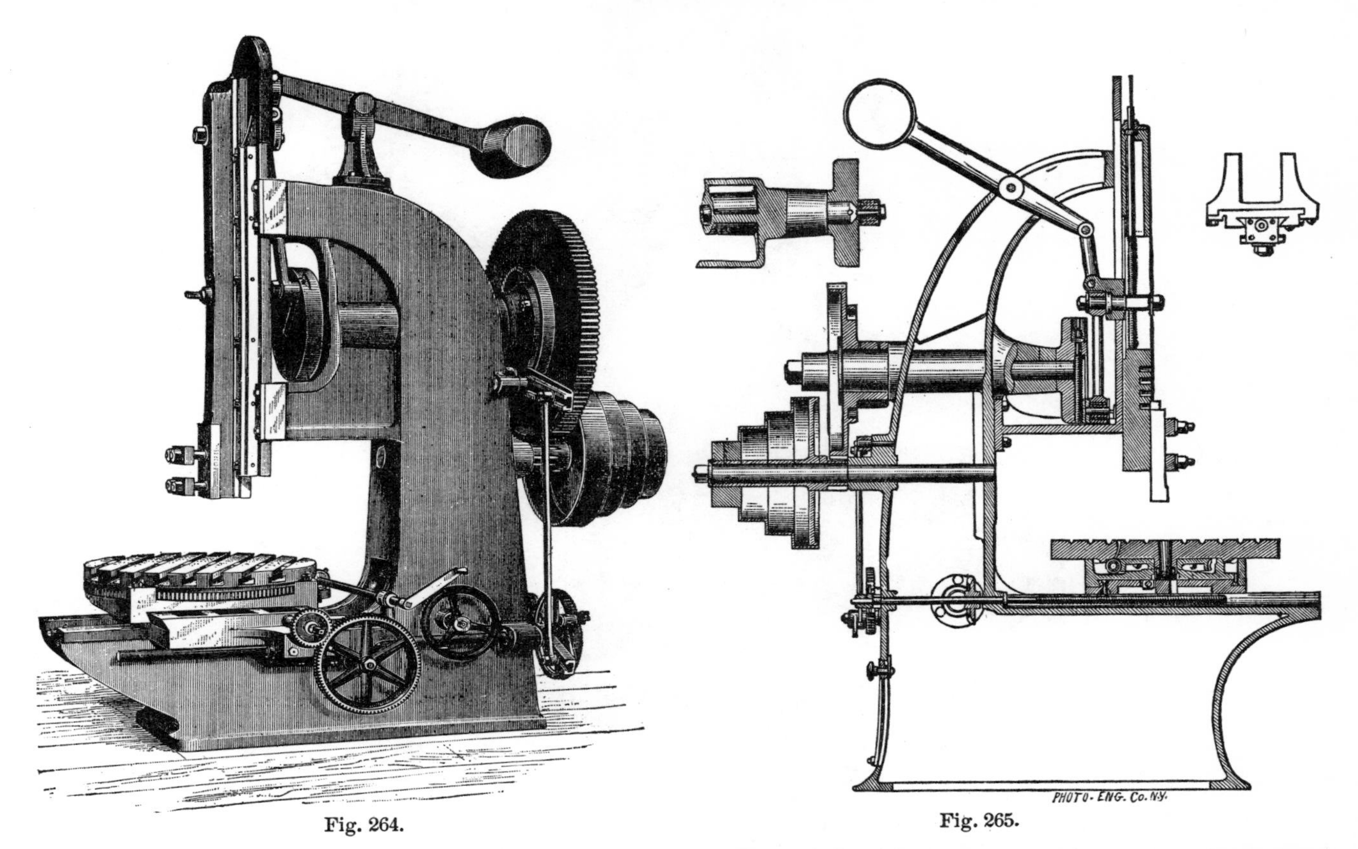

Fig. 264. Fig. 265.

spring forces the bit against the shoulder when it is released from its work (Fig. 267). For larger work an apron may be bolted to the end of the slide, acting similarly with the larger tool (Fig. 268). In the tool shown in Fig. 269 an especial device for the relief of the tool is one of the features. On the inoperative stroke of the feed-levers a motion is given to a screw of steep pitch which backs off the work from the tool-point. When the tool is up, this steep motion is restored and the feed is given in addition by the reverse motion of the levers. In this tool, and in that shown by Fig. 264, the adjustment for the slide-pin is made by the hand-crank on the squared arbor in front. A pair of bevel-wheels turns the screw on which the pin is borne. The quick return is effected by elliptical gear.

The slotter tables have three motions. They move forward and backward, to the right and left, and in addition will turn around a center by a tangent-screw combination. To prevent undesired rotation the circular top of the table may be clamped to the upper traversing slide by grooves in its periphery. The feed is given by a slotted lever, worked by a grooved cam on the crank-shaft. This gives motion to a dog-lever, which may turn slip-gears loose or with splines on the various arbors, which work the tables by screws. The tool-slide is counterpoised by a weighted lever connected to it by a link.

Some of the larger slotting-machines are driven by a rack upon one side of the slide. This rack is either with straight teeth, or the teeth may be made of the V-shape for smoothness. The designs of this latter class have the pinion for the rack driven by a worm on the belt-wheel shaft. There are pulleys of different diameters on it for the quick return, with open and crossed belts shifted separately. The stroke is controlled by dogs in a slot of the slide. Some of the older and larger slotters attain the quick return from one belt. This is shifted from a pulley fast to a shaft which carries a small bevel-wheel, to a pulley on a sleeve turning on the first shaft, which carries an equal bevel-wheel, facing the other way. These bevel-wheels turn others of different diameters on the first shaft of the pinion-train, and thus operate to reverse and to cause the quick return, when the belt is shifted by the motion of the tool-slide.

Fig. 266.

For the very largest slotters, a screw of steep pitch moves the tool-slide. On a tool of this class for the heaviest work, the piece is chucked to a heavy floor-plate, and the upright which carries and guides the holder

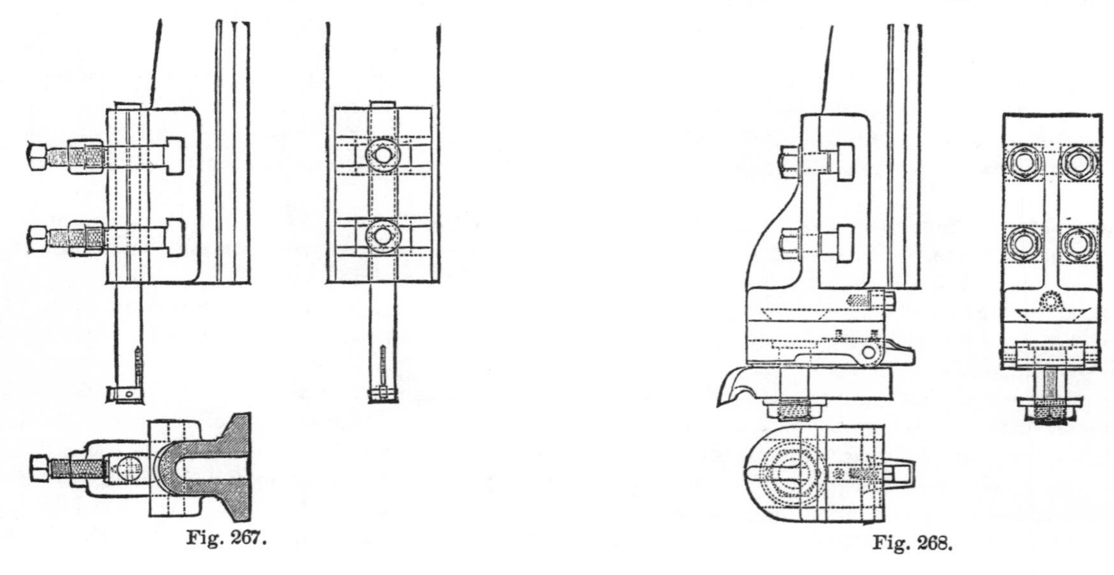

Fig. 267.

Fig. 268.

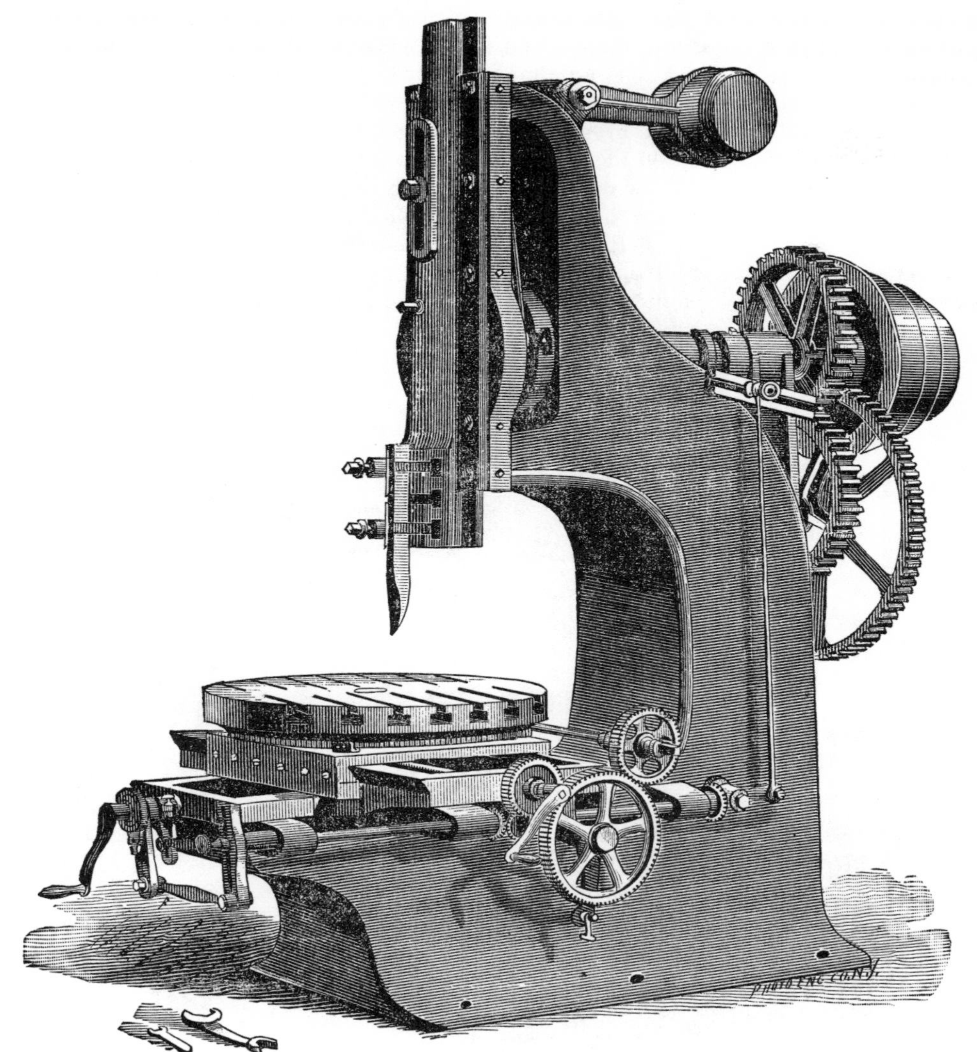

Fig. 269.

Fig. 270.

slides in front of it as fed by a screw. The quick return is given by two belts to a geared splined shaft in the bed below the upright which drives the cutting-screw. The shifting is effected by dogs on a horizontal slotted disk, and the feed is controlled by shields which may admit any desired engagement of ratchet-dogs in either direction. Some heavy slotters, self-contained, have been built with two heavy pillars bolted to the bed-plate which carries the compound table. These pillars are at the two ends of the bed, and support a heavy entablature upon which the train of driving-gear is carried. When these tools are used for heavy profiling, the cutter is pivoted in the holder between cheeks. The long tail of the cutter acts as the spring of the smaller holder previously shown, to permit release on the up-stroke, and to bring the cutter to the shoulder of the holder for the cut.

Fig. 270 illustrates a special form of slotter for dressing the welded frames of locomotive-engines. The two heads face each other, and are driven and operated separately from the splined shafts at the rear. The slide is borne upon the cross-rail, and has automatic feed across the table, while the entire head may receive longitudinal

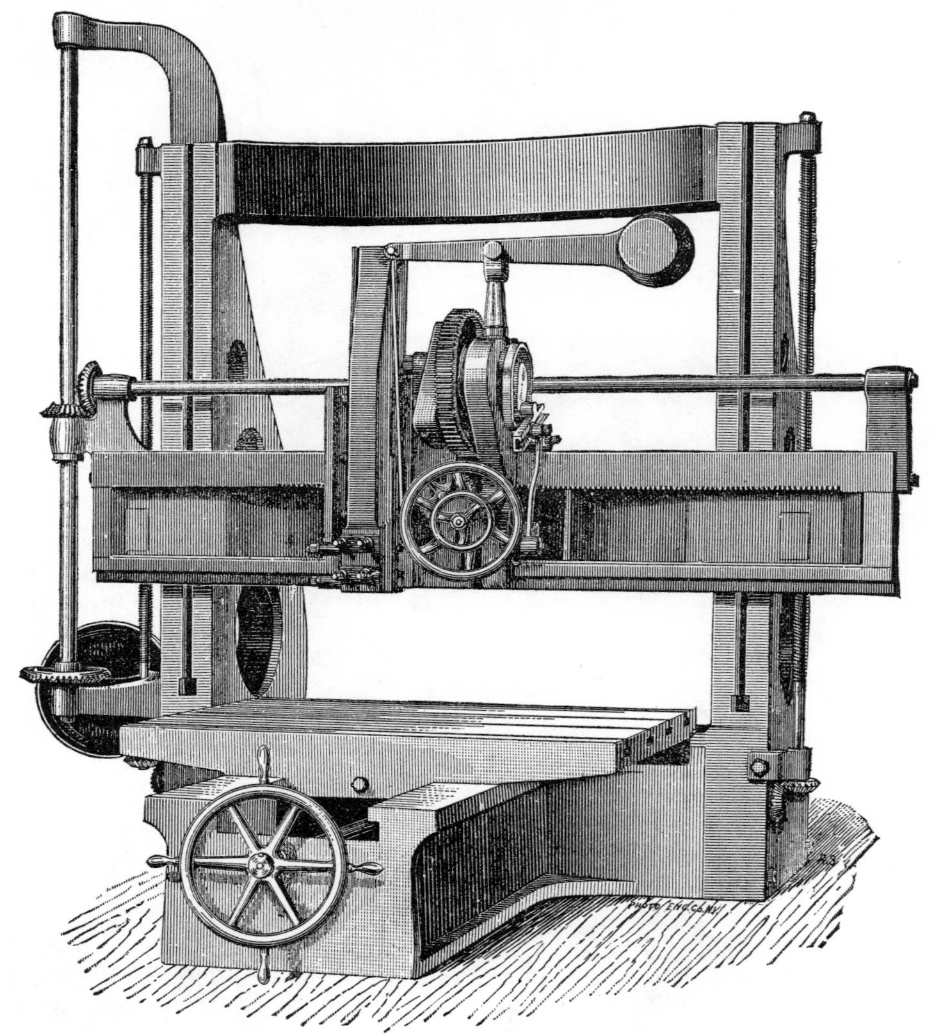

Fig. 271.

feed. The feed-cam is made adjustable upon the gear-wheel which turns the slide-crank to bring the feed in any desired relation to the end of the stroke. For slotting the jaws for the boxes of the driving-wheel axles the heads have an angular adjustment by a pinion and sector, so as to cut obliquely to the line at 90° with the axis of the bed. The saddle has a rapid motion by hand-wheel and rack.

Fig. 271 shows another form of plain traveling-head slotter. The slotting-machine is especially adapted for profiling of heavy work, especially where the profile is much broken. The work may be secured to the table with ease, since gravity assists in holding it there. The table also opposes a direct resistance to the cut, so that the strain of holding the work does not come upon the chucking devices with increasing leverage as the dressing progresses. Large cranks and similar work could be as easily dressed into shape upon no other tool, and for cutting off and cutting up scrap for reforging it serves an admirable purpose.

Fig. 272 shows a tool upon the dividing line between the slotters and the milling-machines. It is for cutting key-seats and similar work. The cutter reciprocates with a quick-return motion from the crank and slotted lever.

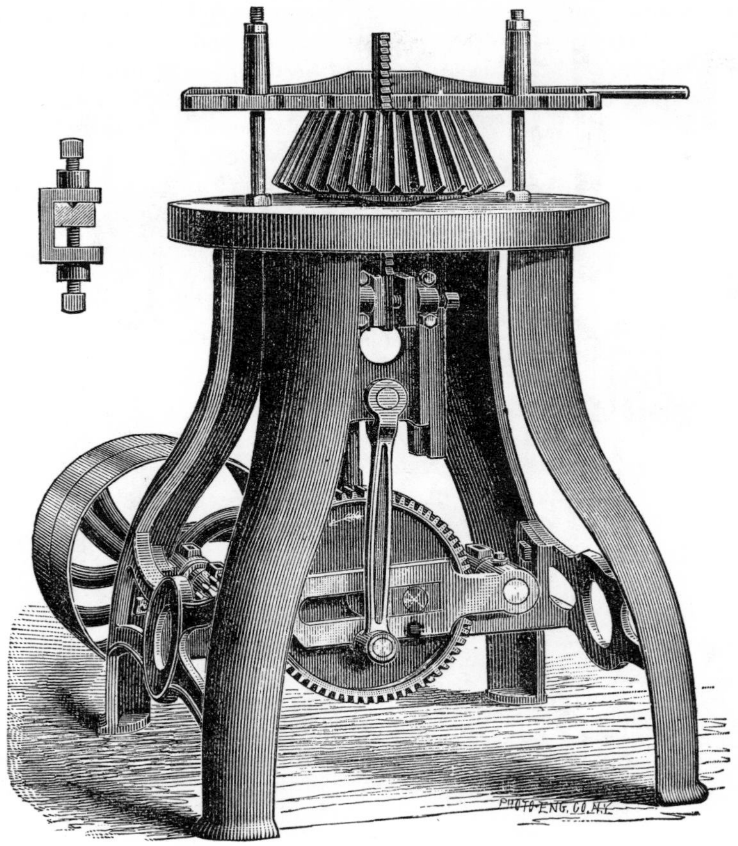

Fig. 272.

The cutting is done by the teeth on the point of a bar which resembles a developed milling-cutter. It can, of course, pass through a hole of quite small diameter.

§ 30.

D.—MILLING-MACHINES.

The term milling-machine may be applied generally to all metal-working tools operating with serrated rotary cutters. Where the cutter is very thin, the machine becomes a metal saw; where especially adapted for one operation, it is often known by a special name; but it still retains enough fundamental features to justify its classification with the typical machine.

The use of the milling-machine is attended with certain conspicuous advantages. These are the result of the revolving cutter, and the resulting elimination of spring in the tool. A great saving of time results from the continuous action of the cutters. There is no return or inactive stroke as in the reciprocating tools. The cutting-edges are very near to their points of support. Therefore exactness of dimensions may be insured and uniformity in duplication of irregular shapes. Again, the cutting-edges of the rotary cutter compel an outline of the work whose form accords with that of the cutter. Hence, if a pattern of cutter be fixed upon by a skilled mechanic, the reproduction of duplicate forms can be intrusted to a less skilled operative. Provided only the cutters are maintained in shape, and the work is properly chucked, the machine can be worked to stop-gauges without the repeated application of standards. For these reasons, the milling-machine in its various forms has become an essential in the manufacture of exact machinery. Operators become easily accustomed to working to a thousandth of an inch, and for fire-arm, electric, and sewing-machine work they have revolutionized the practice of earlier days.

One of the earliest forms of milling-machine for gun-work is illustrated by Figs. 273 and 274. In both the machines shown great improvements have been made over the original machine as made many years ago. The driving-spindle rises and falls in the uprights, controlled either by two screws geared (Fig. 273) or by one screw, equalized between the two boxes by a cross-head and stiff plungers (Fig. 274). Lost motion is prevented by the

Fig. 273.

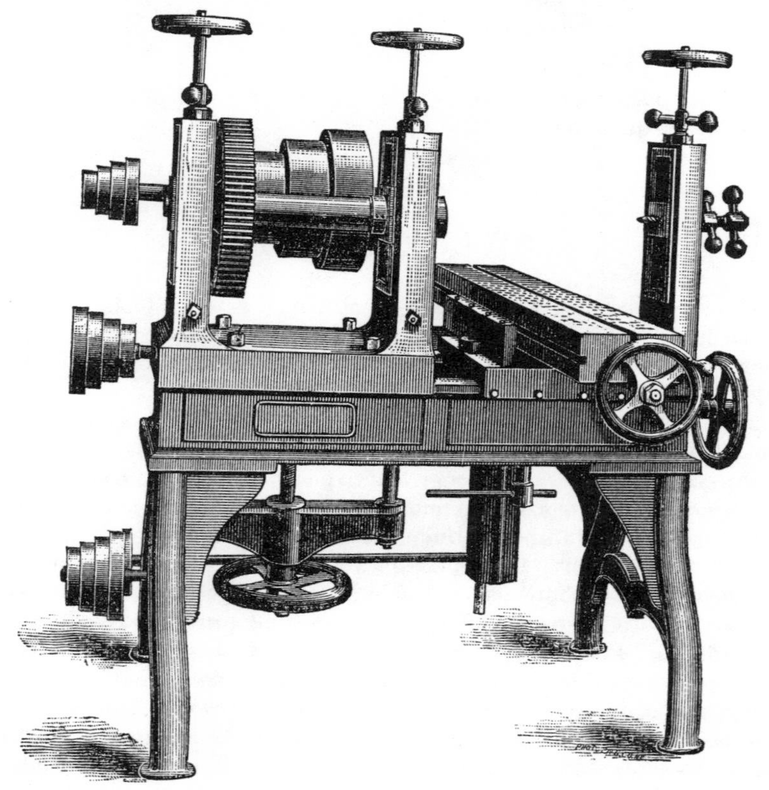

Fig. 274

jam-nuts on the top screws. The cutters are held on a mandrel, which fits into the end of the spindle, the outer end being borne by an adjustable center. This has a motion independent of that of the spindle, for convenience of taper work. The spindle is geared to a pulley-shaft, the latter shaft being adjustable laterally for various elevations of the spindle. There will be three or four grades on the cone-pulley. The piece to be operated upon is clamped in a vise or chucked to a table, which may have two motions. The motion along the axis of the cutter-mandrel is quite short, and is usually by hand only, for adjustment. The motion at right angles to this line and against the cutters is much longer and is automatic. A worm-shaft is driven by small cone-pulleys, and turns a worm-wheel,

Fig. 275.

which meshes into a gear on the cross-feed screw. The worm-shaft is carried on a swivel-bearing at the head-stock, and the further bearing is connected to a pivoted lever. When this lever is latched up the worm turns the wheel. The release of the latch, either by an automatic stop or by hand, permits the worm to drop out of gear with the wheel, and stops the feed. The worm is made long so as to operate wherever the table may be in its longitudinal traverse.

Fig. 275 shows the construction of a machine, which is in some respects an improvement on the earlier forms. The spindle is held on a flat plate sliding in slots to which it may be clamped by bolts. It is adjusted by one large screw, and has a stop-screw below. The pulley-spindle swings on a yoke and is linked to the main spindle, rendering the lateral adjustment of its bearings automatic. The heavy slide insures parallelism of the main spindle at all times, which the unequal wear of the gears and screws of the earlier form was liable to vitiate. The feed-motions of the table are as before. Instead of a back-carrier stand, adjustable for mandrels of different lengths, an outside center support is attachable on an arm from the carrier. These will all move together and can be adjusted while the machine is in motion. A similar design is shown by Fig. 276. Milling-machines of this type are known as

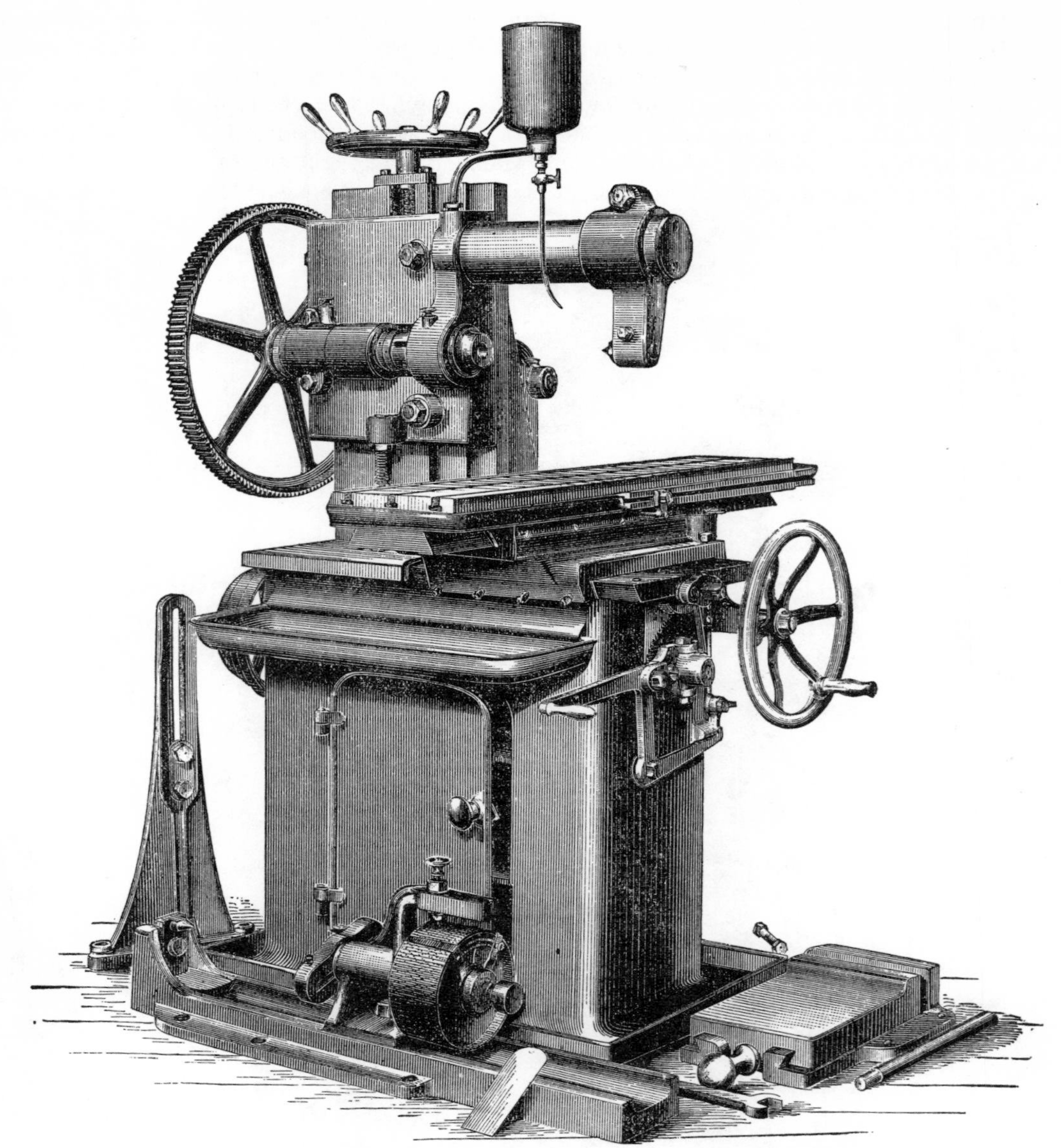

Fig. 276.

Fig. 277.

Fig. 278.

Fig. 279.

Fig. 280.

Fig. 281.

"plain" milling-machines. A milling-machine of a slightly different construction, but similar in principle, is shown by Fig. 277. The vise receives the vertical feed, and both the main and tail spindles have set-over motions. The tool illustrates the application of the lathe principle to milling purposes.

The second form of milling-machine is what is known as the "standard" machine. The working parts are borne upon a column or standard, which in many designs makes a convenient tool-closet for the attachments.

Figs. 278 and 279 illustrate types of the hand-machines. The spindle is driven directly by belt and the knee-table gives a vertical adjustment while the back-and-forth and right-and-left motions are given to the compound table. These are adapted for work with small cutters only, which turn at high speed, and the feeds are by screw or by rack and pinion by the levers.

Fig. 280 illustrates a larger design of standard miller with power-feed across the front. The screw on the hand-wheel shaft is turned by bevel-gear from the vertical telescopic shaft in front, which is driven from a worm-shaft at the base of the tool, as shown by Fig. 284.

Fig. 281 shows another way of producing the feed-motion by a long worm which may be disengaged by hand-lever in front. To compensate for rise and fall, the cone-pulleys are connected to the worm by two universal joints and a telescopic shaft. The double joint also prevents the irregularity of feed from being as noticeable as it would be with but one. There is an automatic stop-motion for the feed, adjustable to any position. There is also a stop by jam-nuts upon the in-and-out hand traverse.

Fig. 282.

Fig. 282 shows the feed-worm driven by belts through a floating cone-pulley shaft. The stiff link swings around the box of the spindle, and an extensible link swings round the worm-shaft. The worm-shaft can thus be more accurately fitted to the adjustable table, and the tension of the driving-belt may be varied at will. The extensible link is forked and bears at both ends of the arbor. The spring latch at the left is acted upon by the adjustable stop under the oil-pan in front. The elevating-screw is turned by bevel-gear and is fitted with a graduated circle

Fig. 283.

Fig. 284.

Fig. 285.

Fig. 286.

Fig. 287.

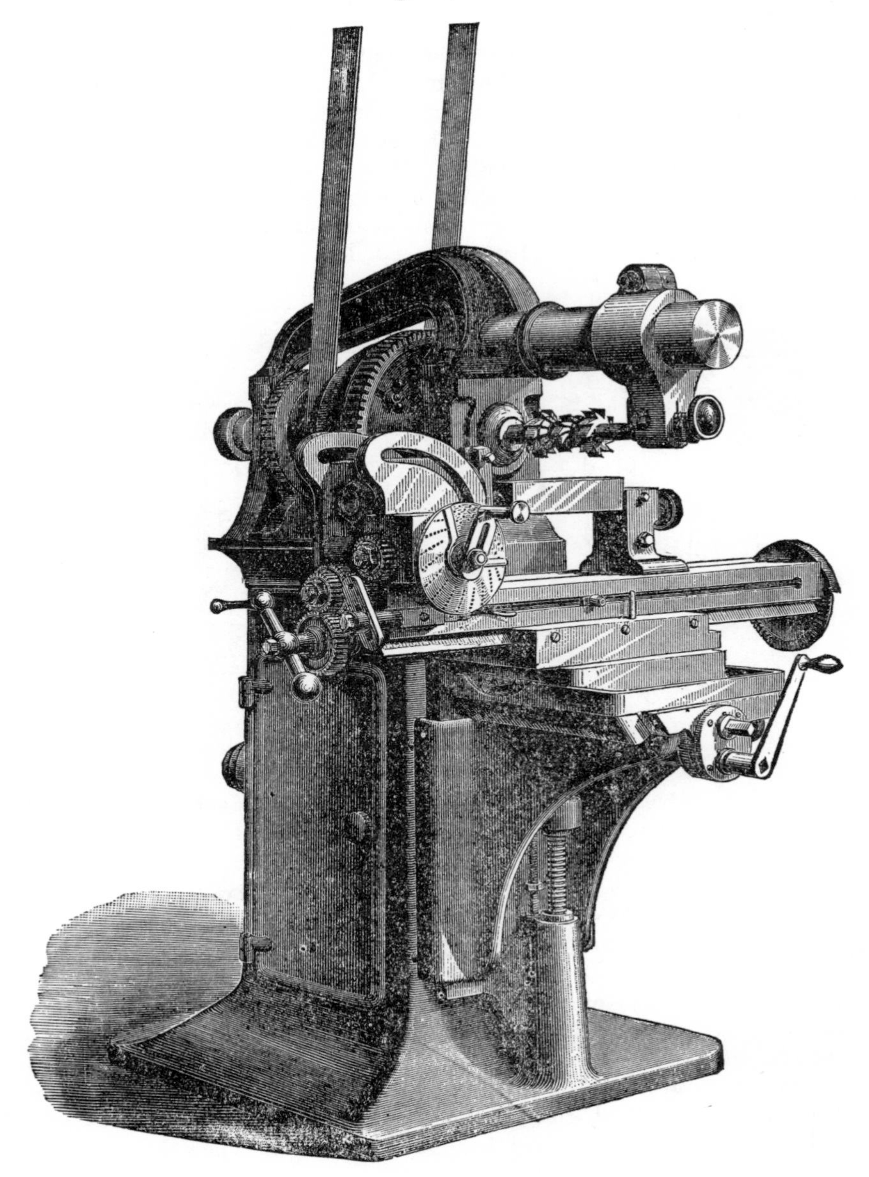

Fig. 2·8.

and index. By dividing the circle into 125 parts and using a screw of one-eighth of an inch pitch, the table may be raised by one-thousandth of an inch, or by one-half of that by ocular bisection of the graduations. The traverse in line with the spindle is by hand over 5 inches only.

Fig. 283 shows a type of back-geared milling-machine, with feed in all directions to the compound table. A twisted round belt transmits motion through a floating stud to a shaft with short worms, right and left. These may be engaged at will with a worm-wheel on a splined shaft which transmits motion by bevel-gears to a second splined shaft at the side of the knee-table. From this the motion is taken off by gears to the cross-feed screw at the end, and for the longitudinal feed. The feeds are disengaged by the short hand-levers shown near the screws. The knee-table is lifted by the screw at the side, the bearing being very long to resist twisting.

For larger tools it is necessary to have an outside center support for the mill-arbor. The strain of the cut might deflect the arbor and cause untruth in the work.

Fig. 284 illustrates an unusual way of accomplishing this result. The arm passes through rings and is set in place by screws, so as to uphold the mandrel by a center. The table has vertical and transverse hand- and power-feed by narrow belts to worm-shafts.

In Fig. 285 the arm for the center is cast with the head, and is not detachable, as is customary. The hanging arm bolts the center through a slot, by which arbors of different lengths may be accommodated. The cut illustrates a tool of this class applied for the special duty of milling out the profile of a carriage-axle at one operation. The square of the axle receives feed-motion by a tangent-screw to the special-holder vise. A type of solid arm, with adjustment vertically, is shown by Figs. 286 and 287. In both figures the compound table has no vertical adjustment for differing thicknesses. This gives steadiness to the table and for its motions, and simplifies the feed connections. In Fig. 286 the casting which carries the arm and spindle is fitted to a concave arc on the standard. The center of the two arcs is the center of the cone-pulley shaft. The movable casting slides on tenons in the arc of the standard, as governed by a screw at the rear, moving tangent to the arc. By this means a vertical adjustment of 6 inches is possible, without interfering with the driving-belt. In Fig. 287 the arm and spindle-casting is hinged at the right, and a pillar-screw and jam-nuts secure the swinging arm in the proper adjustment. The motion takes place around the center of the gear-axis as before.

The most familiar types of the universal standard milling-machine are shown by Figs. 288 and 290. They embody the highest refinements of construction for exactness and finish, many of which are applied in the smaller machines as well, or may be omitted or replaced in designs of less elaboration. In Fig. 289, which shows part of

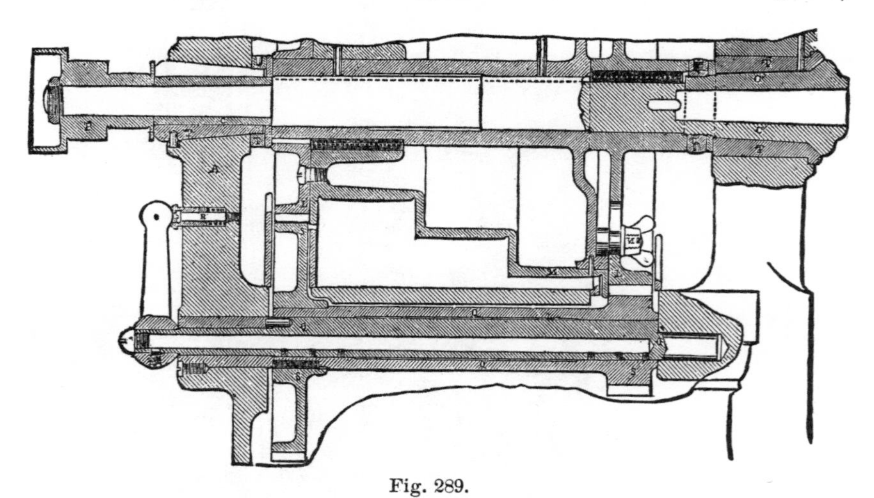

Fig. 289.

the detail of the head of the machine, the spindle C C′ is of hammered steel, hardened and turning in hardened boxes. The spindle is ground at front of box to tangents to the Schiele curve to receive the thrust on the end. A long taper socket is made in the spindle to receive the ends of mandrels. The front box is solid, forced into the supporting casting. A capstan-nut with set-screws on the spindle can take up any lost motion from wear, by drawing inward the conical bearing. The rear box is split, and wear is taken up by a capstan-nut which compresses the box upon the journal as it draws inward the cone of the outside of the box into the casting. Back-gearing is applied below the main spindle, a spring catch holding the engaging-arm in place. The outside center support is bolted to the top of the uprights of the spindle-bearings, and the center clasps the finished arm by a bolt, which closes the split. The dead-center has also a fine adjustment by a milled head on a screw, this having also a split clamp. The vertical and back and forth feeds are by hand. The transverse feed is from the cone-pulleys on the spindle to a complementary nest at the side of the standard. By two universal joints and a telescopic shaft motion is transmitted through a jaw-clutch to the bevel-wheel on the end of the feed-screw. This jaw-clutch can be disengaged by an adjustable stop on the table. It has all the usual and necessary attachments, to be alluded to in the sequel.

Fig. 290 shows a universal standard milling-machine differing from the preceding in several points. The bearings for the spindle are cylindrical, and the thrust of the mills is borne by composition washers on a step-screw at the tail. The journals are of bronze split at one point, and wear is taken up by capstan nuts on each side of the castings of the standard. The arm for outside center has a long cylindrical fit in the cap casting, with about

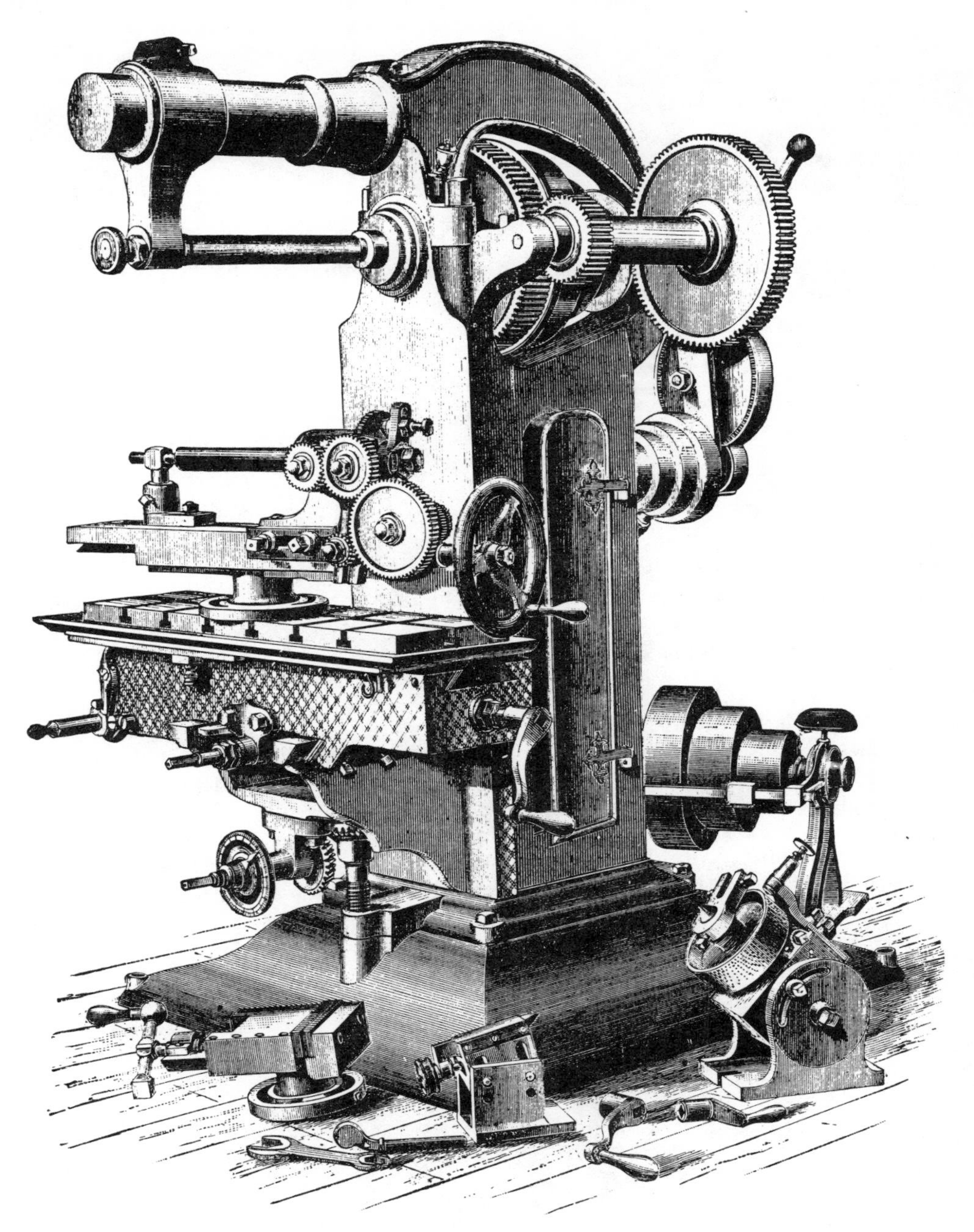

Fig. 290.

1 inch of thread. When screwed home to refusal the split is tightened to prevent the arm from jarring itself loose. The back-gears are at the side, and the feed-shaft is driven by shielded gear and belt through a floating cone-pulley shaft linked to driver and follower. Wear in the feed-screws can be taken up by double nuts. The same fine graduated motion to the table is obtained as in Fig. 282. The main spindle is hollow for convenience of driving out mandrels. In these tools of this class the workmanship is of the best and most accurate. The surfaces are scraped with the greatest care and regard for truth, and so accurately is the work fitted to gauges that in the T-slots in the tables a tenon gauge may be pressed in by hand, but must not fall in easily. From this exactitude in the machine it follows that its work can be correspondingly exact. Units which were formerly thought so small as to be rather in the field of the physicist are now of frequent occurrence in our workshops.

Fully to entitle these milling-machines to the term "universal" certain attachments are required to go with them. These will bolt to the top of the table in the **T**-slots, of which there will probably be one longitudinal and four or six transverse. The first of these will be a vise, which can swivel to any horizontal angle (Figs. 291 and

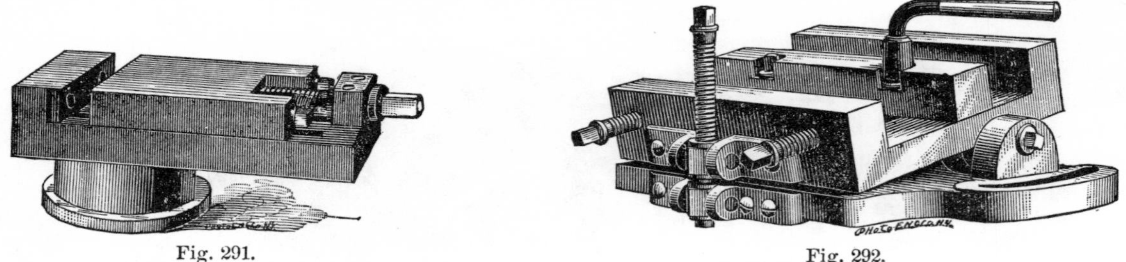

Fig. 291. Fig. 292.

292), and one design permits vertical swiveling also. Any form of holder may be designed for any especial shape or process.

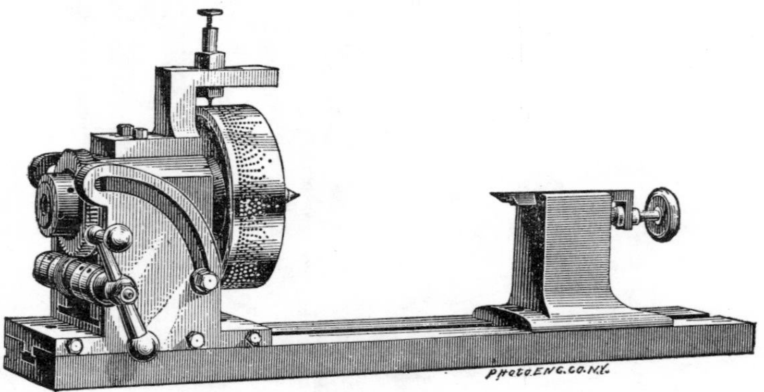

Fig. 293.

The second attachment is a universal head, which can also be used as a simple pair of centers. Fig. 293 illustrates a usual form. The head center is hollow, for rods of any length, and is fitted with a screw in front to hold a chuck or dog-jaw. The spindle may be revolved through any number of degrees by the tangent gearing, the divided cylinder in front serving as index and stop-gear. The whole center has a motion around the axis of the worm, by which an elevation may be given to it for working out tapers with a straight parallel mill. The stationary center has a short pin adjustment when clamped in place.

Fig. 294 shows a similar head with patent back center. The upright is faced on the inside, and fits the inner

Fig. 294.

block, which carries the spindle proper. The two parts bolt together by bolts through the curved slots of the inner block. The center is therefore capable of elevation and depression, but can also be set at an angle, so that tapered work can be finished without danger of throwing the point out of the center line of the countersink and wearing both surfaces unduly. These heads will permit gear-cutting, both spur and bevel. The index-dial will divide in an average size of head all numbers to 25, all even numbers to 50, and several others up to 120. One large head has been made by these builders which will divide a circle into eighteen thousand parts with the highest limit of accuracy, and it will divide it even into fifty-four thousand parts. The worm-wheel is made with sharp **V**-threads, and contains 180 teeth. The wheel is in two parts, and no matter how the two disks may be screwed together any two half-teeth form one without perceptible error. A graduated disk receives a spring pawl, by which exact record can be kept of the turns of the worm. There are arrangements to take up wear longitudinally by check-capstan nuts and vertically by hollow capstan-nuts on the block with through clamp-nuts.

The other attachment for the milling-machine table is a spiral cutter. While the work is fed longitudinally by a screw against the cutter, it receives also a motion around its own axis (Fig. 295). This second motion is derived from a worm on the screw by a train of change-wheels, and spirals may be originated and cut with pitches varying between 2 and 72 inches. The spiral may be cut upon a cone as well as upon a cylinder by a special device.

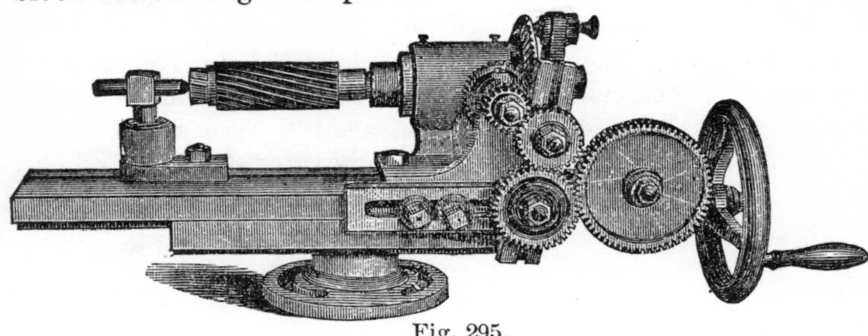

Fig. 295.

Of course for any special manufacture special appliances may supplement these standard attachments. With such devices the application of the machine to all kinds of work becomes most simple. Its use is extending, and is having a most important bearing upon exact manufacture.

§ 31.

SPECIAL FORMS.

For the use of drop-forging apparatus it is necessary that the steel dies be carved out to the exact shape desired. This manufacture of dies is called "die-sinking", and has given rise to a special form of milling-machine. Fig. 296

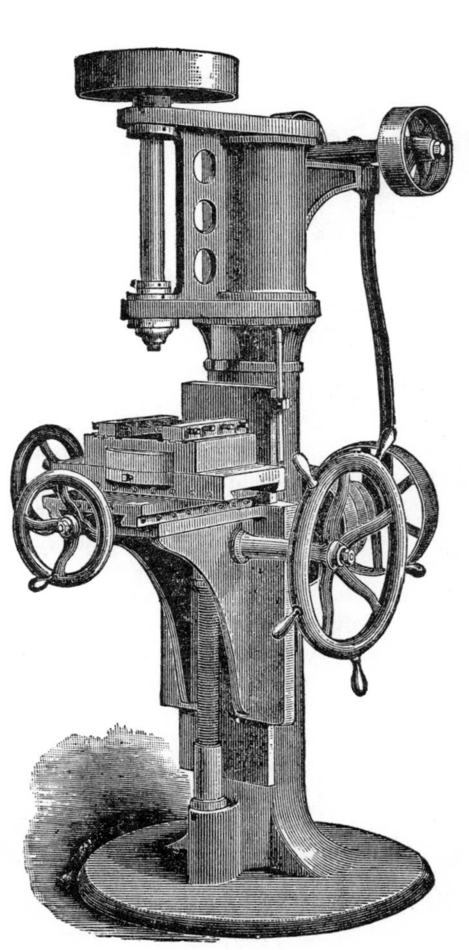

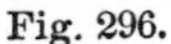

Fig. 296.

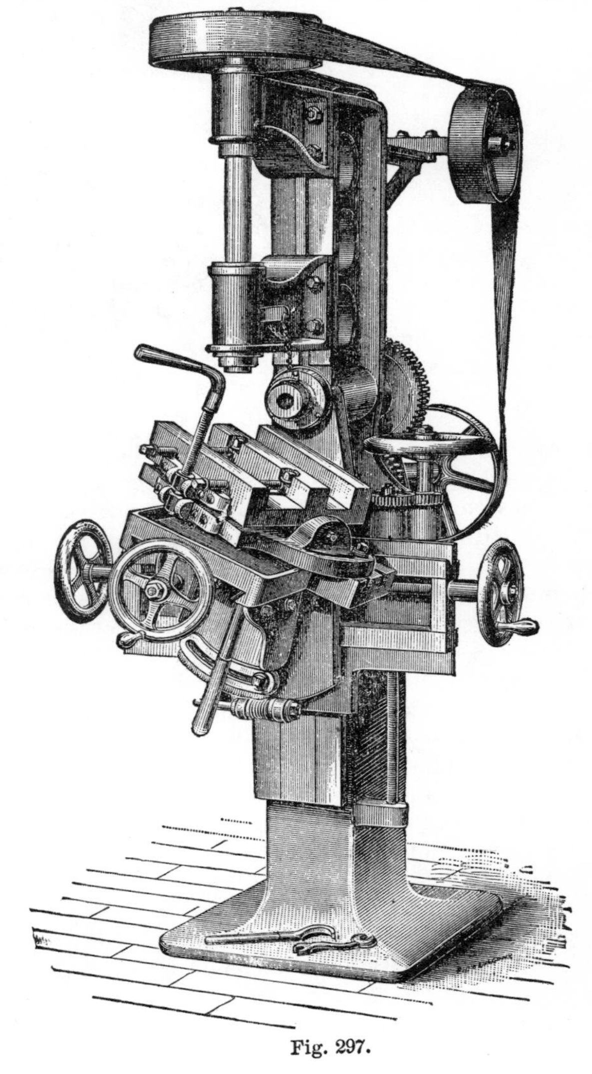

Fig. 297.

illustrates a type. The cutter is vertical, driven by a belt over guide-pulleys. The mill usually cuts on both face and side. The vise has compound motion by hand, and the knee-table can be raised and lowered. There are special devices for taking up thrust and lost motion at the bearings. Very often the motions to the table and vise are given by levers.

Fig. 297 shows a machine with both horizontal and vertical spindles and universal motion to the vise. A saddle has two motions in a vertical plane, and a swivel table, controllable by a worm, holds the slide which receives the vise. All the motions are controlled by hand-wheels within convenient reach of the operator. Such a machine, of course, can be used for any of the small work of miscellaneous milling.

For edge-milling or profiling the irregular shapes of several classes of manufacture the type of machine shown in Fig. 298 is approved. The pieces to be dressed are clamped to the table, which receives a backward and forward

Fig. 298.

feed by rack and pinion from the ball-handle. The mills are carried in the vertical spindles, which are borne on a saddle, which receives transverse motion by a pinion on its under side through the ball-handle on the right. A former is secured to the table, and the operator controls his two feeds by that. The spindles have vertical motion by the hand-levers between adjustable stops for depth, and are driven from the long drum at the rear. This machine has a patent device for cutting formers without reversing the fixtures. The guiding-pin may be driven by gear from one spindle, and the cutter and pin exchange places, while the model is secured to the place which the work is to occupy in the future. The cutter on the guide-pin cuts the forming pattern in the exact position it will retain in use. The gearing and rack are made double, so as to be adjustable to prevent any back-lash in the feeds. This is essential for accuracy of irregular work, and especially in turning corners. Such a machine can also be used as a jigging and die-sinking machine. There may also be three spindles. A rotary cutter has been mounted upon an arbor transverse and parallel to a planer bed, and is used to mill out the flats of locomotive-rods. It is then known as a slabbing-machine, and will take a 4-inch cutter the full width of the rod. For cast iron a larger cutter may be used with advantage. Where, however, heavy work is to be done, the use of inserted cutters is expedient. The work done will then be proportional to the number of cutters, as compared with reciprocating tools.

An example of the economic application of this principle is shown by Figs. 299 and 300. The tool (Fig. 299) is designed to face off the ends of bridge and other girders to exact dimensions. The work is bolted to a stationary table, and the mill traverses in front of it. Several may be secured at once, and each is held independently by a set-screw through the clamp. The mill consists of a solid wrought-iron disk of tough and homogeneous metal. It is 2 inches thick and weighs 400 pounds. Eighty-four teeth are inserted in the rim, on edge and face alternately, and since the disk is 28 inches in diameter the alternate system permits a tooth upon every inch of circumference. The teeth are of steel, $1\frac{1}{8}$ inches face by $\frac{7}{8}$ of an inch thick, and are fitted in milled grooves. The milling-disk is driven by a large steel worm on a splined shaft, by which a vertical adjustment of the slide is possible. The whole head is fed along by a screw either by hand or by power, through a worm-gear from cone-pulleys, and the feed can

Fig. 299.

be varied from $\frac{1}{8}$ of an inch to 1 inch per revolution. Such a machine can square and finish six 15-inch beams per hour, allowing $\frac{1}{2}$ inch of metal to be cut from each end. If less is taken off the feed may be more rapid. In Fig.

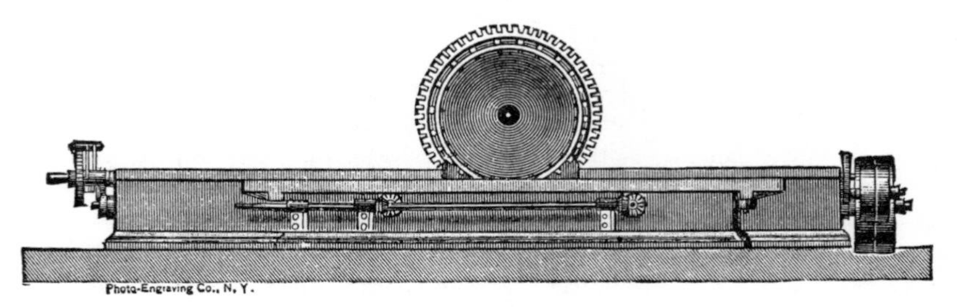

Fig. 300.

300 the cutters are twenty-eight in number, on a 25-inch plate wheel, which is banded with wrought iron. The wheel is driven as in the other tool by worm-gear, and the whole head is made to travel by an automatic variable feed.

§32.

GEAR-CUTTERS.

Any of the universal millers can be used as gear-cutters by means of a universal head, with worm-wheel and index. They can usually cut both spurs and bevels. There are certain tools, however, which are built for that especial purpose, and may properly be discussed by themselves.

Fig. 301 illustrates the type which has been in very general use. The blank from which the spaces between the teeth are to be cut is held firmly upon the end of a vertical arbor. Upon this arbor is secured the index-plate, with its stop-pin, adjustable legs, and clamp. The cutter is borne upon a slide which has a power-feed across the face of the blank, and the whole upright has adjustment for different diameters of blank. To compensate for the motion of the cutter-arbor the belt passes over a hinged binder-frame overhead, which is weighted to maintain a constant tension on the belt.

Fig. 302 illustrates a standard type of machine. The cutter-carriage is swung from a fulcrum on the standard, and may be set to cut bevels of any angle. The cutter is fed automatically across the face of the blank, and has a stop-gear. The mandrel for the blank may be adjusted for different radii of wheels. The wheels are divided by a worm-wheel.

To increase the adaptability of the milling-machine for bevel-wheels such machines as Figs. 303 and 304 have been produced. In Fig. 303 the index-plate is attached to the bottom of a hollow spindle, which swivels around a

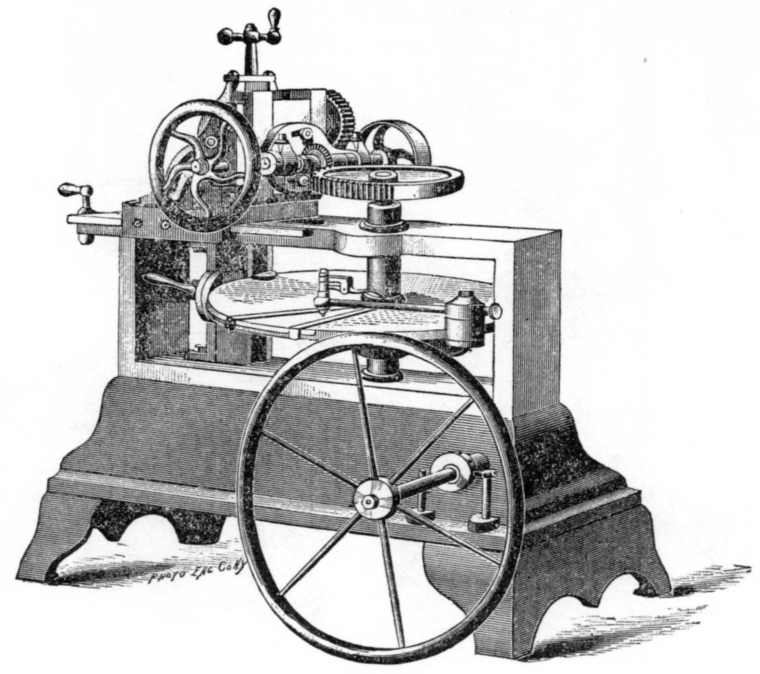

Fig. 301.

center on a vertical slide. The spindle can take a vise or centers or any attachment, and can be set at any angle between 0° and 180°. The vertical slide has a perpendicular traverse of 2 inches and a horizontal adjustment between stops for different diameters. The machine can therefore cut spurs and bevels and worm-teeth. The cone-spindle has a horizontal movement by hand-lever limited between check-nuts.

In Fig. 304 the mill-arbor is driven by bevel-gear from the splined shaft to avoid the necessity for the binder-frame. The vertical spindle has the same motions and adjustments as in the previous machine. As this is designed for general work also, the vertical spindle is arranged to clamp so as to relieve the index-plate from strain, as in the preceding type.

Fig. 305 illustrates a machine specially adapted for racks. The cutter is borne on a horizontal slide driven by gears from the cone-pulley, and more than one cutter may be used at once. The cutters are fed forward by power automatically, and the pitch for the rack is given by a spring stop into the teeth of a change-wheel. The train can be so arranged relative to the pitch of the traverse screw as to have the two pitches commensurable, and the pin should pass over always the same number of teeth.

In the best practice for larger wheel-work the drilled index-plate is replaced by a large worm-wheel, and motion to the worm is transmitted from a crank by a train of change-wheels, as in Fig. 302. The crank is arranged to lock with a spring latch or by a jaw of some sort, so that any number of entire revolutions of the crank may be so multiplied or divided as to effect any subdivision of the circumference of the worm-wheel. By this means the errors of fractional subdivisions are avoided, and also possible inaccuracies from the division or wear of the index plate. Moreover, when the worm-wheel is large, any errors in it are reduced in cutting-wheels of smaller diameter than itself, which will always be most numerous. The only source of error is from the danger of making the wrong number of turns of the crank-shaft. The combinations and numbers of turns can all be worked out and tabulated in advance.

The most advanced types of gear-cutters are those which are automatic. They are made by several of the best builders, and after adjustment of the blank and the combinations they will operate without supervision from the attendant. It is therefore possible to keep four machines full and earning their own interest, with the cost of the labor of but one operator to be divided among the four. Beside, the automatic machine is likely to work more rapidly than a similar machine worked in part by hand. There is a general resemblance in the mechanical devices for securing automatism, though the machines differ widely in outward form and appearance and differ in their adaptedness for large and small work.

A Providence machine for wheels up to 18 inches diameter, with 3-inch face, is shown by Fig. 306. It will cut wheels of any angle by the sector adjustment of the cutter-slide, which carries a graduated arc and index. The cutter-mandrel is driven by belt, with idle-pulley, for equality of tension. The wheel is secured on the horizontal

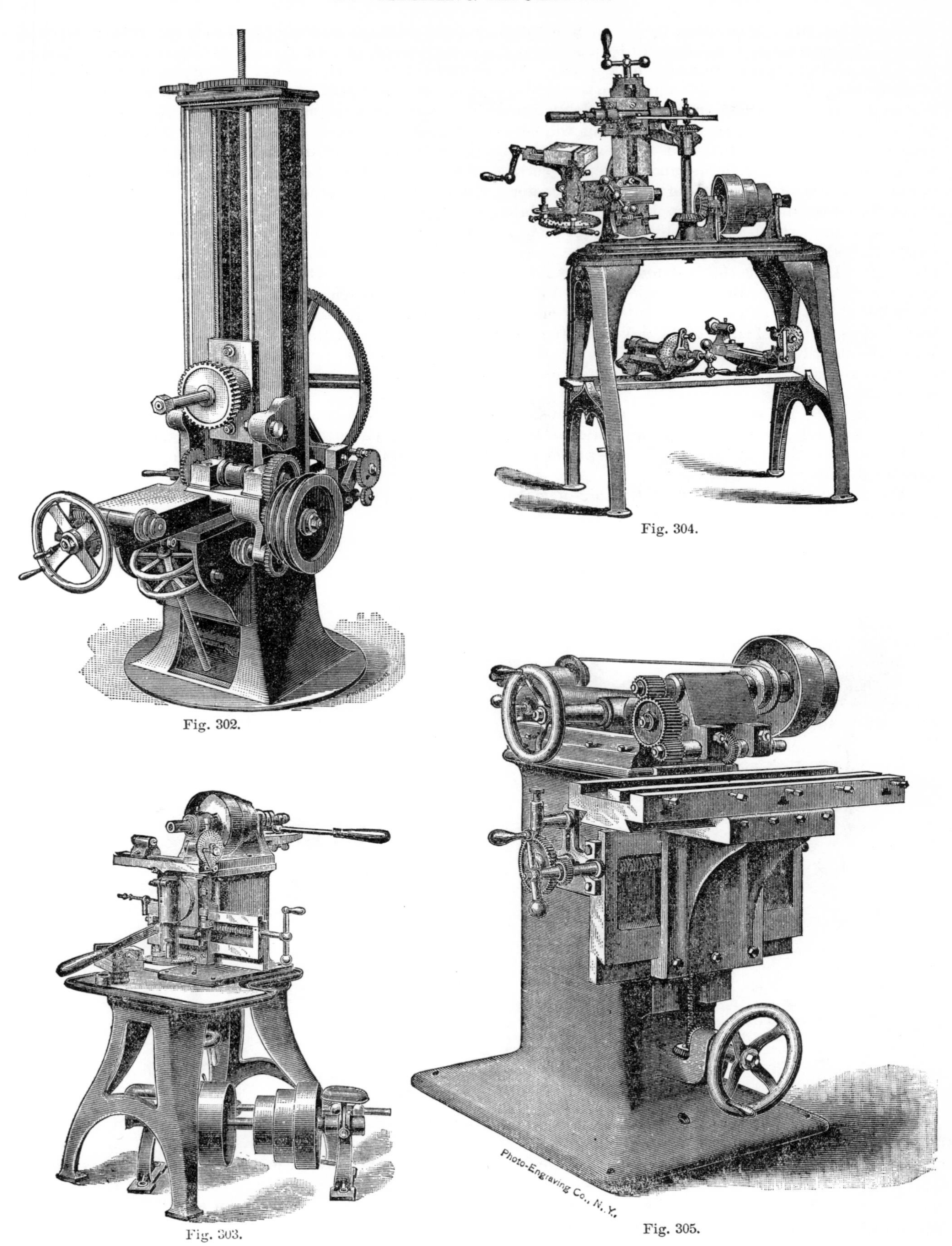

Fig. 302.

Fig. 304.

Fig. 303.

Fig. 305.

arbor, and the latter is adjusted by a scale graduated to thousandths of an inch for exactly the proper depth of tooth. The cutter-slide is fed forward by a screw at the proper speed, cutting through across the face, and when the cut is made the slide returns at quick speed. This is effected by a clutch between bevel-gears on opposite sides of the driving-shaft, and of different diameters. The shifting device is prevented from stalling by wedge-points, one on the clutch-lever and one on a movable stud pressed forward by a spring. As the two wedges cannot hold by their sharp edges, the compressed spring will certainly throw the clutch to one side or the other. To give the proper rotation to the blank, that the next cut may be properly made, the mandrel carries a worm-wheel. The worm which drives it is borne upon a splined vertical shaft, driven from below by change-wheels. The spline permits adjustment for wheels of differing diameters, and the worm is turned and locked by a special device. When the cutter-slide has retreated it engages a clutch, which puts a train in motion, turning the worm. On this clutch-shaft are two wheels, side by side, with their faces plain, except a notch in each. One wheel is fast on the shaft; the other is loose, and is driven in the direction opposite to that of its mate by internal gearing from an idle shaft. It is obvious that a detent can only fall into the notch of either wheel when that of each shall coincide under it. This detent can be so shaped as to lock both wheels and to disengage the clutch which is driving them. Since the wheels are driven in opposite directions, it is simply necessary so to arrange a train of change-wheels that the two notches shall coincide only when the proper number of revolutions of the worm shall have been made. When the shaft has gone round the standard number of times, the notches coincide, the detent falls into them and locks the worm-wheel and blank, and disengages the driving-gear. The detent is loosened by the return of the cutter-slide.

In one of the Philadelphia designs the worm-shaft is driven by a train of change-gears, which must change the speed of the driving-arbor by proper alteration of the six revolutions which the latter always makes when engaged by the return of the cutter-slide. This series of six revolutions is secured by the action of dogs upon two equal wheels with different numbers of teeth.

Fig. 307 shows a special automatic pair of machines, one for spur-wheels and the other for bevel-wheels of small dimensions for light machinery.

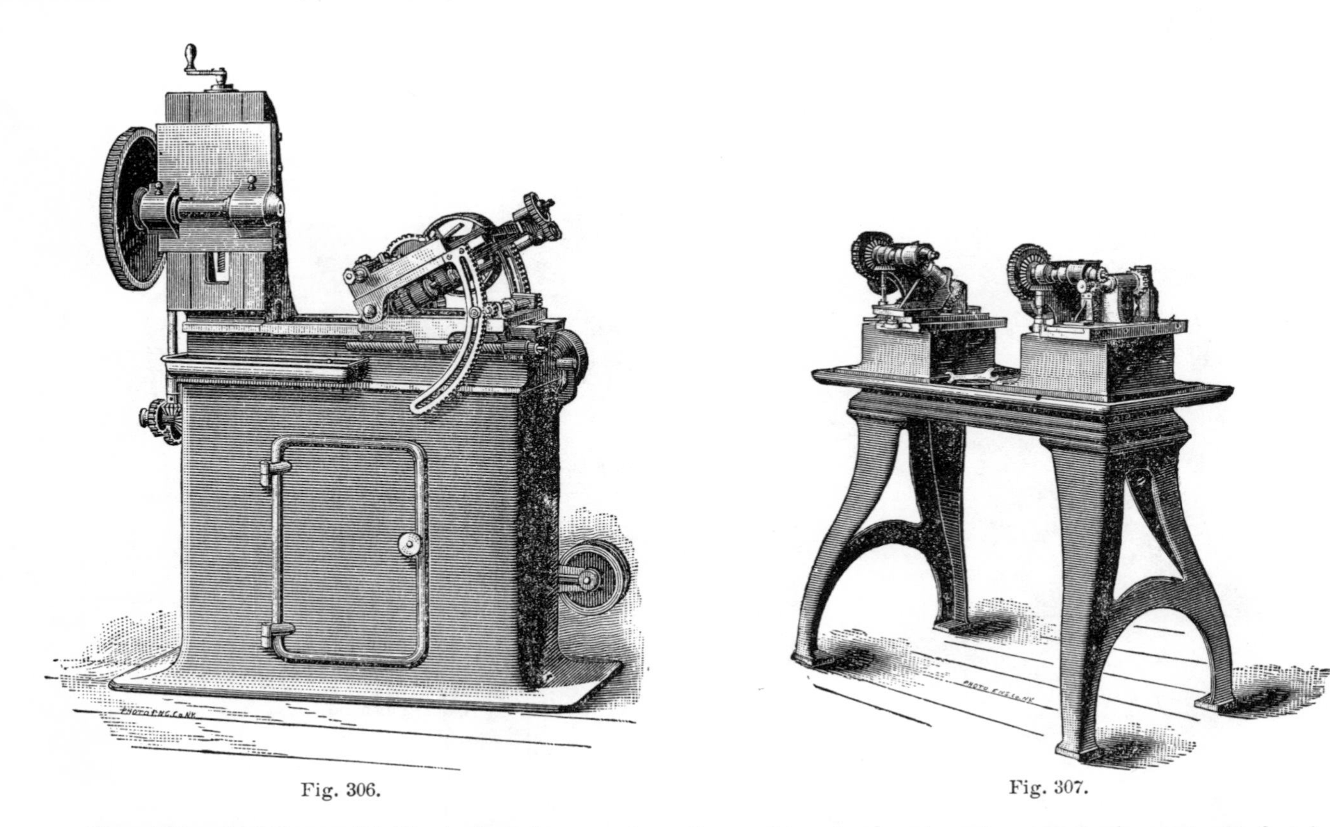

Fig. 306. Fig. 307.

Figs. 308 and 309 *a* and *b* illustrate a large automatic machine for bevel- and spur-wheels up to $4\frac{1}{2}$ feet in diameter and of 12 inches face. It will divide the circumference of wheels containing from ten up to three hundred and sixty teeth. The cutter is borne upon a horizontal slide, with variable traverse and return motion. It is driven by bevel-gear from the cone of belt-pulleys, the belt passing over a counter-weighted tightener-frame. The feeding and dividing motions are obtained from the central vertical shaft. By supporting the outer end of the mandrel for the blanks a large number of thin wheels may be cut at one cross-traverse.

Fig. 308.

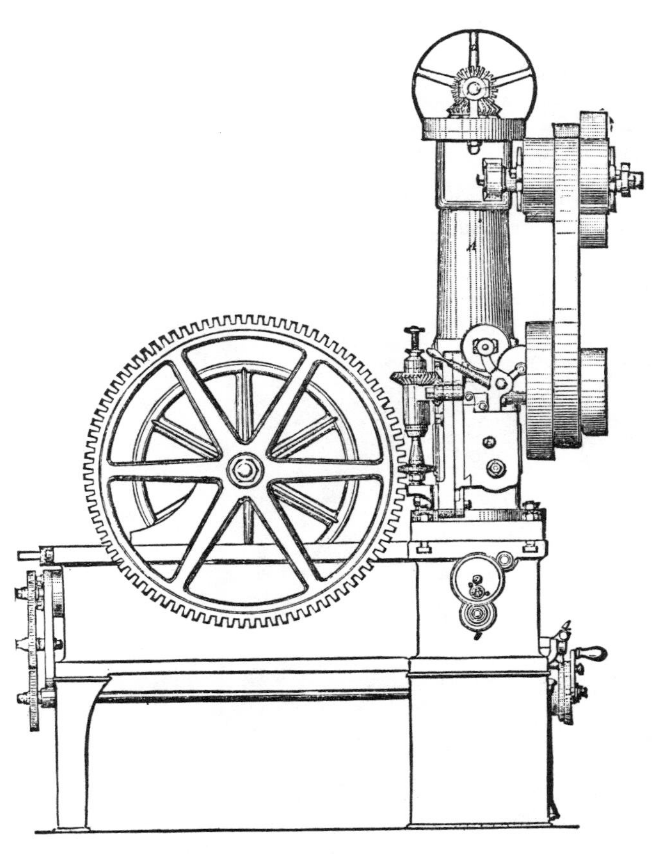

Fig. 309 *a*.

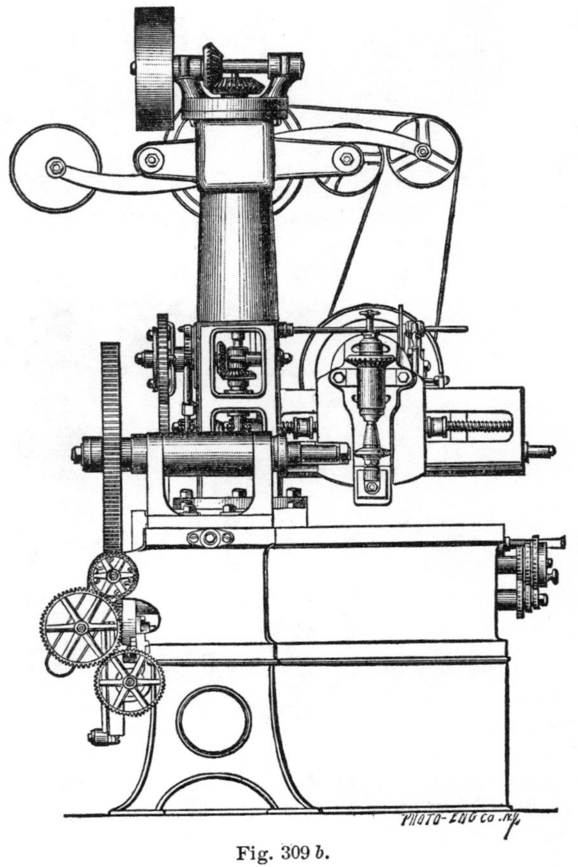

Fig. 309 *b*.

For the rotating cutters for these machines a very general type of patent cutter is shown by Fig. 310. Such cutters are so constructed that they can be sharpened by grinding upon the flat front face without spoiling the profiles of the side edges. The relief necessary for the top of the cutting-face obliges the profile to retreat toward the center. If only the top retreated, each successive grinding would make the space cut in the blank more and more shallow. To avoid this, each cutter is turned in a relieving lathe. The forming-tool receives a special forward motion from the tip to the root of each cutting-tooth as the mill being shaped revolves on a mandrel. This forward motion is imparted by a cam under the former-slide, which revolves once for each cutting-tooth of the mill (Fig. 311). To make the forming-tool, the true profile is worked out and a male chisel is made from it. By this male tool a female tool is planed out, and this latter is used to turn the spiral profiles of the mill itself. By distributing the numbers of teeth in each circular pitch among eight cutters the errors from inexact profile are made quite small.

Fig. 310.

In another system (Pratt & Whitney, Hartford, Connecticut) an especial tool is used for producing an exact epicycloidal profile in the templet from which the mill is to be shaped. Fig. 312 shows a side view, and Fig. 313 gives a view in oblique plan. By this means is eliminated the variableness of profile of hand-made equivalents. From this templet, mechanically exact, as a former, the profile of the mill proper is reproduced. If the edge of a templet,

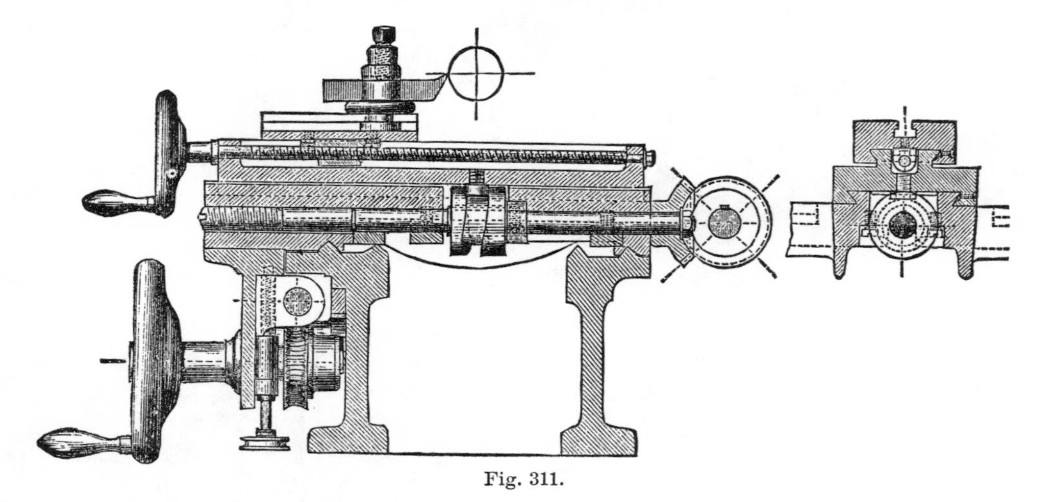

Fig. 311.

T T (Fig. 314), has been shaped by a cutter traveling on a true epicycloidal curve, a roller, P, running along the profile of T T, will make another cutter, N, on the axis of P, reproduce a profile, R S, which has a constant

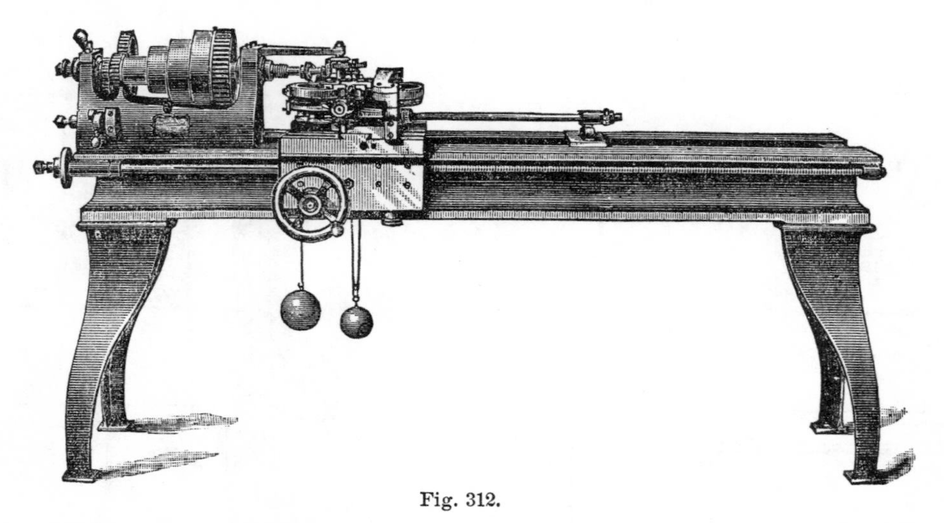

Fig. 312.

normal distance from T T. The reproduction of such curves for cutters is done by turning the cutter nearly to the required form and notching it for the cutting-edges. It is then put upon the pantographic cutter engine (Fig. 315), by which the exact profiles are produced for any other pitch by reduction with a simple device. The pantographic engine will reproduce any type of tooth profile other than the epicycloidal, if supplied with the corresponding templets. This method gives exceedingly satisfactory results. It is open to the theoretical objection that even a roller of the same size as the original milling-cutter will not retrace completely the cycloidal path in which the

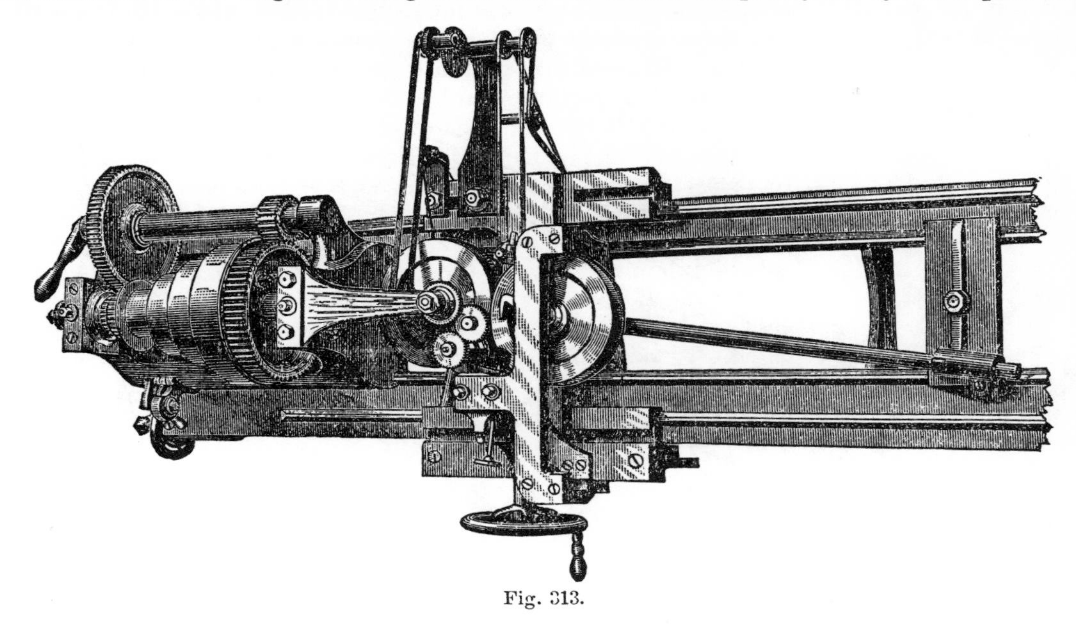

Fig. 313.

latter moved. But this objection is found to cause an inaccuracy of profile in practice so small as to defy detection. Very large wheels are always cut from a former, which guides the cutter. It becomes impossible to use a cutter which shall fully fill the spaces and reproduce itself in large pitches. Hence a cutter is used which dresses the profile by acting upon successive elements, with frequent traverses, and which is controlled by working up to a suitable former.

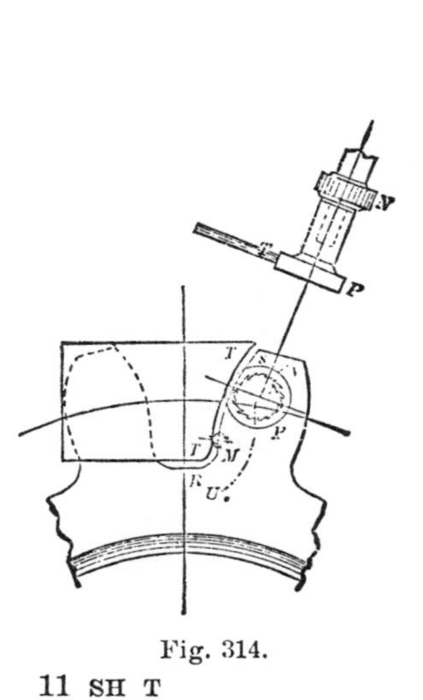

Fig. 314.

Fig. 315.

For bevel-gear the largest type of machine is that (Fig. 316) of Mr. Corliss, of Providence, Rhode Island. The blank is held upon a horizontal mandrel, on the end of which is an index-wheel of 15 feet diameter. By the use of such a large wheel any errors in it are reduced in the work. The blank is so secured that the apex of its conical surfaces shall coincide with the point through which the path of the tool-point always passes. By guiding the tool-slide by a large former, against which the rear of the slide shall be held, the path of the cutting-point at each

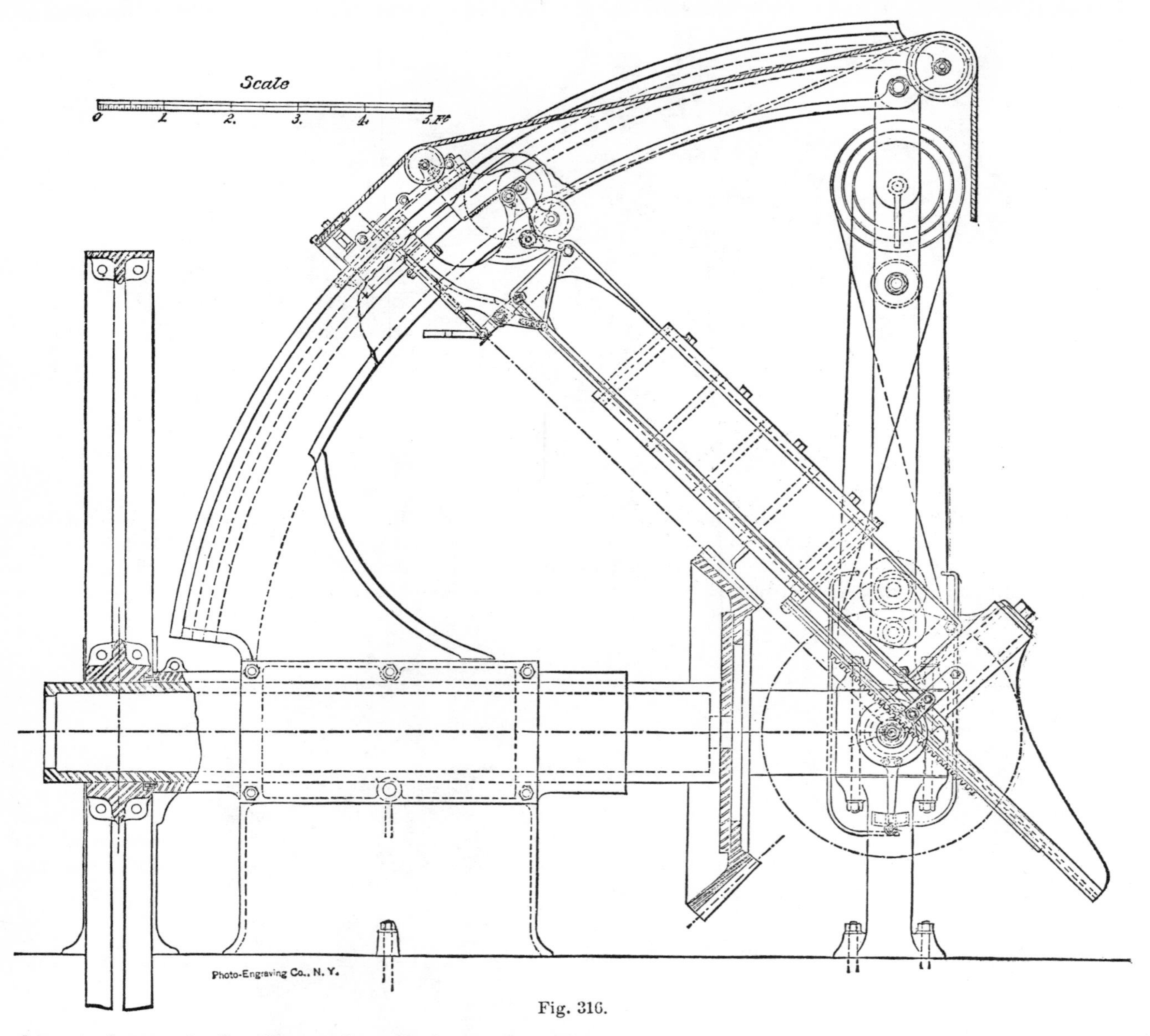

Fig. 316.

element of every tooth will pass through the apex and be tangent to an exact profile at the base of the cone of which the blank forms a short frustum. Profiles of great accuracy will thus result. A smaller machine on similar principle is built by the same makers.

Fig. 317 shows a gear-dressing machine by Gleason, of Rochester, New York. It will act on both spur- and bevel-wheels up to 100 inches in diameter. The wheel to be cut is mounted on the horizontal mandrel, which carries the worm-wheel and train from a crank. For iron wheels the tool-slide is driven by a crank from the central shaft in the upright post, whose center is the center of all cones in bevel-wheels. The end of the radial bar is laid off in degrees for convenience in this work. The tooth-former is put under the tool-holder, and the latter is fed over it. To dress wooden teeth inserted in rims or for patterns a thick circular saw is held in the tool-post, and is driven by belt over guide-pulleys from a radial drum overhead. The radial bar will swing to any angle with the mandrel between 0° for spur-wheels to 90° for crown-wheels. It is also hinged, to permit a vertical movement for bevel-wheels. With greater capacity than the preceding design, it is much less bulky and more rigid vertically.

Fig. 318 shows the Holmes machine working upon a similar principle.

While these latter machines scarcely belong to the class of milling-machines, yet they attach themselves so closely to the milling gear-cutters as to be presented at this point.

The milling-machine in its larger sizes, for locomotive, pump, and engine shops, is becoming increasingly popular. While at present practical considerations often overweigh the theoretical advantages which the tool possesses, and which would lead to its introduction, yet the tendency is toward higher appreciation of the value of

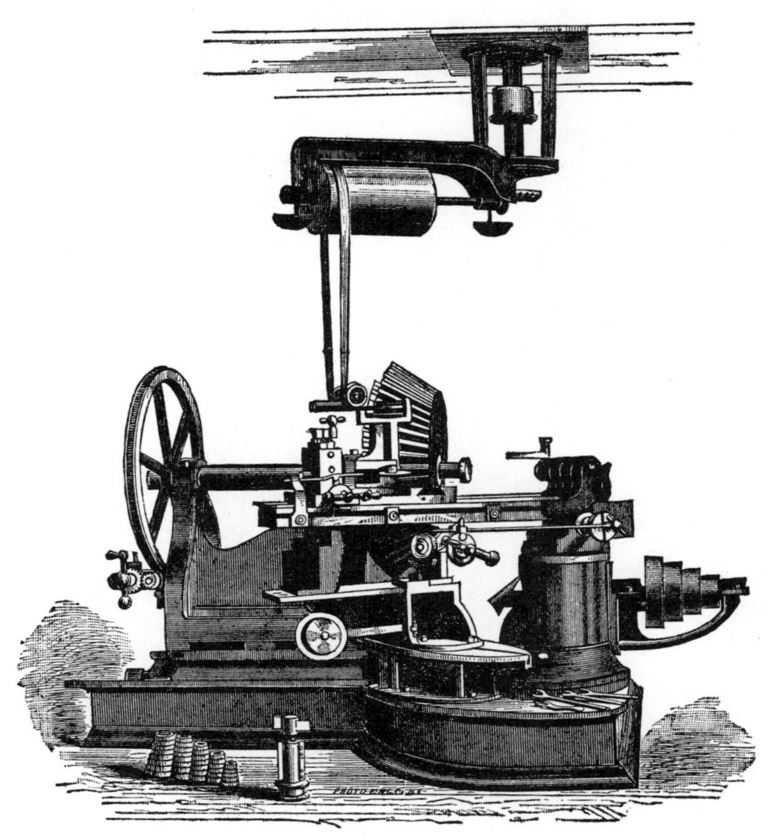

Fig. 317.

the tool. It may also by comparison be called a distinctively American tool in the forms in which it is most frequently met, because the greatest improvements in it have originated in the genius and necessities of this country. By its means production of certain specialties has been cheapened to a degree which would at one time have seemed entirely impossible with the existing high prices of skilled labor.

Fig. 318.